THE COMPLETE DIVER

A GUIDE TO DIVING IN THE 21ST CENTURY

WHAT EVERY
DIVER
SHOULD
KNOW

THE COMPLETE DIVER

The History, Science and Practice of Scuba Diving **By Alex Brylske, Ph.D.**

FIRST EDITION, NOVEMBER 2012

Copyright © 2012 by *Dive Training* LLC
All rights reserved. No part of this publication may be reproduced, used on the Internet,
or transmitted in any form by any means, electronic, photocopied, or otherwise, without prior
permission from the publisher.

Published in the United States by *Dive Training* Magazine, 2012.

The Library of Congress has cataloged this edition as follows:

Brylske, Alexander Frederick Ph.D. 1952, July, 1 -
The Complete Diver: The History, Science and Practice of Scuba Diving/by Alex Brylske, Ph.D. –
1st U.S. ed.

ISBN: 978-0-615-72133-0

© 2012 by *Dive Training* LLC
All rights reserved. First edition 2012
Printed in the United States of America

Book cover and interior design by Doreen Hann
Cover photos by Joseph C. Dovala
Interior photos by Joseph C. Dovala, Barry Guimbellot and Cathryn Castle Whitman
Gene Gentrup and Cathryn Castle Whitman, editors

Dive Training Magazine
5201 Crooked Road
Parkville, MO 64152

Dedication

The Complete Diver is dedicated to my favorite diver in the world, Miss Olivia Skweir, and the thousands of other young scuba enthusiasts who will determine the future of diving.

THE COMPLETE DIVER
The History, Science and Practice of Scuba Divng

Table of Contents

SECTION IV
DECONSTRUCTING DECOMPRESSION: UNBENDING THE BENDS

SECTION V
DOING THE RIGHT THING: DIVING TECHNIQUES RE-EXAMINED

SECTION VI
SEA TREK: THE FUTURE OF DIVING

Acknowledgements

One of the most important scientists of all time, Isaac Newton, once remarked in a letter to yet another brilliant scientist, Robert Hooke, "If I have seen further it is by standing on the shoulders of giants." Indeed, nothing of significance ever happens without the contribution of others. So, too, is the case of *The Complete Diver*. I take credit for originating only some of what you'll read herein. Much more was taken from the words and deeds of others who are far smarter than I am.

Some of the folks whose ideas I've included in the forthcoming pages, and whom I'd be remiss not recognizing, are Dr. Jennifer Hunt, Dr. David Sawatzky, Dr. Glen Egstrom, Dr. Peter Bennett, Joel Dovenbarger, Dr. Chis Logue, Dr. Ernest Campbell, Dr. Dudley Crosson and Dr. Raymond E. Rogers.

Still others helped out in a much more direct way by reviewing specific chapters, and devoting far more time to the task than I could have asked for in correcting errors and giving me direction. These individuals deserve special recognition and include Dr. Sally Bauer, founder of the History of Diving Museum, for her invaluable comments on chapters 1 and 2 (the history of diving); Karl Huggins for his insights into Chapter 3 (history of decompression theory and models); cardiologist and technical diver Dr. Douglas Ebersole for making Chapter 11 (diving and the cardiovascular system) more accurate and clear; tech diver and Divers Alert Network (DAN) Research Director Dr. Neal Pollock for his thorough work on chapters 14 (heat loss in divers) and 27 (exercise and decompression); DAN Medical Director and COO Dr. Nick Bird for his extensive, meticulous and considered comments and suggestions on the physiology and medicine of decompression sickness in chapters 26 and 28; and PADI Technical Development Executive Karl Shreeves for his expert input into chapters 40 (technical diving) and 42 (rebreathers). This book would be a poor attempt on my part without them, and I thank them deeply.

A warm thanks also goes out to my publishing family at *Dive Training* magazine. First, to Executive Editor Cathryn Castle Whitman, who has had the challenging task of editing my work longer than anyone else except my wife. For nearly two decades her considerable talents have turned my meager writing ability into comprehensible prose. Likewise, I'd like to give a tip of the hat to another real pro who has helped me become a better writer over the years and who made no small contribution to this book, Managing Editor Gene Gentrup. I was also honored to have Doreen Hann — the best graphic artist in the dive publishing industry — design the book. And last but certainly not least I'd like to acknowledge the person who made this book, as well as much of the last 20 years of my career possible, *Dive Training*'s publisher, Mark Young.

A most heartfelt recognition goes out to my oldest dive buddy of almost 50 years, and best friend in the world, Joe Heidel. From the dives we barely survived as teenagers until today, our time together underwater has taught me more about diving than any other experience or source. His contribution to Section 5 was incalculable; and I thank him for all our years together.

And finally to my dive buddy for life, my wife Deb, who brings meaning and substance not only to my writing but to my life.

Preface

The Complete Diver:
The History, Science and Practice of Scuba Diving

Scuba diving has seen a dramatic transformation over the past few decades. Technological innovations, along with changes in training methods, have fundamentally changed the face of the sport. Today, almost anyone in reasonable health can become a scuba diver. And not only has learning to dive become an easier and friendlier experience, its safety record has improved as well. In fact, if measured by the risk of injury — and by "injury," meaning a trip to the emergency room — scuba diving is now, per capita, safer than bowling!

But in the head-long rush to make diving as simple and easy as possible, some — including myself — believe that we have lost something. Like most other activities today, diver training has been driven by the I-want-it-yesterday, multitasking nature of life in the 21st century. For example, computer-based instruction now makes it possible for would-be divers to complete their "academic" training (akin to ground school for pilots) without ever reading a book or setting foot in a classroom. In addition, responding to the time-crunched consumer demand, many certification courses are now taught over a single weekend (a process that once took months). And at almost any resort destination in the world one can

become a fully certified diver — start to finish — in only three or four days. Although today's train-in-a-hurry divers are, for the most part, technically competent, they simply do not — cannot — possess the level of knowledge that was seen in their predecessors.

Some say that an in-depth knowledge was never a necessity for safe diving, and point instead to skill development as the hallmark of competence. While I agree that skill and experience are the primary attributes of a competent diver, I still find it somewhat sad that so much of the history, science and nuance that was once part of becoming a diver has all but disappeared from modern diver training.

Yet many claim that in-depth knowledge has not been banished from diving; what's changed is how it's approached. Gone is the once-common comprehensive training course, where divers learned everything there was to know about being underwater. Instead, today's divers are taught the rudiments of knowledge in a course that stresses practical skill development. To emphasize its intended purpose, the very name given to those with an entry-level certificate is "Open Water Diver." Many have described this qualification as a "license to learn."

Those interested in pursuing more in-depth knowledge and skills are encouraged to pursue continuing education and become "advanced" or "specialty" certified. This concept is laudable, but it ignores one important fact: It doesn't really work for the vast majority of divers. The simple reality is that most folks who are certified never go beyond the Open Water level. Personally, I don't find this surprising because people pursue scuba diving as only one of many recreational interests, and often don't have either the time or interest in becoming certified as an "advanced" participant.

In my view, what diving educators should strive for is not convincing an Open Water Diver to become an Advanced Diver, but instead concentrating on making all divers what I term a "complete diver" — someone who possesses both the skill to dive safely and the knowledge to fully understand and appreciate the underwater experience. That's what this book is all about.

The Complete Diver is a product forged from my nearly half-century of experience as a scuba educator. In that time I've learned an awful lot about diving, much of which has never found its way into textbooks or certification courses. Some of what I've learned has come from the school of hard knocks, and a not-too-small dose of luck. The other information that I'll present was gained the old-fashioned way, through exhaustive research and actually interviewing those in the vanguard of their field. Some of what you'll read about has never been addressed before in books on diving, at least not in the way I'll try to present it.

Ironically, I never planned to write this book; it simply evolved from the more than 250 feature articles that I was privileged to write for *Dive Training* magazine since joining their staff in 1991. The project actually came from a comment made by a colleague that it was a shame few could appreciate the full effect of my work, as it was pieced out monthly over more than two decades. He pointed out that what I'm writing about today in *Dive Training* is probably being read by the children of those who read my articles as kids, themselves. (With friends like that, who needs enemies?) I'll leave it to the reader to decide whether there's any real effect from my effort, but I will say that it was a rare and wonderful experience revisiting, updating and revising much of what I had almost forgotten I had done.

Of course, to those of you versed in either literary or diving history, my title may sound a bit familiar.

Indeed, it pays homage to Izaak Walton's 17th-century classic, *The Compleat Angler*, and to a little known but important book — *The Compleat Goggler* — published by a 20th-century American expatriate living in France by the name of Guy Gilpatric. (You'll read more about Gilpatric and his contribution to the history of diving in Chapter 2.) I make no pretense of having the literary prowess of Walton, nor expect my book to have the influence of Gilpatric's. But I do believe that all three of us have the same intent: to treat a subject that we care about passionately in a thorough and considered manner.

In the final analysis, *The Complete Diver* is unique because it seeks to achieve a middle-of-the-road approach between the "see Spot run" of basic textbooks and the dry, technically challenging sources available on the more advanced topics of diving. In a phrase, what I try to provide in the following pages is both a comprehensive and comprehensible discussion of what I see as the knowledge base of a truly complete diver.

Like all books on scuba diving, mine is not designed to replace the guidance of a trained and experienced instructor. It simply recognizes that, once divers complete their initial certification, most will never take another formal course of instruction. I'll admit that that's a shame — and I wish that many more divers would pursue further training — but it's reality. So, in the absence of a guiding hand, perhaps you'll benefit from a guiding voice.

Alex Brylske
Summerland Key, Florida
July 2012

Foreword
Cathryn Castle Whitman

I have a sign in my office that reads, "Make it fun. Let it be easy." In my job as an editor, this simple sign reminds me to enjoy the creative process and not get mired down in a mess of deadlines and difficult edits. After all, at the end of the day we're talking about words on a page, not rocket science or nuclear disarmament.

The sign works for scuba diving, too. Most of us who engage in the sport of scuba diving got into it purely for the fun of it — the ease of drifting weightless along a wall or the excitement of exploring a sunken ship.

Scuba diving carries a certain degree of risk, so it's important that we receive expert training and adhere to safety rules. But there's more to being a competent scuba diver than memorizing and following a set of "do this, don't do that" instructions. Yes, we're better off following rules like, "breathe continuously and never hold your breath," but it's critically important to know the why behind the how — the reason we should do a certain thing (or not do it). Not knowing the reason why is ignorant. And ignorance can put us in danger. In fact, research has shown that individuals with only superficial knowledge of a subject may be worse off than those who know absolutely nothing. Physicist Stephen Hawk-ing cautions, "The greatest enemy of knowledge is not ignorance, it is the illusion of knowledge."

This is precisely why *The Complete Diver* is such an important book — not just for beginning divers and instructors, but also for anyone who dons a set of scuba gear and submerges. It is a comprehensive guide to the history, science and practice of scuba diving. It reinforces our initial training and fills in any gaps of knowledge. It connects us to a fascinating timeline of undersea exploration and innovation, and helps us envision a future in which we'll have the ability to probe deeper into the vast expanse of innerspace.

Alex Brylske is perfectly suited to the task of writing *The Complete Diver*. Alex has spent the last several decades as a scuba educator and author of scuba texts and training systems and he's been atop the masthead of *Dive Training* magazine as senior editor since 1991, contributing his expertise to every issue. A college professor of marine science, he possesses a unique combination of Ph.D. and pragmatism that makes it easy for him to carve the most complex subjects into little bites of information that are easy to swallow — and very satisfying.

The Complete Diver is fun to read and easy to understand. Without it, no diver's book collection is complete.

CHAPTER 1

Ye Olde Divers:
The Evolution of Diving

One of life's lessons is that few things ever turn out the way you plan,

or even dream. In my case I'm fortunate in that, in almost every case, things have turned out much better than I could have ever hoped for or imagined. A case in point is my career. When I entered college, I planned to become a history teacher, and graduated with a major in history and philosophy. Science, back then, was relatively unimportant to me; somewhere in the liberal arts was where I'd spend my career. Yet, life set me on the path to become an oceanographer and professor of marine science. Of course, not everyone is so fortunate. The world is full of folks with unfulfilled dreams and life plans that somehow wrecked along the highway of life.

For someone who turned out to be a scientist, one might conclude that my early training in the liberal arts was of little use, if not an outright waste of time. But I can assure you that nothing could be further from the truth. My liberal arts background has been a useful supplement to me as an oceanographer. How so? It enables me to appreciate the evolution of science more deeply than many scientists who lack my historical perspective. And as a science educator it inspires me to address subjects like the history of science, and its influence on society, in every course that I teach.

I remember as a young history major continually facing doubt from peers and family who questioned my decision to study history. The inevitable question was, "What use is studying the past?" Of course, my standard off-the-shelf response was the famous quote by philosopher George Santayana: "Those who do not remember the past are condemned to repeat it." But as I grew older I realized that the value to studying history was more important than learning how to avoid mistakes. Regardless of who you are and what you do, not knowing where you came from makes it impossible to know where you

are. What's more, if you don't know your history, you don't even know that you're lost. So, you never ask the question of where you are in the first place. That's what studying history does — it provides context and sense of place. To me, not knowing history would be like waking up every morning having forgotten every event that ever happened to you.

Diving, too, has a long history that, sadly, is largely forgotten. Thus, aside from perhaps references to Jacques Cousteau, how divers got where they are today is hardly mentioned in diver training courses at any level. That's unfortunate because our past is both rich and instructive. So, if we're to understand where we are, let's take a look at where we've been.

Ancient Divers

Since the dawn of human existence, men have entered the water to collect food, so it's impossible to trace the exact date or origin of diving. We do know from artifacts that the people of Mesopotamia engaged in diving as a form of commerce — usually collecting pearl oysters — as long as 4,500 years ago. By the third millennia before Christ, the Greeks of Thebes also had a thriving pearl diving industry, which was soon followed by the Chinese.

References to sponge fishermen are mentioned by Homer as early as 1000 B.C. Tethered to the surface, their technique involved plummeting to depths of 100 feet (30 m) or more by holding a heavy rock. They, of course, knew nothing about the anatomy of equalization. So to try and compensate somewhat for the increasing pressure on their ears, they poured oil into their ear canals, and took a mouthful before descent. Once on the bottom, they spit out the oil, cut as many sponges free from the bottom as their limited breath-holding capacity would allow, and were then hauled back to the surface by the tether. It was certainly a grueling and painful way to earn a living.

The most famous divers of antiquity were the Greeks Scyllias of Scione and his daughter Cyana. The pair was commissioned by the Persian King Xerxes (the same guy who had such a difficult time with 300 Spartans at the Battle of Thermopylae) in the fifth century B.C. as treasure salvors during one of the numerous wars between the Persians and Greeks. Not wanting to lose this valued diving duo, Xerxes refused to allow them to return home after finishing their commission. Using reeds as breathing tubes to avoid detection, they slipped into the water under the cover of darkness and escaped. Years later, they destroyed one of Xerxes' fleets by diving into a stormy sea and cutting the mooring lines of the vessels at anchor. For their bravery, statues of Scyllias and Cyana were erected in the Greek city of Delphi. Parenthetically, one contemporary writer noted that Cyana's diving experience proved that "young women may dive into the sea without fear of losing their virginity." Until then, it was believed that the water pressure that could so easily break eardrums could in the same way compromise the virtue of young maidens.

Divers were also enlisted into military operations long before the birth of Christ. The Spartans and Athenians were the first to employ combat divers, but history usually credits Alexander the Great in his famous siege of Tyre (Lebanon) in 332 B.C. He used "demolition divers" to remove obstacles from the harbor. In fact, Aristotle reported that Alexander himself made several dives in a crude diving bell to observe the work in progress.

By the first century before Christ, a thriving salvage industry sprung up throughout the major trade routes

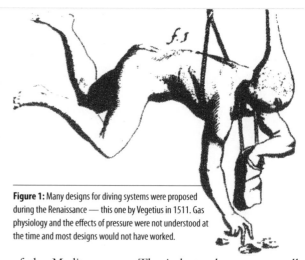

Figure 1: Many designs for diving systems were proposed during the Renaissance — this one by Vegetius in 1511. Gas physiology and the effects of pressure were not understood at the time and most designs would not have worked.

of the Mediterranean. The industry became so well-organized that laws were on the books mandating the fee structure for the services of salvors. Generally, the fee depended on the depth of the wreck. For example, in depths of 25 feet (7.5 m) or greater, the salvor's share was one-half of all goods recovered. From 25 to 12 feet (7.5 to 3.6 m) the share was reduced to one-third; and in water shallow enough to stand, the share was only one-tenth the value of the goods.

Greece and Mesopotamia did not hold exclusive license on diving. Collecting pearl oysters and seafood by diving was a common activity throughout the world. From the Ama divers of Japan and Korea to the Maya of Central America to the Yahgan Indians of the Cape Horn region, freediving has a long and rich history. Even Columbus found a thriving pearl diving industry on the coast of what is now Venezuela. Interestingly, in all of these cultures, the divers were usually female.

The Middle Ages to the Industrial Revolution

In Europe, freedivers continued to make significant contributions in warfare up through the Middle Ages. From Denmark to the Mediterranean, divers were used to cut anchor rodes, drill holes in ships' hauls and ferry supplies to besieged coastal cites.

The first diving apparatus is credited to an Egyptian named Ahsan-ul-Ghawasin, also known as Issa. He served in the navy of the Turkish Sultan Saladin during the third Crusade. As a means of getting supplies through to the city of Acre, he is said to have constructed a device from a bellows. Weighted by a heavy stone, the device let him remain submerged just below the surface and swim past the Christian defenders. The record contains colorful accounts of Issa's horror at witnessing the hundreds of Arab bodies strewn on the seafloor "serving a feast for eels, octopus and crabs." He, too, became one of those bodies after he was spotted by a Crusader patrol and shot dead by an arrow.

With the dawn of the Renaissance and profusion of scientific inquiry, inventors experimented with various designs including breathing tubes (most of which were impractical) and diving bells. Leonardo da Vinci, in particular, penned a number of drawings of diving systems and even sketched what could be considered the prototype of modern goggles and fins.

In 1772 a Frenchman named Sieur Freminet produced what he called the "hydrostatergatic machine." It consisted of a brass helmet with eyeholes. The air was supplied by a bellows into a small air reservoir, then pumped down to the diver. Clearly, Freminet's invention had its flaws, as he died from hypoxia after being in his own device for only 20 minutes.

In 1786 John and William Braithwaite developed an improved version of the helmet as did a German, Karl Heinrich Klingert, in 1787 (see Figure 2). Still, the advances in diving technology of the 18th century came from improvements in diving bells rather than helmets.

Further refinement of the self-contained system came in 1825 from English inventor William James. His design employed a cylindrical iron "belt" attached to a copper helmet. The belt held about 450 psi of air, which allowed for a dive of only about seven minutes.

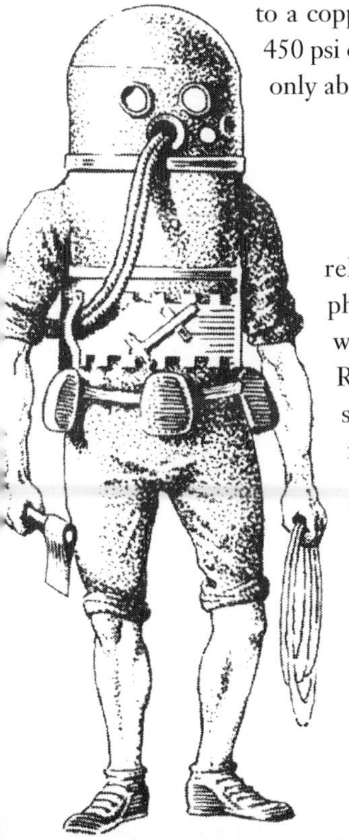

The Evolution of Diving Bells

Although their design was relatively haphazard and unsophisticated, diving bells did meet with limited success during the Renaissance. One of the first successful salvage operations using a one-person diving bell oc-

Figure 2: Klingert's diving system consisted of a large copper helmet and waistband attached to a leather jacket. One design was surface-supplied. Another version allowed it to be attached to a submersible air reservoir, making it perhaps the first self-contained diving system.

Figure 3: This primitive diving bell, designed by an Italian named Lorena, was used to salvage a Roman Galley in Italy's Lake Nemi in 1531.

curred in 1531 in Lake Nemi near Rome (see Figure 3). As the bell carried with it only the amount of air trapped within it once it submerged, it provided only a short bottom time. In addition, the buildup of excess carbon dioxide was a problem, though one which was unknown to scientists and inventors of the time.

In 1669 George Sinclair, a professor at Glasgow University, wrote a treatise describing the theory and techniques for using diving bells. Based on Sinclair's theories, in 1685 one of the most famous early salvors — Sir William Phips — used a bell to recover nearly $1 million worth of treasure from the wreck of the Spanish galleon *La Nuestra Senora de Almiranta* in the West Indies (see Figure 4).

Figure 4: The Cadaques bell — named for the Spanish city where it was designed — was made of wood and used iron ingots around the rim to make it sink. William Phips used this crude but effective bell to salvage the *Almiranta*. He was knighted for his effort.

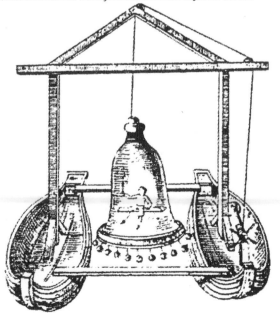

Figure 5: Lethbridge's "diving engine," built in 1715, was one of the most successful diving systems used in the 18th century.

At about the same time as Sinclair was writing about diving bells, a contemporary named Sir Robert Boyle was making important discoveries concerning the behavior of gases under pressure. Using Boyle's research, a French priest named Abbé Jean de Hautefeuille wrote in 1681 *The Art of Breathing Underwater*, explaining for the first time why, "It is not possible for man to breathe air at normal atmospheric pressure when he is himself under water at depth." These ideas culminated in the more sophisticated diving bells designed by famed English astronomer Sir Edmund Halley (the same guy "Halley's comet" is named for) and an enterprising commoner from Devon, England, named John Lethbridge.

Unlike the traditional bell design, Lethbridge's idea was to place the diver in a large sealed cylinder, allowing his arms to remain free to work (see Figure 5). He called his device a "diving engine." Once sealed, a diver could remain submerged about a half-hour to a maximum depth of about 60 feet (18 m). Then the engine was hauled up and the air supply refreshed with a bellows. Lethbridge and his son traveled throughout the world for nearly 30 years successfully salvaging wrecks for sponsors such as the famous Dutch East India Company. He is credited by many as the forerunner of the modern commercial diver.

Edmund Halley's design was a more traditional bell, but it was far more sophisticated than those of his predecessors'. Like Lethbridge's engine, it was constructed of wood, but it was also encased by lead to give it negative buoyancy. Unlike Lethbridge's design, it contained a valve to purge stale air, and a system of weighted barrels connected to a hose to replenish fresh air while the bell was underwater. Divers could even leave the bell for short periods using a special helmet, called a Capp of

Maintenance, and closed leather suit allowing the diver to work outside the bell with air provided through a flexible waterproof hose. Halley used a cock mechanism to regulate the flow of air to the diver. His piping system also enabled the diver to work below the level of the bell by using a bellows to deliver air. In 1693 Halley added a thick glass window to the top of the bell and reported on the addition of a manometer to show the depth of the bell (See Figure 6).

On one excursion Halley himself dove to 60 feet (18 m) in the bell and remained there for 90 minutes. He reported a pain in his ears, "as if a quill had been thrust into them." Although unknown at the time, it's also interesting to note that such a bottom time is well in excess of any no-decompression limit. There is, however, no mention of Halley experiencing bends symptoms. Soon after Halley's design was published, a French mathematician, Denis Papin, suggested replenishing the air supply in diving bells continuously via hoses and bellows.

Figure 6: Edmund Halley's diving bell, using a system of weighted and sealed barrels, was the first to allow replenishing the air supply underwater.

Halley's bell design was refined by a famous English engineer named John Smeaton in 1788. Smeaton incorporated several improvements, including a bell made from cast iron, the first efficient hand-operated pump to sustain the air supply via a hose, an air reservoir system

and nonreturn valves to keep air from being sucked back up the hoses when the pump stopped. This was the first truly modern diving bell, and by the end of the century virtually every major harbor in the world had one for salvage, construction and repair operations. From this point on, bottom times began to increase dramatically and working underwater was becoming commonplace.

The Dawn of Modern Diving Systems

In 1820, a farm near Whitstable, England, caught fire and ignited a spark that would eventually result in the standard equipment used by divers for almost 150 years. Because of the dense smoke, rescuers were unable to get into the stable to save a team of valuable horses. The small water pump of the local fire brigade had little effect on the blaze, and a disaster was surely in the making. But an ingenious, burly man in the crowd had an idea. Borrowing a helmet from a medieval suit of armor on display at a nearby home, he asked the fire brigade to pump air, not water, through the hose. Placing the hose under the helmet to provide a continuous air supply, he bravely walked into the stable through the dense smoke and saved the entire stock. That man was John Deane.

Realizing the implications of his improvised invention, John and his brother Charles went into business producing a firefighting apparatus that they patented in 1823 (see Figure 7). But John had a grander vision for his invention. He believed it could be used for diving, and by 1828 the original firefighting apparatus evolved into "Deane's Patent Diving Dress." He modified the fire helmet design by adding larger viewing ports, and

countered the effects of buoyancy with weighted shoes. A heavy fabric suit was worn to protect the diver from the elements, but the helmet did not attach to the suit. It merely rested on the diver's shoulders and secured to his waist by straps.

As the helmet wasn't attached to the suit, air escaped at the bottom. This was the system's major flaw, as the diver had to continually remain in an upright position. If the diver bent over, or even fell, the helmet would flood and he could drown. Still, the Deane's system was very successful and soon the brothers became well-known salvage operators. In 1836 they produced what was probably the first diving manual. A truly remarkable man, John Deane continued diving until the ripe old age of 56, even diving under the ice in the Black Sea to salvage Russian warships after the Crimean War.

Most historical records tend to forget about the Deane brothers, and instead concentrate on a German instrument maker by the name of Augustus Siebe. He refined the Deanes' design by inventing an efficient way of sealing the helmet to the suit, and improving the exhaust system. By 1840 the "Siebe Improved Diving Dress" was introduced; and Siebe went on to found Siebe Gorman and Company, one of the most famous diving companies in the world. It was Siebe's system that became the true predecessor to the famous deep-sea diving dress familiar to everyone.

Figure 7: A patent drawing of the Deane smoke helmet, which was later modified into a prototype for the modern commercial diver's dress.

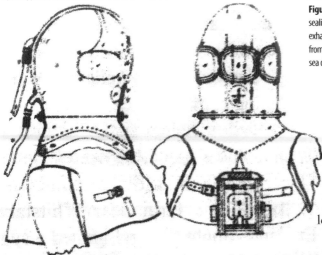

Figure 8: Siebe improved on the Deane brothers' design by sealing the helmet to a waterproof suit and improving the exhaust system. Even in its earlier stages — this system is from 1837 — the suit is recognizable as the standard deep-sea diver's dress for well into the 20th century.

Salvage of the HMS *Royal George*

In 1783 the British warship *Royal George* sank in a freak accident while home for repairs in England's Portsmouth Harbor. It was a devastating tragedy with an inordinate loss of life, including 250 visiting women and children. As it was in a busy harbor in only 65 feet (20 m) of water, the ship was a major hazard to navigation. In 1839 the task of salvaging the vessel fell to a remarkable colonel in the British Royal Engineers named William Charles Pasley. Many historians believe that Pasley's operation brought diving into the modern era; and given the number of innovations and discoveries that resulted from the salvage of the *Royal George* from 1839 to 1842, it's a hard conclusion to dispute.

The salvage operation was on the cutting edge of early 19th-century technology, and one of Pasley's objectives was to evaluate various diving systems. Abandoning most systems because they were either too cumbersome or dangerous, he selected the Siebe Improved Dress and recommended its adoption as the standard for the Royal Engineers. This certainly was one reason the Siebe design went on to become so universally popular.

One of the reasons the *Royal George* operation gained fame was because salvors used underwater explosives for the first time. Incredibly, the exploding devices were made from lead-encased oak barrels filled with gunpowder and welded shut by a brave crewmember. They were detonated by a wire that ran from inside the device to a battery on deck.

Of interest to recreational divers were the numerous historical milestones generated from the *Royal George* operation. For instance, one of the regulations Pasley invoked was that his divers had to operate in pairs. This became the first recorded use of the buddy system for diving. In addition, the historical record is replete with the exploits of one particular diver known only as "Corporal Jones." On one occasion, Jones' umbilical became hopelessly entrapped in a load of pig iron ballast as it was being loaded in a cargo sling. Miraculously, Jones managed to cut free from his umbilical, kick off his weighted boots, and ascend back to the surface from 60 feet (18 m) while continuously exhaling. He thus became the first person in recorded history to make an emergency swimming ascent in a full diving dress.

Another unfortunate milestone for the salvage crew was the first medical account of a massive diver squeeze. Early diving helmets did not have nonreturn valves. This meant that if a hose was severed, the high-pressure air surrounding the diver rapidly and with incredible force escaped from the helmet. At even a modest depth, the tremendous negative pressure created by the escaping air caused an extreme and often life-threatening squeeze on the diver. This is exactly what happened to Private John Williams. Fortunately, even though "his face and neck were swollen and livid, his eyeball capillaries ruptured and blood was flowing from his ears and mouth," Williams survived. But he never returned to diving.

In extreme cases, the negative pressure caused by a severed air hose could actually suck flesh and soft tissues up into the pipe and much of the diver's body into the helmet. Stories abound among old-time commercial divers in which so much of a diver was sucked into his helmet that it was buried in place of a coffin. (And you thought an ear squeeze was painful.)

Over the three years the salvage operation was under way, Pasley's crew received extensive and colorful coverage in the press. Eventually, their exploits came to the attention of the Royal Navy. (There was quite a bit of jealousy because the Royal Engineers were a contingent of the British *Army*.) But swallowing their pride, the Navy allowed Pasley to take a complement of 13 petty officers from the HMS *Excellence* and set up the first Royal Navy diving school. The first instructor was the indomitable Corporal Jones. At the conclusion of the *Royal George* operation, Pasley said of him, "Whatever success has attended our operations is chiefly attributed to the exertions of Corporal Jones, of whom as a diver I can not speak too highly."

CHAPTER 2

The Untethered Diver
and Daddy Scuba

Ask divers what inspired them to take up diving

and you're likely to hear a variety of reasons. I'll wager the list will include the challenge diving presents, the chance to explore an entirely different world, a lifelong love of the sea, to escape the stress of the everyday world, and probably more than a few votes for "a friend talked me into it." But I'll also bet you the farm that a lot of folks of my generation will specifically credit one of two individuals for their choice of avocation (and in cases like mine, vocation). For those who began diving in the mid-1960s, as I did, or before, that person would be Mike Nelson (played by actor Lloyd Bridges) from the landmark 1950s TV series, *Sea Hunt.* For those who got started a bit later, it was Jacques Cousteau, based on the wildly popular TV series from the 1960s and '70s, *The Undersea World of Jacques Cousteau.*

Before his death, Jacques Cousteau was one of the most recognized people on the planet. Like Thomas Edison, the "aqualung" inventor sparked a revolution. Not only did the device create an entire industry, it also extended our scientific understanding of the ocean more than perhaps any other invention in history. But the idea of the aqualung didn't just spring forth into Cousteau's mind out of nowhere. While an individual is normally "credited" with an invention, the truth is that inventions are the result of a historical, evolutionary process in which new ideas and technology build on older ideas and technology. So, too, is the story of modern scuba. Unfortunately, once an invention is "perfected," the accolades for the inventor normally drown out any recognition for those who came before. But by ignoring those on whose shoulders an inventor stood we do both a great injustice to earlier pioneers, and fail to grasp the true nature of world-changing technological advances. So, giving Cousteau his due, let's take a more thorough look at how self-contained diving came to be.

While references can be found in the writings of both the Renaissance scientists Leonardo di Vinci and Giovanni Borelli, credit for the first workable self-contained diving system design should probably go to the English inventor William James. As shown in Figure 1, his apparatus consisted of an iron reservoir, secured

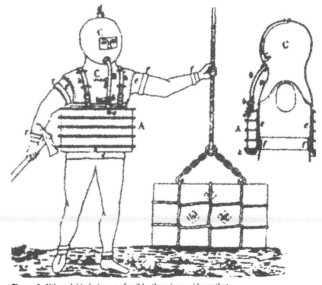

Figure 1: Although his design was feasible, there is no evidence that William James' self-contained diving system was ever put to practical use.

around the diver's waist. The air was injected into a helmet, regulated only by a free-flow on/off valve. Although his design dates back to 1825, there's no evidence that it was actually used. The first functional system was actually invented on the other side of the Atlantic.

An American, Charles Condert of Brooklyn, manufactured and used the first functional self-contained diving system in 1831. As depicted in Figure 2, his design consisted of a gutta percha- (pliable substance made from latex) impregnated suit that was partially inflated by a horseshoe-shaped air reservoir secured around the waist. Glass ports allowed him to see out, and expired air escaped from a small hole in the top of the hood. Air was periodically replenished via an on/off valve. The air reservoir was "charged" at the surface by a pump Condert built from the barrel of a gun. Condert also had to carry a 200-pound (90 kg) ballast to counteract the system's enormous positive buoyancy. Yet, crude as it was, Condert's system worked, and he is reported to have made numerous dives to a depth of about 20 feet (6 m) in the East River. But on one fateful dive in 1832, he experienced a problem that severed the hose that provided air to the suit. He drowned as a result.

Figure 2: Although he designed the first functional self-contained diving system, inventor-diver Charles Condert became an early victim of diving technology. He drowned in New York's East River when his air line was accidentally parted.

In 1863 another American refined Condert's design. T. Cato McKeen added a large back-mounted air reservoir and fabricated a rubber suit. Perhaps the most ingenious part of McKeen's apparatus was the addition of a second air system to inflate the suit and bring the diver to the surface. (Although this has been described by some as the forerunner of the modern buoyancy compensator, an Argentinian, Manuel Theodore Guil-

laumet, actually received a French patent for an inflatable vest in 1839.)

Unquestionably the most famous self-contained design of the 18th century was developed by a French mining engineer, Benoit Rouquayrol, and his associate, French naval officer Auguste Denayrouze. In 1865 they built the Aerophore. This apparatus was similar to earlier designs — an air reservoir was carried on the back — except that it was the first to incorporate a regulator to control the air delivery. Using a crude diaphragm-like device, their regulator was similar in concept to the modern demand valve. In fact, expired air was expelled into the water through a one-way valve, much like in a modern scuba regulator.

While the Aerophore was designed primarily as a surface-supplied device, it could function completely independent of an external air supply. The Aerophore enjoyed widespread popularity, and was the inspiration for the diving suits described by a contemporary — Jules Verne — in his classic adventure novel *20,000 Leagues Under the Sea*.

Self-contained systems were extremely inefficient and required large air reservoirs. So, by the 1870s interest shifted to developing an oxygen system that could scrub and recirculate the breathing gas, a system that we today call a rebreather.

Though designs for oxygen rebreathers date back to the Napoleonic Period, the first practical design is often credited to Frenchman Pierre Aimable De Saint Simon Sicard for his patent in 1849. Close on Sicard's heels was a 1853 patent by German biologist Theodor Schwann (he became much more famous for his contribution to cell the-

Figure 3: The most famous self-contained diving system of its time, the Aerophore was the inspiration for the divers in Jules Verne's 20,000 Leagues Under the Sea.

ory). In 1878, Englishman Henry Fleuss developed an apparatus consisting of a rubberized fabric hood, a breathing bag and a copper cylinder containing oxygen compressed to 30 atmospheres (440 psi). The tank, along with a carbon dioxide scrubber, was worn on the back. As the diver rebreathed his expired air, the system needed periodic recharging from the oxygen supply.

Fleuss' system was used in one of the most incredible commercial diving operations in history. In 1880 a tunnel under the Severn River in England flooded, and couldn't be pumped out unless a hatchway door was closed. Unfortunately, that hatchway was not only at 60 feet (18 m) of depth, but also 1,000 feet (300 m) back into the tunnel. In a death-defying feat, one of the most famous commercial divers of his time, Alexander Lambert, made the excursion using the Fleuss oxygen apparatus.

The most remarkable thing about Lambert's dive is that neither he nor anyone else knew that breathing pure oxygen was toxic below a depth of about 25 feet (7.5 m). But he found that out three years later when a similar problem occurred and he was asked to make the dive again. This time Lambert almost died from an "oxygen hit" (massive convulsions). His experience pointed out the system's major drawback — a diver's depth and time are limited when breathing pure oxygen.

Regardless of its limitations, Fleuss' apparatus was far from a failure. Later he redesigned it, placing the oxygen tank and breathing bag on the diver's chest. This was a prototype for the oxygen rebreathers used by the frogmen of World War II. A modification of the Fleuss device became the first successful submarine escape apparatus. Interestingly, a similar system was used in filming the first underwater feature movie — the J.E. Williamson's 1915 version of — what else? — *20,000 Leagues Under the Sea.*

In 1900 the inventor and early underwater photographer Louis Bouton went back to an air-based design. He became the first to solve the air reservoir problem by adding high-pressure tanks capable of holding 200 atmospheres (about 3,000 psi). The self-contained diver was finally beginning to look like his modern counterpart.

By 1918 a relatively obscure but highly successful system was developed in Japan — the "Ohgushi Peerless Respirator." Ohgushi incorporated many of the ideas of his predecessors, but his major contribution was using a more modern mask design, which was similar to the one used by early scuba divers. The major flaw in the system was the

Figure 4: One of the first systems to use a compressed air tank, the Ohgushi Peerless Respirator used a regulator requiring a very complex breathing process in which the diver had to breathe in through his nose and out through his mouth.

complex way in which the regulator system worked. To breathe, the diver had to clench his teeth against a valve, inhale through his nose, then exhale through his mouth. Nonetheless, the device was adopted by the Japanese Navy and there are records of its use in salvage operations to depths of more than 200 feet (61 m).

The Genesis of a New Sport

Most of the diving systems we've described so far were custom-made by the inventor. But by the early 1920s some visionaries were beginning to see a need for mass-manufactured equipment. Some even foresaw diving moving beyond the realm of commerce and becoming a recreational activity. One of those visionaries was a Frenchman named Yves Le Prieur.

Le Prieur learned to dive in the navy during the early years of the 20th century. But his zeal for improving diving systems didn't occur until 1925 when he saw a demonstration of an underwater torch used to cut metal. What impressed Prieur most wasn't the cutting tool, but the breathing system the diver used. It had been invented back in 1912 by Maurice Frenez. Soon after the demonstration, Prieur and Frenez collaborated on an improved system using tanks of compressed air, and by 1933 had a very functional apparatus, as shown in Figure 5. The major flaw in Le Prieur's device, however, was that it wasted so much air. Lacking a demand-type regulator, it was a free-flow system. The diver manually controlled the air flow from the tank, allowing it to enter directly into the mask. The expired air — along with a lot of unused air — escaped under the mask seal. Still, the "Le Prieur Improved Diving Apparatus" made a major contribution and helped spawn recreational diving.

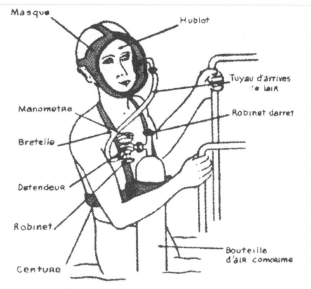

Masque
Hublot
Tuyau d'arrivée de l'air
Manomètre
Robinet d'arrêt
Bretelle
Détendeur
Robinet
Bouteille d'air comprimé
Ceinture

Figure 5: The "Le Prieur Improved Diving Apparatus" used a successful full-face mask. But lacking a demand regulator, it wasted most of the valuable air supply as it free-flowed into and out of the mask.

In 1935 Prieur gave a series of demonstrations of his device in Paris, which sparked the imagination of many. One observer was Jean Painleve who that same year founded the first amateur diving club — Club des Scaphandres et de la Vie Sous L'Eau.

Birth of the Man-Fish

In the years after the First World War an expatriate American named Guy Gilpatric was living on the coast of Southern France. And although his name is virtually unknown today, Gilpatric, more than perhaps anyone else, was the modern inspiration for recreational diving. An ex-aviator, Gilpatric began spearfishing in the Mediterranean using a crude pole spear and a pair of his flying goggles he had sealed with putty and paint. Gilpatric became quite an accomplished spearfisherman and well known in the local community. In 1928 he published an important book describing his adventures — *The Compleat Goggler* (to which this book pays homage). This work went on to spur the first generation of freedivers much as Cousteau's later book, *The Silent World*, inspired the first generation of scuba enthusiasts.

Strangely, Gilpatric never wore fins, even though prototypes came on the scene by 1930. By 1933 a French inventor named de Corlieu received the patent, and by 1935 fins were available commercially for the first time. Fins were brought to America by yet another diving pioneer, Owen Churchill, who produced the de Corlieu design under license. Churchill's fins went on to become

standard issue for both the frogmen of World War II and early sport divers. Incredibly, you can still see an adaptation of the Churchill design in use even today. (I have a pair in my own dive locker.) The stubby, odd-shaped fins are extremely popular among boogie boarders and body surfers.

Like fins, the diving mask can be traced back to the 1930s. The modern diving mask, of course, evolved from goggles. The first person to improve on their primitive design was a Russian, Alec Kramarenko, who was inspired by the equipment and technique of the Ama pearl divers. Kramarenko replaced the double lens with a single plate; using a molded rubber skirt, the plate was held in place by a wooden frame.

Because his design did not enclose the nose, the diver couldn't equalize the internal pressure with the external water pressure. This allowed the diver to descend only about 20 feet (6 m) before succumbing to a serious mask squeeze. To solve this problem, Kramarenko added rubber bulbs at each end. On descent, these bulbs were squeezed, forcing more air into the mask itself, and counteracting the external pressure. While it was rather bizarre looking, the design did work. The final evolution of enclosing the nose as well as the eyes in the mask is credited to yet another Frenchman, Maxime Forjot. He received a patent for his innovation in 1938.

Communication among freedivers of the time was very poor, and parallel development of technology certainly occurred. For example, American diving pioneer Jack Prodanovich independently developed an improved diving mask about the same time as Kramarenko and Forjot.

Creation of the snorkel is a little less clear in the historical record. Gilpatric credits his friend Englishman Steve Butler for the device. But the patent eventually went again to Maxime Forjot in 1938.

The Forgotten Men of Diving

At the same time freediving technology was advancing, an important step forward was made in breathing apparatus design. The first completely automatic scuba system was produced by George Commeinhes, one of the spearfishermen inspired by Gilpatric. By chance, Commeinhes' family owned a company that manufactured valves for the mining industry.

Using his mechanical knowledge and family's ample resources, Commeinhes improved on Le Prieur's design. He retained the full-face mask concept, but placed the compressed air tank on the diver's back. But more significantly, Commeinhes' device abandoned the free flow design of Le Prieur, replacing it with a demand valve mounted between the diver's shoulders.

In 1937 the Commeinhes unit was approved for use by the French Navy, and was tested to depths of more than 150 feet (45 m). Unfortunately, while the Commeinhes device held great promise, the inventor was killed in combat during the war. One can only speculate how the history of diving might have been altered had Commeinhes not met such a tragic and untimely end.

Another future notable inspired by Gilpatric was a young Austrian zoologist, Hans Hass. But unlike Gilpatric's fascination with spearfishing, Hass turned his interest to underwater photography. After a successful journey to take underwater photos off the Dalmatian coast, Hass planned a more elaborate expedition to make an underwater film. Although he originally intended to film in the Red Sea, the mounting international tensions of prewar Europe convinced him to change his plan. He instead chose the island of Curaçao, and thus the first feature-length underwater documentary was shot in the Caribbean in 1939. The film contained the first close-ups of sharks in the wild, which is particularly amazing considering that much of it was shot while freediving.

Serendipity and Creation of Modern Scuba

The influence of Guy Gilpatric on diving's early pioneers was very significant. And one of the earliest converts to the new sport was a French Naval officer named Philippe Taillez. Coincidentally, a friend of Tailliez, also a Naval officer, was involved in a serious car accident, and was reassigned to duty in the French coastal city of Toulon. As part of his rehabilitation, he began to do a lot of swimming. One day Taillez introduced his friend to Gilpatric and the history of diving would never again be the same. That accident victim was Jacques-Yves Cousteau. Together with Taillez and another well-known spearfisherman, Fredric Dumas, the trio would go on to ensure that the fledgling sport of diving would become what it is today.

Cousteau's experience with the Le Prieur device led him to believe that a great potential existed for the recreational use of underwater breathing equipment, but only after significant design improvements. Initially Cousteau experimented with oxygen-based systems. But by 1939 personal experience — including a bout with oxygen convulsions — convinced him that oxygen was too dangerous for use in a recreational system.

In the fall of 1942 Cousteau went to Paris on leave along with his friend Taillez. The trip had two objectives. First, they wanted permission to make more underwater documentary films. (Cousteau had made his first underwater film, *Ten Fathoms Under the Sea*, in 1940.) The second reason was to meet with Emile Gagnan, a talented engineer who worked for the Air Liquide Corporation. (Today Air Liquide, and its U.S. affiliate, the Liquid Air Corporation, are the parent companies of U.S. Divers.) The reason Cousteau contacted Gagnan was because of his expertise in building specialized valves.

Gagnan agreed to help and proposed a valve based on a design he'd invented to convert automobiles from gasoline to natural gas, as gasoline was a scarce and valuable commodity during wartime. Their original design was only marginally successful. In fact, Cousteau nearly drowned during the first test dive in the Marne River. They then redesigned the demand valve and positioned it on the diver's back between his shoulders — similar to the Commeinhes apparatus. But unlike previous designs, Cousteau and Gagnan abandoned the full-face mask, opting instead to supply air to the diver via a mouthpiece. The mouthpiece connected on one side to an intake hose, which delivered the air, and to an exhaust hose on the other side, which directed the expired air away from the diver.

The refined and patented Gagnan valve design was successfully tested in the summer of 1943. After more than 500 shallower test dives, Cousteau's friend and associate Frederic Dumas made a 220-foot (67 m) dive, confirming the reliability of the Cousteau-Gagnan invention. With a simple, safe and reliable breathing apparatus, the final piece had been added to the puzzle, and the stage was now set for the creation of the new sport of scuba diving.

Scuba American Style

The publication of Guy Gilpatric's articles in the *Saturday Evening Post* magazine in the early 1930s gave Americans their first exposure to his undersea exploits. The effect was almost immediate. By 1933

Californians Glenn Orr, Jack Prodanovich and Ben Stone formed the first spearfishing club in the United States — the famous San Diego Bottom Scratchers. By 1939, the Bottom Scratchers added yet another diving trailblazer, Wally Potts; and together the group pioneered the design of more effective equipment and refined the techniques of freediving.

The aqualung was brought to America in 1948 by a Navy UDT commander, Doug Fane. The next year, Cousteau sent six units to Rene Bussoz, a sporting goods dealer who owned a store near the UCLA campus. Seeing the potential value of scuba for scientific investigation, a young graduate student, Conrad Limbaugh, convinced his professor to buy two of the units. Soon after, Limbaugh, along with an associate, Andy Rechnitzer, began diving throughout the Southern California coast. In 1950 the two enrolled in the Ph.D. program at San Diego's Scripps Institution of Oceanography. There they informally tutored a few of their colleagues in the use of scuba until 1952, when a student diver at another California university died in a diving accident.

Alarmed by the death, the Scripps administration asked Limbaugh to create a training course and manual for teaching students to dive. The result was the first formal scuba program and textbook in America. Likewise concerned over the hazards of this increasingly popular sport, in 1954 the Los Angeles County Department of Parks and Recreation sent three representatives — Al Tillman, Bev Morgan and Ramsey Parks — to San Diego to take Limbaugh's course. This was the first scuba instructor program conducted in America. Returning to Los Angeles, the trio formed the nation's first recreational scuba training program. By 1955, of the total worldwide sales of aqualungs (some 25,000 units), 80 percent were purchased in California. The United States clearly had the largest population of recreational divers on the face of the planet.

In 1960 Conrad Limbaugh died in a cave diving accident in France. His position was soon filled by another member of the Scripp's dive team, James Stewart. Over his 30-plus-year career, Stewart went on to pioneer many of the scientific diving techniques that today are the mainstay of academic diving programs throughout the world; and he helped establish the American Academy of Underwater Sciences (AAUS).

During this period another development was under way that was to have equal significance to diver train-

ing. The National YMCA formed a committee to publish a text based on the then-available resource material related to scuba diving. By 1957, the committee, headed by National Physical Education Director Bernard Empleton, published the results of their work under the auspices of the Council for National Cooperation in Aquatics — the textbook, "The Science of Skin and Scuba Diving." Significantly revised, of course, this text is still in use today in some diving programs. In August 1959, the YMCA conducted the first national instructor training program.

By 1960, Neil Hess felt that diver training should be more organized, and instructors training more controlled than could be achieved through the informal process of his Instructor's Corner column. His idea was to start a national training organization using Los Angeles County's diver training program as a model. For guidance Hess turned to Al Tillman, who headed the Los Angeles program. The two organized an instructor certification course in Houston in 1961 that attracted more than 60 of the top diving educators in America. Initially, Hess planned to call the new group the National Diving Patrol, a tribute to the highly successful National Ski Patrol. But that name had already been taken by another entity, and it was decided to call the fledgling organization the National Association of Underwater Instructors (NAUI). Many participants of that first instructor course would eventually go on to have a significant influence on diving, and many are still active today.

Over the next few years a small contingent of divers from the Midwest grew increasingly dissatisfied with the existing diver training infrastructure, contending that it was unresponsive to the needs of inland instructors. In response, Ralph Erickson, an aquatics instructor from Chicago's Loyola University — and graduate of the first NAUI Instructor Institute — along with his friend and diving equipment sales representative, John Cronin, formed the Professional Association of Diving Instructors (PADI) in 1966. In 1973, seeking to establish a more national perspective, PADI moved from Chicago to the mecca of the American diving scene, Southern California.

Meanwhile, believing that their needs were not being addressed by the existing training programs, a group of diving retailers led by John Gaffney formed the National Association of Scuba Diving Schools (NASDS) in 1967. Three years later, after an internal dispute, a group within the NASDS organization led by Bob Clark broke off to form Scuba Schools International. The landscape of recreational diver training as we know it today had been formed.

In diving's early days yet another important entity was the Florida Skin Divers Association. FSDA was formed in 1952 out of a group of Florida-based scuba clubs. That same year they also formed their Scuba Training Committee, and began formally training scuba instructors. In 1976 the Scuba Training Committee voted to split from FSDA, and was renamed the International Diving Educators Association (IDEA). FSDA lineage can be traced to many of diving's early pioneers, including legends like Poppy Taylor, Bob Axelrod, Paul White, and Sheck Exley, Jim Hollis, Ken Brock and Dr. Doug Williamson.

The Transition to the Modern Era

Early divers were a macho crew of daredevils whose activities, like their freediving predecessors, centered primarily on spearfishing. Not surprisingly, their training programs reflected this commitment to hunting and other testosterone-enriched activities. Many early instructors were ex-military and modeled their courses on the requirements, content and activities used in military training. For example, diving's most popular (in fact, only) instructional films were U.S. Navy productions. Featuring about as much staged gore as a slasher movie, these classic films painted vivid impressions in the minds of divers and went a long way in establishing the "deep, dark and dangerous" image of diving in its early years.

Reflecting the rigorous nature of early scuba training, students were required to undergo long hours of esoteric classroom instruction. In fact, by the time these students earned the coveted c-card, they had likely spent 30 or more hours in the classroom exposed to discussions ranging from in-depth physics and mathematics — complete with more than a dose of algebra — to enough equipment mechanics to qualify graduates for admission to engineering school.

This arduous regime just got more difficult when it came to skills training. If fun was what you were after, an early-day scuba course was not the place to go. Many exercises, lifted right out of military course curricula, required the stamina of a marathon runner and the watermanship skills of an Olympic swimmer. The highlight of many programs was the ubiquitous "harassment training" in which the instructor and gleeful staff would swim around a group of students turning off air, releasing buckles, and flooding masks to "simulate" the reality of an unexpected emergency. (To add yet more flare to the exercise, some instructors often required students to wear blacked-out masks during this exercise.)

The idea of early diver training was simple: Before you could call yourself a diver, you had to prove you had what it takes. And what it took was surviving training. Diving might be fun, but fun had little place in learning to dive.

In defense of the very earliest days of diver training, however, there was a solid rationale for the militaristic approach. After all, equipment was unsophisticated and notoriously unreliable; much of it was homemade or surplus military issue. There was no such thing as a buoyancy compensator or submersible pressure gauge. (Part of the math learned in training was supposedly to teach a diver how to calculate how long an air supply would last.) The complete diver's ensemble was considered to be a mask, fins, regulator and tank (and maybe, if you were lucky, a depth gauge). In colder water, an exposure suit was handy, but that was something you would have to make yourself, assuming you could find enough neoprene rubber and a pattern. It was little wonder then that divers often encountered situations in which the only thing between survival and death or injury was their own stamina and physical prowess. Fortunately, that situation was not to last for long.

By the late 1960s the loose confederation of amateur aficionados and garage mechanics had evolved into a true industry. Several full-time diving equipment manufacturers were producing reliable equipment, and technology had improved enough that the diver no longer had to assume that the gear would eventually malfunction.

The problem was, education did not keep pace with advances in technology. Divers were still being trained in the late 1960s and early 1970s in essentially the same way they had been a decade earlier. Still, modern technology — as well as a burgeoning interest in diving among the general public — was not about to be held back by antiquated instructional methods. By the mid-1970s, the face of diver training began to change.

When scuba training was first formalized, learning to dive involved classroom and pool instruction only. Training in open water was considered an afterthought and was not even required (although many instructors did choose to include a check-out dive in the classes). By the late 1960s, this concept of a checkout — a single brief dive in which the student could demonstrate a few rudimentary skills — became a standard practice.

By the 1970s, realizing the true importance of training in the actual environment where diving takes place, a second open-water training dive was added and even more were recommended. By the 1980s, the current standard of four training dives for entry-level certification had arrived, although some organizations adopted this idea of expanded open-water training several years earlier.

Likewise, instruction began to change in the classroom and pool. Classroom instruction was revised to reflect not only changing technology, but also that much of the esoteric training of earlier days was not necessary or even relevant to the modern diver. Subjects such as rote memorization of gas laws, confusing medical jargon, and manipulation of complex formulae soon were replaced by basic, relevant nuts-and-bolts information. Less time was spent with theory and more in practical application.

In the pool, buoyancy control devices and alternate air source regulator — both inventions of this period — caused a revolution in how divers maneuvered in the water and handled out-of-air emergencies. Soon, training programs began to de-emphasize rigorous, irrelevant skills of the past and concentrate on the essence of what a good diver needed to know — buoyancy control, equipment familiarity, and how to deal with problems in a thoughtful, relaxed manner. Without these changes in teaching practice, scuba diving certainly would not have become the mainstream activity that it is today.

What the Future Holds

The future promises to be an exciting time for diver training. As with most other aspects of society, it has been greatly influenced by computer technology. Already, computer-based programs enable classroom instruction to be delivered at the convenience and pace of each learner. In fact, many students today complete the entirety of the academic instruction online, and never even meet an instructor until they are ready for skill training.

In the skills realm also, diver training will be influenced by technology. Already, microprocessors are giving us unimagined access to information. Instruc-

tors, for example, now have the capability to remotely track the bottom time and air supply of their entire class during an open-water dive. Although outside the reach of the average diver's wallet, there's even an underwater GPS enabling instructors to track the location of their charges.

Additionally, buoyancy control systems are now more sophisticated than ever and will probably require a re-examination of teaching techniques. (With integrated weighting systems, for example, weight belts seem to be going the way of the double-hose regulator.) Dry suits, too, are becoming so commonplace in many cold-water locations that some instructors are training entry-level students in their use. This will have significant consequences on instructional methods and course requirements.

One of the most interesting aspects of diving is that even though we have come a long way down the road, many of the pioneers of our sport are still with us. It's as though the Wright brothers were still alive when Neil Armstrong walked on the moon. ✆

CHAPTER 3

Unbending the Past:
The Evolution of Decompression Theory

While the history

of diving may be interesting to some, to others I'm sure it's less than enthralling. After all, not everyone enjoys a day at the museum. However, regardless of your predilection for history, there is one topic that affects all divers — decompression. Still, you might ask why knowing the history of decompression theory could be of any real value to today's divers? The answer lies in what I call "black box diving." By this I mean our willingness to blindly allow microprocessors to control our behavior and decision making. We all realize that decompression sickness (DCS) lurks somewhere in the distance of any dive not much deeper than a swimming pool. Yet, we place little or no value in understanding exactly how the dive computers we use keep us out of a recompression chamber; only that they do so.

I've devoted the entirety of Section 4 to an in-depth examination of the science of decompression sickness (DCS). This chapter, instead, examines its historical roots and early development. My goal is to address the unfortunate but common human tendency to gladly surrender common sense to technology. Frankly, getting a bit lazy in the face of ever more sophisticated technology is probably unavoidable. Where we get into trouble is when we unquestionably embrace technology with no regard nor interest in what makes that technology function, or how it came to be. I'm not advocating that you need to be a scientist or engineer to be a diver. But by the same token, you need to know more than merely how to press a button.

How It All Got Started

Historical roots often run deep, and modern decompression theory is no exception. Most attribute its beginnings to one of the great scientists of the 17th century, Sir Robert Boyle. (The same guy you'll read about in Chapter 6 who gave us Boyle's law.) Sometime around 1650 a German scientist by the name of Otto Von Guericke invented the first vacuum pump, which could remove or compress air. Boyle, who had long been fascinated by the behavior of gases, decided to build one himself, and in 1670 used his newly constructed device to subject various unwitting creatures to certain death, including a snake, in what he called his "exhausted receiver."

Writing about his observations, Boyle said, "I observed the viper furiously tortured in our exhausted receiver which had manifestly a conspicuous bubble moving to and fro in the waterous humor of one of its eyes." This was the first recorded account of the phenomenon we now know as decompression sickness. So, the first bends victim in history turns out not to be a human, but a snake.

In the early days of science the vacuum pump, like other technology, was used mainly to inspire curiosity and entertain guests at dinner parties. What was needed to take the next step was a true practical application of the technology, and that would have to wait another 150 years.

The 19th century was defined by the Industrial Revolution, and what powered the revolution was the steam engine. What's important to our story is what powered the steam engine: coal. With increasing demand, easily mined coal reserves near the surface in most places in Western Europe were becoming exhausted. Meeting the demand required digging deeper. But deep mines have one nasty characteristic: They flood. But not to worry; technology to the rescue.

Necessity being the mother of invention, the English quickly figured out that pumps could play a key role in flood prevention. To keep the water out, all one had to do was seal off the mine and pressurize it. But while the English were still busy thinking, the French actually went and did it. In Chalons, France, in 1841 they constructed the world's first pressurized mine. Soonafter, there were reported the first cases of a mysterious disorder that would come to be known as decompression sickness. Doctors at the time reported that the afflicted miners showed symptoms of "pain in the ears, a nasal quality of speech and joint pains." And the suggested remedy to "rub the affected area with spirits of wine" was, not surprisingly, ineffective.

Other scientists began exploring the problem, and two French physicians named Pol and Wattelle described the curious nature of the disorder in 1854. "The danger," they said, "does not lie in entering a shaft containing compressed-air; nor in remaining there a longer or shorter time; decompression alone is dangerous." They became the first to realize that the problem arose from first subjecting a person to increased pressure, and then reducing it. By 1857, another researcher named Felix Hoppe-Seyler concluded, based on autopsies of both animals and humans, that bubbles were responsible for this mystery disease. As your own instructor explained to you during training, Hoppe-Seyler deduced that the bubbles formed when gas was liberated too quickly from blood and tissue by excessive decompression. To reduce the likelihood of the disease, he suggested slowing the decompression rate.

While we've discussed problems encountered by miners, it should be obvious that divers can succumb to a similar fate. After all, be it underground or underwater, pressure is pressure.

Another characteristic of technology is that, once invented, it often applies to a wide diversity of circumstances; often far different from those for which it was intended. And so was the case with pressurization. Engineers soon applied the French method to underwater construction. By building a pressurized chamber called a caisson

to keep out the water, men could work on the seabed to build bridge foundations, tunnels and other large-scale structures. Caissons were first used in the United States to build bridges in 1869 — initially a railroad bridge over the Pee Dee River in South Carolina. That same year the more ambitious Eads Bridge project crossing the Mississippi River at St. Louis was begun. Just like the miners, caisson workers soon begun turning up with the same mysterious problems that plagued miners. During the St. Louis project, workers were subjected to a pressure of 80 psia (pounds per square inch absolute) (equivalent to almost 147 feet of seawater), a record for the time. But the higher pressures had tragic consequences. There were 35 cases of serious neurological decompression sickness, including six fatalities. This gave rise to the first popular name for the disorder, the "caisson disease."

As there was still little understanding of the caisson disease, there was certainly no consensus on how to treat it. So in the absence of certainty, physicians have to go on speculation about what they know about the cause of a disorder, and a modicum of gut feeling. Realizing that his own workers were certainly going to fall victim once his company began using caissons, the chief surgeon of the New York Bridge Company, Andrew Smith, suggested recompression as a treatment. Sadly, his advice was ignored during construction of the Brooklyn Bridge, and many men died or were permanently disabled as a result.

Meanwhile, important events were taking place back in France. The story now introduces one of its most brilliant champions, and a true Renaissance man of the 19th century. His name was Paul Bert, and in addition to a distinguished career as a physiologist and physician, he also managed to become a lawyer and even a noted champion of women's rights. Bert's first important discovery came in 1872 when he analyzed the gas bubbles in decompression experiments and found them to contain primarily nitrogen. He, like Hoppe-Seyler, concluded that the bubbles were indeed the cause of the bends. In 1879 he clinically described his theory in his landmark book, "La Pression Barometrique." This 1,800-page treatise was so significant and authoritative that it is still in print and cited today in medical literature on decompression sickness. Like many before him, Bert recommended that caisson workers be brought back to surface pressure slowly, allowing nitrogen gas to escape before it formed bubbles.

But Bert's major contribution involved his recommendation for treating decompression sickness. He, like Andrew Smith, suggested the victims be recompressed, then again slowly returned to surface pressure. But here's an example of a truly great mind at work. Unlike any of his predecessors, Bert deduced that, as the bubbles were composed mainly of nitrogen, victims would benefit from breathing pure oxygen to help flush the nitrogen from the body. Today, we recognize oxygen administration as the single most important measure taken in treating a DCS victim, and the advice was offered at the same time Thomas Edison was inventing the first commercially successful incandescent light bulb. Bert made still another landmark discovery during his research. He became the first person to describe the toxic effects of high-pressure oxygen. In deference, the now well-known sign of oxygen acute toxicity — convulsions — was given the formal name, the "Paul Bert effect."

Bert's techniques were employed in 1893 during the construction of the tunnel connecting New York with Jersey City. And they worked. There was a marked decrease in the number of decompression sickness cases, and a reduction in the number of fatalities. Yet, there was still an unsolved problem. Bert's technique did not prevent all cases of DCS. What was needed was a more definitive approach.

Great Scot!

With the dawn of the 20th century, technology lunged ahead at a breakneck speed. Marine technology was no different. Even though hard-hat diving had been around for a few decades, diving systems were improving, as well as other innovations in underwater construction. Military commanders were also beginning to understand the possibilities and implications underwater technology might have on warfare. However, as is often the case, there was a widening gap between what machines could do versus human beings. By the turn of the century, improvements in their equipment enabled divers to reach depths of more than 200 feet (61 m). But, due to the effects of decompression sickness, the practical limit for diving was only about 120 feet (36 m). So, something had to be done.

In 1905 the British Royal Navy took the first step in what would become the birth of modern decompression technology. It commissioned a renowned Scottish physiologist, John Scott Haldane, to explore the problem of decompression. Haldane was a member of the Royal Navy's Admiralty Deep Water Diving Committee, and had conducted research into improving the ventilation of diving helmets, so he was already familiar with diving operations. Now, his challenge was to provide a systematic method to safely decompress divers. And in the end, not only did he succeed, but he extended the operational diving range to almost twice what was believed possible: 210 feet (64 m).

Yet, there are more reasons to understand Haldane's methods than mere historical significance. The concepts and procedures he devised are still used in designing dive tables to this day. And while his ideas have been greatly revised and expanded — as well as disputed — a full appreciation of modern decompression theory is impossible without understanding what Haldane did and why he did it.

Drawing on the work of Bert and others, Haldane understood that the formation of nitrogen bubbles were the likely cause of decompression sickness. These bubbles formed when, upon ascent, the pressure of nitrogen in the body was significantly greater than the pressure of the air the diver was breathing. As not all divers or caisson workers got the bends, he deduced that a person could tolerate a certain degree of excess nitrogen pressure without bubble formation. The problem was determining exactly what this "certain" amount was, and how the pressure could be reduced in a predictable way to avoid bubble formation.

As a good scientist, Haldane first wanted to observe the phenomenon he was studying to form a working hypothesis. From his observations of diving operations in a construction project in Gibraltar harbor, he already knew that divers could safely dive for long periods of time in shallow water without getting DCS. But he now needed a more controlled way of studying the phenomenon. Luckily, he was fortunate enough to have access to one of the only experimental hyperbaric chambers in existence — a boiler that had been converted for this purpose by Dr. Ludwig Mond.

Even though he could get willing volunteers, Haldane realized that the preliminary tests would be too uncertain and potentially dangerous to use human subjects. The first problem, then, was determining exactly what animal would be appropriate. This is a bigger problem than you might think. For example, he found that mice, rats, rabbits and guinea pigs were extremely difficult to bend. Mice, he found, could be taken to a depth of 168 feet (51 m) for more than an hour and brought back to the surface in less than a minute symptom-free. This same dive would require hours of decompression for a human. And there was yet another problem with these smaller animals. How do you know when they're bent? Signs of joint pain, for example, would be extremely difficult to detect in a rat or a guinea pig.

Finally, Haldane found a suitable animal that mirrored human physiology well enough: goats. Due to their size and circulatory dynamics, goats more closely approximated humans than the smaller animals. In addition, Haldane found them more manageable than other larger animals such as monkeys. It was also easy to tell when they experienced pain by the way they lifted or favored the affected limb. Incidentally, Haldane's selection and use of goats turned out to be spot-on. They are still used today as test subjects in decompression studies.

Based on these experiments, Haldane noted a constant relationship: Decompression sickness did not occur as long as the pressure the subject was exposed to did not exceed twice the ambient pressure. This is the origin of his famous "2:1 ratio." He noted, for example, that goats could be taken to 2 atmospheres (33 feet [9 m]) and brought up immediately to 1 atmosphere. Similarly, they could be pressurized to 6 atmospheres (165 feet [50 m]) and brought immediately up to 3 atmospheres (66 feet [20 m]). He postulated that a diver could be brought immediately up to any depth provided the 2:1 ratio was not violated. Once the 2:1 ratio was achieved, the remaining portion of the ascent must proceed much more slowly to allow for elimination of the excess nitrogen. This was the genesis of the idea for decompression stops, or what is known as "stage decompression."

The 2:1 ratio finding, however, was just a preliminary finding, and Haldane realized that designing precise schedules would require significant refinement and evaluation. He knew that the phenomenon he was studying was actually extremely complex because gas absorption and elimination isn't constant for all parts of the body. It varies greatly due to the amount of blood flow to the tissue (how quickly gas gets to and from the tissue), and the density of the tissue (how quickly gas disperses throughout the cells). This means that some tissues would absorb and eliminate gas very quickly, while others would do so very slowly.

To solve the dilemma, Haldane formulated an ingenious approach that's still used in many decompression models today. He knew that while there are probably hundreds of actual rates of absorption and elimination, it was neither possible nor necessary to consider every one. Instead, an overall picture could be described by looking at certain representative "tissues." This was the origin of what's termed the multi-tissue model of decompression.

While many are aware of Haldane's concept of "tissue" compartments, this is also a subject of the greatest misconception. He did not intend for the term "tissue" to be taken literally. Rather than real human tissues, Haldane was using a theoretical construct to create a mathematical model. Therefore, in terms of decompression theory, his "tissues" were merely the mathematical values he used in his equations to predict rates of absorption and elimination. In fact, scientists today prefer to use the term "compartment" rather than tissue to avoid this widely held misconception.

Another of Haldane's assumptions was that both the absorption and elimination of gas occurred at an exponential rate, and Haldane needed a way to describe them. He turned to a common form of mathematical description used even today in fields such as nuclear science and pharmacology: a half-life or half-time. As with exponential relationships, there's nothing mysterious about the concept of half-times.

A half-time is simply the amount of time something (in this case a tissue compartment) takes to either fill or empty half of what it's assumed to hold (in this case nitrogen gas). For example, Haldane's model contained the half-times five, 10, 20, 40 and 75 minutes, and it assumed four half-times for saturation to be complete. To illustrate the concept let's look at his fastest compartment: five minutes. In the first five minutes the compartment will fill to 50 percent. In the next five minutes, it will fill half its remaining capacity (75 percent full). Five minutes more will take it halfway again for a total of 87.5 percent. After the fourth half-time it will be 93.6 percent full. Note that if you continue to a fifth half-time the compartment reaches 96.9 percent, and after a sixth half-time or 30 minutes (6 x 5 = 30), the compartment is at 98.4 percent. Mathematically, it can never reach 100 percent.

Haldane also deduced that different compartments would reach their maximum levels according to the diver's depth (pressure) and bottom time (duration). In his model, he provided for the compartment that came closest to the maximum allowable pressure to exercise "control" over the decompression requirement. Without the aid of a computer, or even an electronic calculator, the tedious and complex computations required to create the tables obviously involved many hundreds of hours.

With a method to calculate nitrogen pressures in any of his compartments, Haldane could then determine the time and depth from which a diver could ascend without exceeding the maximum allowable nitrogen pressure in any compartment. If the diver exceeded the maximum compartment pressure, then a decompression stop was required. Halting the ascent at predetermined intervals allowed for reduction of the nitrogen pressure in the diver's tissues. Once the stop was completed, the compartment pressures were reduced and the diver could then ascend to the surface.

In 1908, along with his associates A.E. Boycott and G.C.C. Damant, Haldane published the results of their research in the article, "The Prevention of Compressed-Air Illness." Included was the first set of tables giving divers specific time and depth guidelines. This article remains one of the most important ever published in the history of decompression theory. Many decompression models used by recreational divers today were derived — with refinements — using the principles laid down by the indomitable Professor Haldane. Anyone who puts on a scuba tank, even today, owes him a great debt of gratitude.

Although Haldane made an incalculable contribution to the field of decompression, his system was far from perfect. In actual use, divers found that his short duration table — dives of less than two hours — to be too conservative. Additionally, his long duration table — dives of more than two hours — did not provide for sufficient decompression. Clearly, there was a need for further refinement.

Another point that surprises many is that Haldane's tables had no provision for making more than one dive a day, or what we now call "repetitive diving." At the time, all diving was surface-supplied and conducted for a purpose. There was no need to consider the consequences of a diver making a second dive after a brief surface interval. The diver simply remained underwater until the task was accomplished, or another diver was sent down to complete the task.

With the advent of mechanical air compressors, divers could go even deeper than with hand-operated pumps. Unfortunately, it soon became apparent that Haldane's principles didn't work adequately at these more extreme depths.

To solve these shortcomings, a project extending Haldane's tables to allow dives to 300 feet (91 m) was undertaken. Assigned to this task was Royal Navy Captain G.C.C. Damant — one of Haldane's research associates — and the diving company of Siebe Gorman & Co. Ltd. After additional animal experiments and actual test dives, they achieved their goal of greater depth by reducing Haldane's original 2:1 surfacing ratio to 1.75:1.

It would be left to others to refine Haldane's work even further, and make dive tables safer and more reliable. And it would take the introduction of scuba to create a need for repetitive diving tables.

Anchors Away, My Boy

Recognizing the importance of John Scott Haldane's work to naval applications, the U.S. Navy took a considerable interest and began constructing its first dive tables in 1912. The Navy's interest was inspired by a maverick young warrant officer and diver by the name of George Stillson. That year he submitted a report to the Naval Bureau of Construction and Repair, the department that did most of the diving in the Navy. In the report, he condemned the inadequate state of diving equipment and technique within the U.S. Navy. (The vast majority of diving at that time did not exceed 60 feet [18 m].) Aware of the advances made by the Royal Navy, Stillson suggested that the U.S. Navy look at adapting a similar approach to decompression diving.

Acting on Stillson's recommendation, the Navy began a series of tests to evaluate Captain Damant's (Haldane's successor) expanded tables. The tests took place in 1913 at the new Navy Experimental Diving Station (later to become the Experimental Diving Unit) at the Naval Ship Yard in Brooklyn, and also aboard the support vessel USS *Walkie*. Eventually, more than 300 test dives were conducted to depths of up to 270 feet (82 m). The Navy refined Damant's tables, primarily — thanks to Paul Bert — by having the diver breathe pure oxygen during decompression. Based on this research, the first Navy tables were pub-

Over the years various terms have been used to describe what we today call decompression sickness (DCS). Just a few examples from the historical record are caisson disease, diver's palsy, tunnel disease, aeropathy, hyperbaric pneumatosis, aerebullosis, pompholyhaemia and even luftdruckerkrankungen. But the name we're most familiar with is, of course, the bends. How the disorder came to be known as such is an interesting aside.

In the late 19th century, most victims of DCS were not divers but laborers who worked on the seabed in pressurized enclosures called caissons. Those afflicted with noncritical forms of DCS sought relief by walking in an abnormal, contoured manner. As it happened, it was also quite fashionable for ladies of the time to walk in an awkward, forward-leaning stance called the "Grecian Bend." Thus, caisson workers suffering from decompression sickness were said to have the Grecian Bend or simply "the bends."

Whether the term came into common use as a result of the Brooklyn Bridge or Eads Bridge in St. Louis is still disputed. While the term "caisson disease" was coined by Dr. Andrew Smith in 1873 during construction of the Brooklyn Bridge, many attribute the term "Grecian bend" to the Eads Bridge project. But regardless of its origin, the term "bends" will be with us long into the future.

lished in 1915. They became known as the "Bureau of Construction and Repair Tables."

The first practical application of the Navy's deep diving tests came very quickly. In 1915 the Navy submarine *F-4* sunk in Amala Bay off Honolulu in more than 300 feet (91 m) of water. Twenty-one men lost their lives. It was also the first boat lost in the Navy's 15 years of experience in submarine operations. The Navy was, therefore, very interested in recovering both the victims and the vessel. The first dive of the salvage operation fell to a small 127-pound (57 kg) Navy diver named Frank Crilley. Using the new tables, Crilley safely returned from the world-record depth of 306 feet (93 m). To this day, recovery of the *F-4* holds the record for the deepest salvage operation ever undertaken using standard deep-sea diving dress on compressed air.

Stillson's tests and the *F-4* salvage operation resulted in the Navy establishing the first deep-sea diving school at the U.S. Naval Torpedo Station in Newport, Rhode Island, in 1916. A bit later, in 1924 the first U.S. Navy diving manual was published. The foundation was now in place for the U.S. Navy to assume a leading role in decompression theory and table development.

The next important development came about in the early 1930s from a researcher named Charles Shilling. Using volunteers, he organized a series of experimental dives and showed that no existing model could adequately predict decompression for prolonged deep dives. In 1935, by analyzing Shilling's data, another researcher, J.A. Hawkins, drew an important conclusion: Haldane was wrong. In his model, Haldane had assumed that the 2:1 surfacing ratio was consistent for all "tissue" compartments. Hawkins concluded that this wasn't the case. Rather than a single ratio, each compartment should have its own surfacing ratio.

In 1937 a researcher named O.D. Yarbrough expanded upon Hawkins' work. He concluded that the five- and 10-minute compartments could tolerate such a large reduction in pressure that they could be ignored. However, accounting for increased gas absorption due to exercise, Hawkins' ratios for the remaining compartments were reduced even further than previous recommendations.

Based on Yarbrough's conclusions, the Navy published a revised set of tables that same year. Eliminating the fast five- and 10-minute compartments, Yarbrough's tables included only the 20-, 40- and 75-minute compartments. In addition, each compartment was given an individual surfacing ratio. This version of the Navy tables soon gained acceptance around the world, and represented the most significant advance in table design since Haldane's original work.

Although an important step forward, Yarbrough's tables — like Haldane's — weren't perfect. They were still unable to handle decompression requirements for prolonged deep dives. However, as World War II approached, the Navy's priorities shifted to other matters. Yarbrough's tables would remain in use by Navy divers through the Second World War.

The Arrival of Scuba

After the war the Navy resumed work on refining its dive tables. A researcher named O.E. Van Der Aue was exploring ways to enable surface decompression. Surface decompression is a procedure in which the diver ascends to the surface — either immediately or after an abbreviated decompression stop — then is rapidly transferred to a recompression chamber where he completes his decompression requirement. This gives advantages in both safety and comfort.

During his tests, Van Der Aue found that Yarbrough's tables were inadequate in many circumstances. For example, in one test to 100 feet (30 m) for 85 minutes, half of his volunteer subjects got decompression sickness. Luckily, very little deep diving with very long bottom times was done using these tables.

By the early 1950s the Navy concluded that they should revise their tables to improve their safety and reliability. Of the staff of researchers assigned the task of refining the tables, two are particularly notable — M. Des Granges and J.V. Dwyer. From their research they concluded that as the depth and time of a dive increase, so must the depth of the decompression stop. They also restored to the decompression model the fast five- and 10-minute compartments.

Another major contribution: They added a much longer half-time compartment — 120 minutes. (The slowest compartment for both the Haldane and Yarbrough models was 75 minutes.) This was done to account for prolonged dives — a major flaw in previous tables. Later, an Exceptional Exposure Table was developed by Robert Workman using even slower compartment half-times of 160, 200 and 240 minutes.

While these new revisions were necessary to increase the safety of decompression diving, another con-

sideration influenced the decision to revise the tables: scuba. Scuba presented a novel problem to table designers: how to deal with a limited air supply. This problem had never been a concern because all diving was surface-supplied. With a virtually unlimited air supply, the diver could always remain at depth until his task was completed. This wasn't the case with scuba. The very limited supply of air in the tank would sometimes require the diver to surface to change tanks. Thus was born the need for making more than one dive a day or what the Navy dubbed "repetitive diving."

The need to exit and re-enter the water presented a unique problem. It required Des Granges and Dwyer to come up with a way to account for the amount of excess nitrogen held over in the diver's tissues after surfacing. This led to the development of methods and terms known to all modern divers, and is still critical to understanding how to use most dive tables in use today. The extra quantity of nitrogen, which they termed residual nitrogen, was expressed using another novel concept — the Repetitive Group Designation or "pressure group." Second, they had to calculate how much residual nitrogen would resolve while the diver was on the surface. Solving this problem resulted in a new component of the dive tables — the Surface Credit Interval Table. Using the 120-minute compartment — the slowest compartment in their model — the new table allowed the diver to calculate how much nitrogen was eliminated in the time between dives. This nitrogen status could then be taken into consideration before re-entering the water for later dives.

In 1958 the revised U.S. Navy Standard Air Decompression Tables were published. Immediately adopted by the fledgling recreational diving community in America, these tables became the standard for decompression procedures. In fact, if one was certified before the mid-1980s, these — in various adapted formats — were the table they would have learned to use.

Dial M for Diving?

The next refinement was one to make the computation process of dive tables easier. Remember, this was a time when computers were merely experimental machines, and the laborious process of calculating was done with slide rulers. To solve the problem, Robert Workman introduced the concept of M-values (short for "maximum values") in 1965. This greatly simplified the complex and mathematically tedious process of comparing various surfacing ratios.

Workman's idea was to define the maximum amount of nitrogen allowed in any compartment not as a ratio, but as an expression of pressure; specifically, pressure in feet of seawater (fsw). For example, let's look at the nitrogen pressure in a compartment at the surface using his method. First, Workman reasoned that another way of expressing the pressure of 1 atmosphere (ATA) is to say it is equivalent to 33 fsw. Thus, the terms 1 ATA, 14.7 psi or 33 fsw are all the same expression of pressure. As our atmosphere is made up of about 78 percent nitrogen, we can say that, at the surface, our tissues contain a nitrogen pressure of 26 fsw (33 fsw X 78 percent = 25.74 fsw). With his system Workman was able to simplify the computation process.

Another example of the advantages of Workman's method becomes clear by looking at how he handled one of the tissue compartments. In the Navy model, the surfacing ratio for the 5-minute tissue compartment is 3.15 atmospheres to 1. This means the compartment is allowed to hold 3.15 times the surface pressure before a decompression stop is required. However, instead of a ratio, Workman expressed this maximum value as 104 fsw. (The surface value of 33 fsw X 3.15 = 103.95 fsw.) As each tissue had its own surfacing ratio under the old ratio system, Workman's system assigned each tissue its own M-value. This method of computing decompression status was far simpler than continually comparing ratios. In fact, it is still used in many decompression models today.

While it may seem like the development of decompression models has a long and rich history, this chapter only brings us up to 1958. In order words, all this happened before recreational scuba diving was much more than a novelty. The next chapter will describe what has happened since. 🐠

CHAPTER 4

Unbending the Future:
Decompression Models In the Modern World

When I learned to dive back in the 1960s, all dive planning was based on the U.S. Navy Standard Decompression Tables for the simple reason that there was nothing else. We viewed these sacred columns and rows as though Moses himself brought them down off the Mount. And we went to bed every night certain that, if we followed them loyally, they'd provide complete immunity from the dreaded divers' disease, the bends.

Of course, much has happened since the 1960s, and today the average diver will rarely ever see a copy of these once-hallowed tables. In fact, most recreational divers, once they complete training, rarely again look at any table. As I heard a diver comment not long ago, "Dive tables are the slide rulers of scuba diving, so why would I use a slide ruler when I have a scientific calculator [dive computer]?"

Most folks who use technology couldn't care less about how a gadget works, only that it does. I prove this point to myself ever so often by asking divers a simple question: "What model does your dive computer use?" Ninety-nine percent of the time they'll tell me the manufacturer. And when I follow up with, "No, the decompression model, not the product model," I invariably get blank stares.

Once in a while this conversation will elicit a sincere desire by a respondent to learn a bit more about what's programmed into their microprocessor. And more often than not they're dumbfounded to learn that there's isn't just one model. "That's one reason why you and your buddy may get very different readouts on the display," I tell them, "even if you stick together like glue during the dive."

Indeed, unlike the early days of diving, there is no longer a single gold standard for decompression planning. Today, not only are there several popular decompression models programmed into dive computers, some even allow the user to select from one or another. So, instead of evolving to a consensus over the years, decompression models have never been so diverse. And, as I admonished in the last chapter, that should motivate you to learn a bit more about your computer than just how to turn it on.

A Bold New World

While J.S. Haldane was the star of the last chapter, make no mistake, his ideas — like all scientific theories — have been challenged. And from these challenges have come important refinements — as well as some radical departures — concerning decompression theory and models. One of the first challenges to Professor Haldane's theory, and still a primary area of debate, centers on the way gas bubbles form. Haldane believed that bubble formation was essentially spontaneous or *de novo*, occurring soon after a tissue's saturation limit was exceeded. Much like being pregnant, one was either bent or wasn't. Scientifically, this is called homogeneous nucleation.

As early as 1942 this concept was challenged by U.S. Naval researcher Albert Behnke. One of the great names in the field of diving physiology, Behnke deduced that small harmless bubbles probably formed before reaching a size that caused DCS. We now know this is true, and you'll read a lot more about these bubbles asymptomatic or "silent bubbles" in Section 4.

The implication of this silent bubble theory was that bubble formation was not, as Haldane assumed, spontaneous. Instead, bubbles formed in a gradual process, developing first from tiny gas micronuclei or "gas seeds." As opposed to Haldane's theory of homogeneous nucleation, this is called heterogeneous nucleation. Still, as there was no technological means to confirm the hypothesis in Behnke's time, it was all just theory.

By the late 1950s important advances in technology were occurring that would confirm the silent bubbles hypothesis. In 1958 two researchers, Shigeo Satomura and Ziro Kaneko, developed the doppler flowmeter, which used ultrasonic waves to monitor blood. In 1968, two other researchers, Merrill Spencer and S.D. Campbell, were the first to detect gas bubbles in the circulation of sheep decompressed from 200 feet (61 m) for an hour. In 1969, the technology was first used to detect silent bubbles in humans.

As Doppler ultrasonic technology could detect bubbles before the onset of decompression sickness, researchers believed they had a more refined way of testing the safety of dive tables. (In the Navy's research to develop its decompression tables, the test criterion was whether the diver got the bends.) The idea was that silent bubbles could be used as a predictor of more serious bubble formation elsewhere in the body. Furthermore, tables could be designed to keep silent bubbling to a minimum.

It's important to note here that, although this theory has been used in testing dive tables for decades, it's nonetheless still unproved. There has been no clear correlation established between silent bubbles and their relationship to DCS symptoms. As a result, some researchers dispute the validity of using silent bubbles as a test criterion.

Regardless of the uncertainty of the relationship of silent bubbling to decompression sickness, the 1970s saw several landmark Doppler studies exploring the U.S. Navy tables. Virtually all researchers found the same result: Significant silent bubbling occurred in divers well before the maximum limits of the tables were reached. To minimize silent bubble formation, many researchers such as Merrill Spencer, Bruce Bassett and Andrew Pilmanis published revised no-decompression limits. They also advocated other conservative practices, such as safety stops before ascending.

New Tables for Recreational Divers

In 1981, one of the first tables was published using the recent findings about silent bubbles. Karl Huggins, then a bioengineering student at the University of Michigan, produced what he called the "No-Bubble Table." Using procedures like those used to design the U.S. Navy tables, Huggins incorporated Spencer's Doppler-derived no-decompression limits. Up until this the advances in table design came directly out of the hyperbaric scientific community. But the situation was about to change.

The next major event occurred in 1983, and was based on the insights of a recreational diver. Dr. Raymond E. Rogers published an article, "The Dive Tables: A Different View," in which he pointed out that the Navy's decompression tables had certain limitations for recreational (no-decompression) divers. He reiterated what many before him had — that the Navy no-decompression limits might be too liberal. But that was far from a radical idea.

More importantly, Rogers introduced recreational divers to a limitation of the Navy tables, which no one else seemed to have noticed: For handling outgassing during surface intervals, the Navy tables were probably more conservative than necessary.

The long surface interval times — up to 12 hours — of the U.S. Navy tables are based on using the very slow 120-minute tissue compartment to control outgassing. This compartment was used because the Navy designed its tables for decompression diving. After a decompression dive, a slow compartment such as this might have to be considered in planning a repetitive dive.

Rogers' hypothesis was that if a diver doesn't decompress — as in recreational diving — then he could be freed from the hefty restrictions of such slow outgassing during a surface interval. Specifically, rather than the slow 120-minute compartment, Rogers determined through extensive computer analysis that a half-time as fast as 60 minutes could control outgassing during a surface interval.

This provocative theory sparked the interest of the Professional Association of Diving Instructors (PADI). Intrigued by Rogers' hypothesis, PADI established a company — Diving Science and Technology Corporation — to finance a scientific assessment. Over the next four years, under the leadership of hyperbaric researcher Dr. Michael Powell, Rogers' theory was confirmed. There were no cases of DCS in nearly 1,400 chamber and open-water test dives. In addition, less than 10 percent of the test subjects even demonstrated silent bubbles. The result was the creation in 1987 of PADI's Recreational Dive Planner.

Used throughout the world today, the Recreational Dive Planner has become the most popular dive table in existence. In fact, many dive computer manufacturers now base outgassing calculations in their devices on the Rogers/Powell research results. (Today this model is often referred to as simply the Powell Model, but in deference to the remarkable man and late friend who was its originator, it should be called the Rogers/Powell model.) For the recreational diver, the Recreational Dive Planner was perhaps the most important advance in table design since the Navy published its revised tables in 1958.

Other refinements to the Haldanean approach were made by Dr. Albert Buhlmann. A Switzerland-based researcher, Buhlmann made significant contributions, especially in adapting decompression models for application at altitude. In fact, a Buhlmann-refined version of the Haldanean approach is another common algorithm (mathematical recipe) found in many dive computers today.

More Models

Many scientists believe that while Haldane's methods may work in helping divers avoid decompression sickness, the theory underlying his methods is fundamentally wrong. (Some now question even the idea that bubbles cause decompression sickness, but more about that in Section 4.) Revisionists contend that ideas such as tissue compartments have little to do with physiologic reality. In other words, Haldane merely came up with a clever way of predicting decompression requirements.

Other researchers take a more moderate approach and say that Haldane's theory works only under certain circumstances; or that his theory explains only part of the picture. This situation points up that modern science actually knows very little for certain about the decompression phenomenon. It's clear that researchers in

the field of decompression are far from unified in either their theories or methods. This has sparked a wide divergence in decompression theory and approaches to decompression technology.

A major refinement of Haldanean ideas came out of Canada beginning in the 1960s from two researchers, D.J. Kidd and R.A. Stubbs, at the Defence Research Medical Laboratory and the Canadian Forces Institute of Aviation Medicine. Unsatisfied using a purely Haldanean/U.S. Navy model to solve the decompression dilemma, they decided to approach the problem in a very different way.

In the Haldanean model, compartments are arranged in what can be termed a parallel sequence. This means each compartment is assumed to be separate — having no interaction with any other compartment. Kidd and Stubbs concluded, however, that it probably wasn't reasonable for the tissues of our body to act independently of one another. They instead developed the first decompression model that considered the interaction among compartments. As opposed to the Haldanean parallel model, this is called a serial model. Between 1962 and 1965 they succeeded in producing a successful, though very bulky, dive computer based on this premise.

In 1971 the Defence Research Medical Laboratory and the Institute of Environmental Medicine merged into the Defence and Civil Institute of Environmental Medicine (DCIEM), and continued research into decompression and dive computers. They drew on earlier work that used ultrasonic bubble detection technology. By 1977 DCIEM scientist Ken Kisman and a researcher from the French Navy, Gerard Masurel, developed the K-M bubble classification code for bubbles detected using Doppler ultrasound. This classification system is still used in most Doppler studies today.

In 1979 DCIEM began a series of studies using the Doppler ultrasonic bubble detection method to investigate the decompression stress imposed on divers using tables based on the Kidd-Stubbs model. For the next four years, an extensive series of Doppler experiments were conducted using this model as a reference.

In 1983 the Canadian Forces decided to construct their own set of dive tables. (Until then, they used the U.S. Navy tables.) Under the direction of Lieutenant-Commander G.R. Lauckner and scientist Ron Nishi,

DCIEM was given the task of developing these new tables. Based on the research conducted over the previous years, and extensive computer simulations, a modified version of the Kidd-Stubbs model known as the DCIEM 1983 decompression model was produced. After several years of testing and validation in recompression chambers using both dry and wet divers in cold-water conditions of 40-50 degrees Fahrenheit (4.5-10 degrees Celsius) the DCIEM Tables were released in 1985. A recreational diving version was published in 1988 by Universal Dive Techtronics, followed by an expanded version in 1990. A technical diving table for cave and research diving was published in 1994.

Today, the DCIEM tables represent a significant advance for diving safety. In addition to being adopted by a number of government and naval authorities throughout the world, they have been adapted by some recreational diver training organizations.

Although the Kidd-Stubbs model differs from a pure Haldanean model in the arrangement of the compartments, there are some similarities. That is, in a symptom-free diver, the nitrogen within each compartment is assumed always to be in a dissolved state. There has been some recent biomedical research, however, to dispute this assumption.

Tiny Bubbles

Microscopic bubbles exist in virtually every liquid or liquid-based substance on Earth — including human tissue. In addition, we now know that for various physiological reasons the human body has a proclivity for making gas seeds or microbubbles, even among those not involved in diving. This has given rise to a whole new approach to decompression theory sometimes called free-phase dynamics, or more popularly, the "tiny bubble model."

Advocates of free-phase dynamics models contend that their approach offers hope of a more accurate biophysical model of inert gas absorption and elimination. Accordingly, they believe that dive tables derived from free-phase models will be more reliable than tables based on a Haldanean model. Pointing especially to the difficulty Haldanean models demonstrate in handling multiple-day repetitive diving, tiny-bubble advocates seek a more complete picture. They have proposed decompression models that recognize that gas micronuclei will inevitably develop into bubbles during a dive. The

key to the success of a decompression model is, therefore, to keep the quantity and size of these microbubbles below a critical limit.

While, as with most issues involving decompression, the jury is still out on which approach works best, the tiny bubble group has made significant strides. Two similar models have developed out of the "tiny bubble" school. The first was the Varying Permeability Model (VPM), developed by David Yount and Don Hoffman of the University of Hawaii in the 1980s, and refined in the 1990s.

More recently Dr. Bruce Wienke, a physicist at the Los Alamos National Laboratory, has developed the Reduced Gradient Bubble Model (RGBM), which uses similar assumptions and methods as the VPM. Today, Wienke's model has been adopted for use in many of the dive computers used for technical diving, and in software for commercial diving operations. A major outcome of the RGBM is the use of deeper decompression stops than called for in Haldanean models. The RGBM was also the first non-Haldanean model adopted by a recreational diver training organization — the National Association of Underwater Instructors (NAUI).

A Conclusion?

It may seem that, given its long and rich history, science has figured out everything there is about decompression. But nothing could be further from the case. We've barely scratched the surface. Although decompression models appear to be getting more reliable, our knowledge of the complex physiology involved is still in its infancy. Furthermore, even if someday we do solve all the questions science can pose, this still will not guarantee bends-free diving. The human machine is just too inscrutably complex. All dives will likely always carry with them at least some chance of DCS, or what scientists call "probabilistic risk."

History teaches us many lessons. But above all, it gives us the insight that enables us to solve or avoid problems in the future. And by knowing more about the history of decompression models, you'll have the insight to make more informed decisions, and not mindlessly hand over all control to your dive computer. Remember, the best computer is always the one between your ears. 🙶

CHAPTER 5

A Focus On Physics:
Understanding the Way Things Work

As visual thinkers humans associate words with images. For example, when you hear the word "jaws" I'll wager that the image that pops into your head isn't of an anatomical structure in the skull used to masticate food. Not even close. Since 1975 at least — thanks to Steven Spielberg — the image swimming through our head is undoubtedly *Carcharodon carcharias*, the great white shark.

Another example is the word "genius." Here it's not an animal that illustrates the concept but a person, probably the famous bushy-haired scientist Albert Einstein. Though less famous, other candidates who might qualify are Isaac Newton and Stephen Hawking. (As testament to the legacy of genius, until his retirement in 2009, Hawking held the same academic chair at Cambridge University as Newton did more than 300 years earlier.)

The unifying theme among this brainy trio is that they weren't just scientists; they were all physicists. Formally, physics is defined as the branch of science concerned with the nature and properties of matter and energy. So, as it's matter and energy that make up the universe, in a sense, physics is really the science of everything.

Perhaps more than any other science, the primary language of physics is mathematics, and that brings us to the heart of, if you can forgive the pun, the matter. Few subjects elicit fear and loathing in us as much as math. So, if someone can climb to the top of a field that most of us can't even begin to understand, they must be not only geniuses, but the smartest people on the planet. This may be true, but with due deference to Einstein, Newton and Hawking, understanding physics on a conceptual level does not require such intellectual prowess.

Certainly, mathematics is necessary to understand the intricacies of physics. But the basic concepts of physics — particularly as it relates to scuba diving — require nothing more than common sense and logic. And the only math requirement is basic arithmetic (although a touch of algebra can sometimes come in handy). Let's look first at the phenomenon of light, sound and buoyancy.

Lighting the Way

While the gift of sight is a wonderfully complex physiological phenomenon, the basic mechanics of how we see is fundamentally simple. "Sight" is really the way we perceive electromagnetic energy within a certain range of wavelengths. Humans can perceive only a very narrow range of electromagnetic energy, between about 390 and 750 nanometers (billionths of a meter). Our eyes function by collecting light (energy) that's reflected off an object. These energy waves are then turned into electrical impulses and sent to the brain by the optic nerve. The brain interprets the signals and we "see."

This means any changes in the energy waves will alter what we see as well.

There are three different factors that can change the behavior of light underwater, including refraction, absorption and turbidity. Let's explore refraction first. As light passes from one medium, such as air, into another, such as water, the speed at which it travels changes. Because water is denser than air, light travels more slowly through it.

This change in speed causes the light ray to bend or refract as it enters the new medium. (See Figures 1a and 1b).

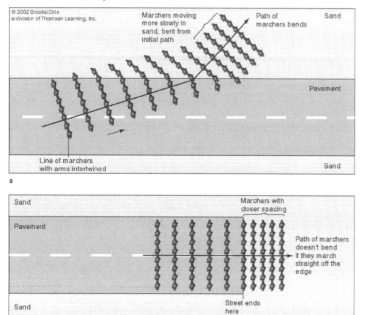

Figures 1a and 1b: Refraction can be understood using the analogy of columns of marchers, with interlocked arms, walking along a paved road. The pavement represent a media such as air, while the sand represents the heavier media, water. Just as the marchers speed changes as they walk through different media—they walk slower in the sand than the pavement—so does the speed of light (or sound) as it changes media.

Having evolved on land, the human eye cannot focus underwater. To see clearly underwater, therefore, we must have an air space in front of our eyes — a mask. But, for light to reach our eyes it must pass through three different media — the water, the glass of the faceplate and the air within the mask. At each interface the speed of the light, and thus its angle, changes (as illustrated in Figures 2 and 3).

This phenomenon acts like a big magnifying glass making everything we look at underwater appear larger and closer than reality. The magnification factor is about 25 percent. For example, a 3-foot (1 m) fish at a distance of 4 feet (1.2 m) may look to us more like a 4-foot fish

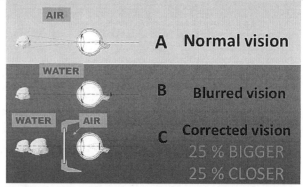

Figure 2: Note that in A the field of focus occurs directly on the retina of the eye. In B, the field of focus is well behind the retina. In C, the field of focus is restored to the retina, but due to refraction, the view of the objects is magnified.

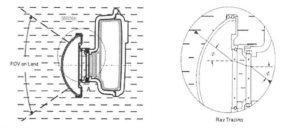

Figure 3: A dome port on a camera functions in a similar manner to what was illustrated in Figure 2. However, the curved dome corrects for the refraction, maintaining the camera lens' original field or view.

only 3 feet way. Much like the trick mirrors in a carnival, it's all the result of the bending of light rays.

The interesting thing about this magnification phenomenon is that it doesn't always work. Factors such as turbidity, contrast and lack of a reference scale sometimes cause objects to appear farther away than their actual distance. As a result, the diver may sometimes overestimate the distance of an underwater object. In general, the closer the object is to the observer, the greater the tendency is to see the object as closer than its actual distance. The more turbid the water, however, the more likely the object will appear farther away than its actual distance. This is a result of human perception rather than physics, and is called the "visual reversal" phenomenon.

Refraction affects even the amount and intensity of light at depth. Maximum penetration of light into water occurs only when the light source is directly above the water (much as the sun at noon). As the angle decreases, less light can penetrate. Once the angle falls below about 49 degrees (measured from the perpendicular) the light will not penetrate the water at all, but reflect. Similarly, the sun is at an optimal angle for maximum light penetration usually between 10 a.m. and 2 p.m. As underwater photographers know, this is the best time to take underwater photos because of maximum light levels.

As mentioned earlier, light is actually a form of electromagnetic energy and it travels in waves. Each form of electromagnetic energy — ultraviolet, infrared, X-ray, cosmic, gamma, microwave, radio — has its own range of wavelengths. Also, each color has its own wavelength. When all visible wavelengths are present, the color we see is white.

Water can gradually absorb light according to its wavelength. The deeper the light penetrates in the water, the more light is absorbed. Absorption begins at the red end of the spectrum. This is why even in the clearest water a nonfluorescent red or orange wet suit appears gray once you descend below 20 feet (6 m) or so. It's also the reason that when we bleed underwater, the blood doesn't appear red, but green.

Likewise, this phenomenon explains the ever-changing color of the ocean. Clear water allows the greatest transparency to wavelengths in the blue range. By contrast, turbid water gives greatest transparency to wavelengths on the green range.

Thus, very clear water appears blue, while turbid water usually appears green.

While color is quickly absorbed underwater, under ideal conditions enough light penetrates to sustain photosynthesis at more than 600 feet (181 m) of depth. Yet, probably some of you have been on dives in which it was pitch-black in only 20 feet. The reason for this isn't the selective absorption of color, but the diffusion and scattering of the light caused by suspended particles in the water. The relative concentration of particles in a given volume of water is called turbidity. The reasons for variation in turbidity can be from physical factors such as erosion bringing mud or clay into the water, or by biological phenomenon such as plankton production. Regardless of the cause, however, the more turbid the water, the less light can penetrate it. Turbidity is usually the most critical factor affecting underwater visibility. (See Figure 4.)

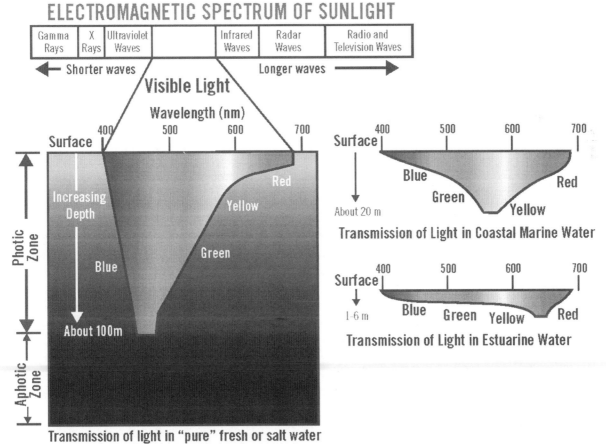

Figure 4: The color of seawater depends not only on the phenomenon of absorption of light with depth, but also absorption of light by the amount and type of particulate in the water column.

Sound Off

Although both light and sound travel in waves, the nature of these waves is vastly different. Light waves are electromagnetic. Sound is caused by pressure waves produced through vibration. As the medium containing the pressure wave comes into contact with another medium, a sympathetic vibration occurs. This transfers the wave pattern to the second medium. For example, a lightning bolt initiates a violent pressure wave in the atmosphere. The wave travels through the air, striking our eardrums. A sympathetic vibration occurs in our eardrum. This mechanical vibration is then translated into a nerve impulse and sent to our brain. We, in turn, perceive this as thunder.

Another way light and sound differ is in how well they transmit through various media. Light travels at optimal speed in a vacuum. But unlike what you've been led to believe by the dramatic battle scenes in "Star Wars," sound cannot travel in a vacuum such as outer space. In fact, the denser the medium, the better sound will travel. Dense media have their molecules packed close together, allowing easier transmission of the wave motion. Submariners take advantage of this property, for example, by using sonar to detect ships at very great distances. The excellent transmission of sound in water also explains why the use of sound (echolocation) is so highly developed in some marine mammals such as whales and dolphins.

As density controls how fast sound travels in water, the actual speed of transmission depends upon several factors. These include the temperature of the water (colder water is denser, thereby allowing it to transmit sound faster) and the salinity (seawater allows sound to travel much faster than fresh). As a comparison, sound travels at only 1,125 fps (feet per second) in air at a temperature of 20 degrees Celsius. In fresh water, it travels 4,915 fps, while in seawater 5,023 fps. But this is still no match for sound's transmission speed in the denser medium of steel. That's a whopping 16,600 fps.

What does all this mean to a diver? Actually, there's good news and there's bad news. The good news is that we can hear sounds much better underwater than on land. The bad news is that underwater it's almost impossible to detect the direction from which a sound emanates. But, as in the visual reversal phenomenon, this isn't the result of physics, but instead human perception.

We perceive the direction of a noise by its intensity and the relative delay in the pressure wave striking one ear before the other. On land, we're very good at this. After all, our brains evolved for millions of years in an environment where sound travels at 1,125 fps. Underwater, however, things are very different. In this alien environment where sound travels four times faster than what we're used to, our brain is fooled. First, the water tends to distribute the sound intensity more equally than in air. More importantly, the brain is unable to detect the much shorter delay in the pressure wave striking one ear before the other. Thus, it assumes the signal is striking both ears at once. We interpret this as the sound coming from all directions.

Because the speed of sound depends on the density of the medium it travels through, interesting acoustical effects occur when diving in thermoclines. The density of water varies according to its temperature. As sound waves attempt to transfer from water of one temperature/density to another — such as when they encounter a thermocline — substantial energy is lost. This tends to isolate sounds within water of a consistent temperature. If the diver isn't in the same temperature range as the source of a sound, he often cannot hear the sound even though it's coming from only a few feet away. Again, submariners learned this trick long ago. Using the acoustical properties of thermoclines is a common way submarines avoid detection from sonar. (Remember the scene from "Hunt for Red October"?)

The Ups and Downs of Buoyancy

Buoyancy refers to the tendency for an object to float. Some objects float quite well and are called positively buoyant. Other objects sink immediately to the bottom and are called negatively buoyant. Objects that neither float nor sink, but remain suspended like an astronaut in outer space, are called neutrally buoyant. Neutral buoyancy is the state we try to achieve and maintain when diving.

Long ago the Greek mathematician Archimedes determined that "any object wholly or partly immersed in a fluid is buoyed up by a force equal to the weight of the fluid displaced by the object." His principle, by the way, applies to all fluids, not just water. It's why hot air balloons can fly.

To determine the buoyancy of an object, we must first know the density or weight of the fluid in which it'll be placed. As divers, we're only concerned with water. Buoyancy calculations require that we use certain constants. In the Imperial system of measurement, the most common constants used by divers for calculating buoyancy are 1 cubic foot of fresh water weighs 62.4 pounds, while 1 cubic foot of sea water weighs 64 pounds. (Seawater is 1.6 pounds heavier because it contains dissolved salts not found in fresh water). In the metric system the constants are 1 liter of fresh water weighs 1 kg (kilogram), while 1 liter of seawater weighs 1.03 kg.

Let's see why these constants are important. Suppose an object displaces exactly 1 cubic foot and it weighs 63 pounds. Will it float or sink in seawater? Because a cubic foot of seawater weighs 64 pounds, an upward force of 64 pounds will be exerted on any object with that same displacement. As the weight of the object is only 63 pounds, 1 pound of more force is exerted keeping it afloat than trying to sink it. Though not by much, the object floats — it has 1 pound of positive buoyancy.

Now suppose the same object is placed in fresh water. It, of course, still displaces 1 cubic foot of volume, and it still weighs 63 pounds. But, a cubic foot of fresh water weighs only 62.4 pounds. This means only 62.4 pounds of buoyant force is exerted. The object now has 0.6 pounds more negative than positive buoyancy, and will sink.

Using these constants we can calculate more complex problems involving buoyancy. Such calculations are useful for gaining a better understanding of the buoyancy phenomenon, and have practical application as well. Let's see how.

Suppose you plan to salvage a motorcycle that you've located at the bottom of a lake in 50 feet (15 m) of water. How big of a lift bag will you need?

From a specification sheet supplied by a local motorcycle dealer, you find that the cycle weighs 470 pounds. And from its dimensions you figure that it displaces about 2.75 cubic feet. The rest is simple.

As it's in fresh water, you know that 171.6 pounds of buoyant force is exerted on the cycle (62.4 X 2.75 cubic feet = 171.6). However, as it weighs 470 pounds, there's 298.4 pounds more negative buoyancy than positive (470 – 171.6 = 298.4). Therefore, you must apply an additional 298.4 pounds of positive buoyancy to make the cycle neutral.

From the constants, you know that for each cubic foot of air you add to the lift bag, an additional 62.4 pounds of positive buoyancy is applied. By dividing 62.4 into 298.4 you find that 4.78 cubic feet of displacement will provide the required positive buoyancy to make the cycle neutrally buoyant. Thus, to complete the salvage operation you must have a lift bag with at least a 5-cubic-foot capacity.

From your training as a diver you probably remember that as the lift bag is brought to the surface, the air within it will expand. As it expands, the displacement, and thus the buoyancy, will increase. Wouldn't it be useful if you could determine just how much it will increase so you knew what to expect as you ascend? You can determine this by applying still other principles of physics involving the behavior of gases.

A Primer on Pressure

The Renaissance scientist Evangelista Torricelli — the guy credited for giving us the barometer — once described humankind as "living submerged at the bottom of an ocean of air." Although an astute deduction, some would find his analogy difficult to accept because we don't normally feel any sensation of pressure as we go about our daily lives. In fact, other than an occasional encounter while flying or driving through the mountains, most people never give the idea of pressure — at least the physical variety — a second thought.

But divers are not most people. Unlike others who spend their entire lives on terra firma, we have an intimate familiarity with pressure. Yet, while divers may have a good understanding of how it affects their bodies, they're often less informed about how our knowledge of pressure evolved, as well as the terminology and systems used to describe it. That's unfortunate because without a complete insight into the pressure phenomenon, a diver can never fully appreciate the science that governs the underwater experience.

The term pressure describes any force or weight acting on a defined area. In the Imperial system, the most common expression is pounds per square inch (psi). In the metric system it's kilograms per square centimeter "(kg/cm²). On land, pressure is a result of the weight of the more than 50-mile-high (80 km) envelope of air we call the atmosphere. While that's an unimaginable quantity of gas, it only exerts a pressure of about 14.7 psi or 1.03 kg/cm². So, we do quite literally live at the bottom of the sea of air Torricelli so aptly described.

A Historical Perspective

The idea that air has substance has been around since antiquity. The Greek scientist-philosopher

Anaximenes of Miletus proposed that air was the basic element from which everything else arose. Furthermore, he believed that although invisible, air was actually composed of tiny particles. Aristotle's observation that wind could exert a force also led him to deduce that air indeed had substance.

One of the first scientists to investigate the phenomenon of pressure was Galileo. He demonstrated that air not only had substance, it actually had weight. His hypothesis was proven by first weighing an empty sealed container. Then, after pumping more air into it and weighing it again, he found that it was in fact heavier. His conclusion: The only thing that could account for the increased weight was the additional air. One of the most important figures in the investigation of pressure was the aforementioned Evangelista Torricelli, a colleague of Galileo's. Torricelli was intrigued by a practical and unexplained phenomenon faced by mining engineers of the 17th century. Using hand pumps, they were able to evacuate water from mines only as long as the rise of the water was less than 34 feet. Torricelli reasoned that the weight of the atmosphere pushed the water up the line into a vacuum created by the pump. Once the water got to a height of 34 feet, however, it equaled the pressure of the atmosphere pushing on it, and it could not be pumped any further. But how could he prove it?

While Torricelli is normally credited with its invention, it was actually his colleague Vincenzo Vivian who built the device that proved his hypothesis — the barometer. Knowing that using water would require an enormously long glass tube, he scaled down his model by substituting a much heavier liquid — mercury. This allowed Vivian to work with a tube that was only about 4 feet (1.2 m) long.

With the glass tube sealed at one end, Vivian filled it with the liquid metal, and blocked off the open end with his finger. He then turned the tube upside down and immersed the open end in a vessel also containing mercury. Removing his finger, he observed — as he expected — the mercury in the tube begin to empty from the tube, but not completely. About 30 inches (76 cm) of mercury remained in the tube.

Vivian knew that the void in the tube had to be a vacuum because air could not have entered it. He concluded that the mercury remained in the tube because as Figure 5 illustrates the pressure of the at-mosphere held it in there by exerting a force on the mercury in the vessel. For the first time in history, someone had demonstrated that atmospheric pressure equaled the weight of a 30-inch (actually, 29.92 inch), or 760-millimeter, column of mercury. His method of using mercury as a "measuring stick" for pressure is still used today in many fields of science, particularly in meteorology.

The French scientist and theologian Blaise Pascal was the next person to advance the study of pressure. Taking Vivian's experiment to full scale, he was able to show that the pressure of the atmosphere could indeed support a column of water 34 feet high (33 feet for seawater). But Pascal did much more than that simple experiment. His interest in hydrodynamics led him to invent both the syringe and hydraulic press. Moreover, he gave us "Pascal's principle" of the transmissibility of fluid pressure. It states that, "any pressure applied to a fluid will be transmitted equally to every point in the fluid." For divers this explains why we must equalize when we descend. The surrounding water pressure is transmitted through the tissues of our body, but acts upon air-filled structures such as our lungs, sinuses and middle ear.

Pascal's experiment also gave us a convenient way to calculate the atmospheric pressure in pounds per square inch (psi). As 1 cubic foot of seawater weighs 64 pounds, a column 33 feet high would weigh 2,112 pounds (64x33). This is equal to the atmospheric pressure acting on a 1 square foot of area of the Earth. By dividing 144 — the number of square inches in a square foot — into 2,112 we have the value known to all divers who use the imperial system of 14.7 psi.

The next player in the story of pressure is the famous English scientist Sir Robert Boyle (about whom we'll hear much more later). Fascinated by the behavior of gases, Boyle took Vivian's experiment a step further. Like Vivian, he used a glass tube sealed at one end. But unlike Vivian's straight tube, Boyle's was bent into a U-shape. He poured mercury into the tube, as shown in Figure 5a. The air trapped in the sealed end of the container was, of course, at atmospheric pressure (14.7 psi). He then began adding more mercury to the open end until the air volume in the sealed end was exactly half the original. It took 30 more inches of mercury — equal to the pressure of the atmosphere — to halve the air volume in the tube.

He then knew the air pressure in the sealed end had to equal the original pressure of 1 atmosphere plus a second atmosphere of pressure created by the added mercury (Figure 5b). So, the pressure of the reduced volume of air was exactly 29.4 psi. In other words, to halve the volume, you must double the pressure, and vice versa. This was the genesis of Boyle's law — an elemental part of diving science.

Terminology and Applications

Describing the pressure phenomenon accurately requires the proper terminology. One system of expression that you probably learned in your beginning scuba course uses as a base the constant pressure of the atmosphere itself. One "atmosphere" (this is usually abbreviated as "ATM") equals 14.7 psi, 2 ATM equals 29.4 psi, 3 ATM equals 44.1 psi and so on. Outside the United States, instead of atmosphere, the term "bar" is used. This is an expression of the mil-

libar system. And although 1 bar is actually equal to 1.013 atmospheres, divers generally use the terms bar and atmosphere interchangeably.

While the standard atmospheric pressure is 14.7 psi, this isn't always the actual pressure that surrounds you at any one time. Variations in atmospheric pressure are caused by high- and low-pressure weather systems, like the ones you've seen on the evening weather report. These are measurements of barometric pressure, and divers sometimes express concern that these fluctuations may affect the accuracy of their depth gauge. While it's true most depth gauges work by measuring changes in pressure, the fluctuations in barometric pressure are very minor. So minor that the calibration range of your depth gauge can't even detect them. (Although many dive computers do take the actual barometric pressure into account when they're initialized.) For the purposes of making any diving-related calculations, you can ig-

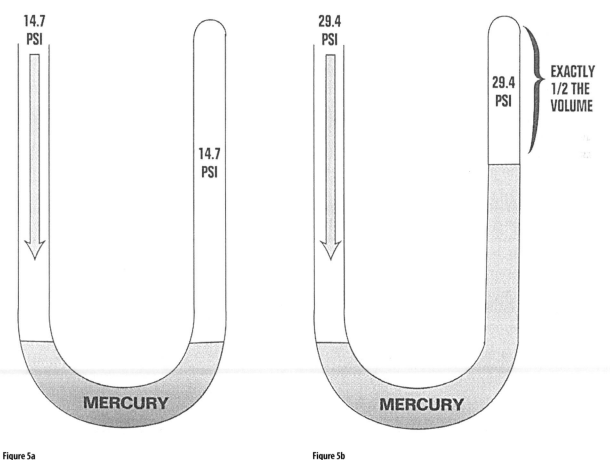

14.7
PSI

14.7
PSI

MERCURY

29.4
PSI

29.4
PSI

EXACTLY
1/2 THE
VOLUME

MERCURY

Figure 5a

Figure 5b

nore the barometric pressure and assume the surface pressure is always 14.7 psi or 1.03 kg/cm^2.

Of course, as you ascend in the atmosphere, the air gets less dense. As there's less air, it exerts less pressure. You've no doubt experienced this anytime you have flown in an airplane or driven through the mountains. At an altitude of about 18,000 feet (5,400 m), for instance, the pressure is half that of the surface or 0.5 ATM.

The more important consideration in calculating pressures involves the difference between gauge pressure versus absolute pressure. Gauge pressure is an expression that uses atmospheric pressure as a 0 point. For example, if you look at your SPG before you put it on your tank valve, it (hopefully) reads 0, not 14.7. That doesn't mean that the pressure of the atmosphere is 0. It just means that because the gauge is designed to measure only the pressure within the tank, it ignores the atmospheric pressure. To avoid confusion, gauge pressure readings are indicated by the letter "g" at the end of the designation, such as psig or kg/cm^{2}g.

On the other hand, absolute pressure is a measure of both gauge and atmospheric pressures. Absolute pressure is also sometimes referred to as the ambient pressure. (Ambient simply means surrounding.) This time the letter "a" follows any pressure designation, such as psia or kg/cm^{2}a. One way to keep it straight is to assume you're about to make a dive. While you are on the surface you're exposed to the pressure of 1 atmosphere absolute (14.7 psia), which is abbreviated as 1 ATA. But gauge pressure ignores the atmosphere, so at the surface the pressure is 0 atmospheres gauge. If you dive to 33 feet (10 m), the pressure doubles. You have the weight of the atmosphere and an equal weight of the water, so you'll be under a pressure of 2 atmospheres absolute (2 ATA) but — because it ignores the surface pressure — only 1 atmosphere gauge.

The water component of pressure is called hydrostatic pressure, and like the atmosphere it increases and decreases in a very predictable way. Water has a density of almost 800 times that of air. So, while it requires over 50 miles (80 km) of air to exert a force of 14.7 psi, it takes only 33 feet of seawater (34 feet of fresh) to equal the same pressure. If we know that 33 feet of water exerts a pressure of 14.7 psi, then we can determine that every foot of water exerts a pressure of 0.445 psi (0.432 for fresh). Also, because water is incompressible, this relationship of increasing

pressure by 1 atmosphere for every 33 feet of water remains constant. At the depth of 165 feet (50 m), for example, the absolute pressure is 6 atmospheres. The hydrostatic pressure accounts for 5 atmospheres, plus the weight of the atmosphere itself pressing down on the water's surface accounts for the sixth.

These are valuable constants because with them you can determine the ambient pressure at any depth anywhere on Earth. At the bottom of your 8-foot-deep (2.4 m) swimming pool, for example, the pressure is 18.15 psia or 3.45 psig. At the bottom of the 36,152-foot (10,995 m) Challenger Deep in the western Pacific's Marianas Trench — the deepest point in any ocean — the pressure is an incredible 16,102.34 psia or 16,087.64 psig. That's almost 1,100 atmospheres or over 7 tons of pressure per square inch. ♋

JOHN DALTON   WILLIAM HENRY

ROBERT BOYLE   JACQUES CHARLES

CHAPTER 6

Scuba Diving's Lawmakers:
All Hail the Good Doctors

The "science of diving"

generally involves the physiology of how our

body is affected, either directly or indirectly, by the increasing pressure of depth. But before we can understand the physiology, we must first understand more fundamental concepts of matter, energy, force, motion, and the way they relate to each other. That was the purpose of the previous chapter. But to proceed further in your understanding of the science of diving, one must devolve into the so-called "gas laws." Whether they're called by name or not, those four immutable laws named for doctors Boyle, Charles, Dalton and Henry control almost everything that occurs to us and in us while we dive. So a cursory knowledge of their rules and applications is certainly a valuable asset to any diver who wants to understand the nuances of the underwater experience.

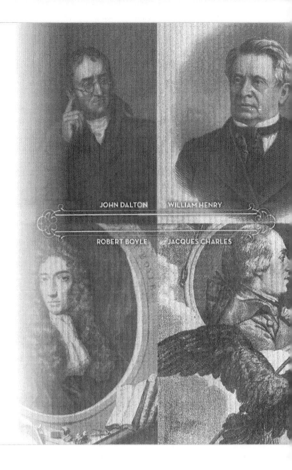

JOHN DALTON   WILLIAM HENRY

ROBERT BOYLE   JACQUES CHARLES

Robert Boyle

The granddaddy of gas experts was a renowned English scientist named Robert Boyle (after he got famous, it was Sir Robert Boyle). Building on Evangelista Torricelli's work, he discovered that when gases are exposed to either increased or decreased pressure, their behaviors are highly predictable. He expressed his prediction mathematically in what has come to be known as Boyle's law. Without all the algebra and scientific mumbo jumbo, Boyle's law essentially says that if you increase the pressure on a gas-filled object — like a balloon — the volume gets smaller. Squeeze a balloon and it gets smaller. Obviously, this stuff isn't rocket science. Of course, Boyle's law acts in the exact opposite way when the pressure is reduced — like when a diver ascends. According to Boyle's law, if we release a sealed balloon at depth, it will expand as it ascends, and if it exceeds its maximum volume, it will burst. So, too, when reducing the pressure on ascent, our lung volume increases. If we do nothing about it — like exhale — we risk lung injury due to overexpansion. Boyle's law is, of course, the rationale

for the most important rule in scuba diving: Breathe continuously; never hold your breath.

Ironically, while Boyle discovered his "law," he could never explain what was actually happening. That took another scientist, the Italian Daniel Bernoulli, who explained that as gas, molecules collide with the container walls. The collective force of these collisions is what causes gas pressure. The more the molecules are agitated, the more collisions occur and the greater the force (pressure). Bernoulli concluded that when the density of a gas increases, the number of collisions also increases. The increase in the number and force of collisions is what causes the pressure increase.

Even if your instructor never actually mentioned the name of Dr. Boyle, every diver is introduced to his law in their entry-level training. But just in case you're a little rusty, recall that for every 33 feet (10 m) of descent, seawater pressure increases by about 15 psi or 1 atmosphere or ATM. (I know, it's really 14.7, but decimals only complicate things here, and 15 is close enough for government work.) This means that at 99 feet (30 m), the pressure is four times the surface pressure; three contributed by the water and one by the atmosphere (99/33 = 3 + the surface pressure of 1 atmosphere = 4 ATA or "atmospheres absolute").

Similarly, a volume of gas in a flexible container, like a balloon or your lung, will also decrease predictably according to the depth (pressure). For example, at 33 feet (2 ATA) the balloon will decrease to one-half its surface volume. At 66 feet (3 ATA) it decreases to one-third, at 99 feet (4 ATA) to one-fourth and so on. The reverse holds true on ascent. The volume of a balloon partly inflated at 99 feet (4 ATA) will increase fourfold if it's taken to the surface.

This constant relationship gives divers a neat little way to estimate how gas volumes change as they ascend or descend. Let's try an example. Assume that a balloon containing 20 liters of air at the surface is taken to 100 feet (4 ATA for all intents and purposes). By expressing the problem as a fraction in which the original surface quantity (20) is the top number — the numerator, for the less mathematically challenged — and the pressure at 100 feet (4) is the bottom number or denominator, we have 20/4 or 5 liters (once the fraction is reduced).

You can solve even more complex problems with this fractional relationship. Let's assume a balloon contains 5 liters at a depth of 66 feet (20 m). What will its volume be if it's taken to 33 feet (10 m)? First, let's see what happens to the balloon if it's taken to the surface. As 66 feet is 3 ATA, the balloon will expand threefold when it reaches the surface and contain 15 liters (3 x 5 = 15). Now, simply use the same fractional relationship from the previous problem: The surface volume (15) over the pressure (2), or 15/2. Then, reduce the fraction to 7.5. Thus, the balloon would change from a volume of 5 liters at 66 feet to 7.5 liters at 33 feet. Neat trick, huh?

The only drawback to this quick-and-dirty method of calculation is that it only works if you use atmospheres as increments. For more precise results, or for problems expressed in terms other than atmospheres, you'll have to use the dreaded mathematics of algebra, and the famous equation $P1V1=P2V2$. The point is that the implications of Boyle's law are easily determined using nothing more than some logic, common sense and simple arithmetic. You didn't even have to use a calculator.

While understanding the relationship of pressure and volume is both vital and obvious to all divers in ex-

plaining why we should never hold our breath, it may not be as easy to see why it has another important effect on gas density. Still, like pressure and volume, understanding the density implications of Boyle's law is also a matter of common sense.

Using the balloon example again, let's see what happens when we squeeze it. First, its volume is decreased, which means the molecules within the balloon have to come closer together. (Think of a conductor pushing a crowd of people aboard a subway car.) Another way of looking at it is that the air gets "thicker," but the more appropriate term is denser. There is one important difference between pressure/volume and pressure/density relationships, however. Note that the former relationship is inversely proportional — if one factor goes up, the other goes down. In the latter, the relationship is directly proportional — if one factor goes up, so does the other.

Luckily, the change in the density of a gas is as predictable as the change in its volume. If, for example, you take a flexible container to 33 feet (2 ATA) the volume will decrease by one-half but the density will double. In turn, at 66 feet (3 ATA) the volume will be one-third and the density will triple; at 99 feet (4 ATA) the volume is now one-fourth and the density quadrupled and so on. This relationship is important because it explains why a diver consumes his air more rapidly the deeper he goes. Here's why.

In freediving (breath-hold diving), as a diver descends, his lungs decrease in size, according to Boyle's law. But this isn't the case when using scuba because a diver fills his lungs completely with every breath. To fill the lungs, the density of the air inhaled must increase to equal the ambient (surrounding) pressure. In fact, as we saw earlier, the air in a breath taken at 33 feet (10 m) will be twice as dense as at the surface. Likewise, to get a lung full of air at twice the density of the surface, twice the number of molecules must be drawn from the tank. So, as the diver is drawing twice the number of molecules from the tank at 33 feet, his air supply will last only half as long as it would at the surface. Similarly, if all other conditions are equal, the air supply will last only one-third as long at 66 feet (3 ATA), one-fourth as long at 99 feet (4 ATA), and so on.

Knowing this relationship gives you an easy way to estimate how long your air supply will last. But be forewarned; this is only a rough estimate. Your actual air consumption rate varies drastically due to factors such as cold, heavy exertion and stress. Additionally, the estimate works only if you plan to remain at a constant depth throughout the dive — something we divers rarely do.

Jacques Charles

Sir Robert Boyle's work dealt solely with the effects of pressure and volume. He did not consider the effect of a third important factor: temperature. The influence of temperature on gas behavior was first explored by a French scientist named Jacques Charles and his colleague, Joseph Gay-Lussac.

Through experimentation, Charles and Gay-Lussac found that if they kept the pressure of a gas constant in a container, the volume of the gas would increase as the temperature increased. Conversely, the volume would decrease when the temperature decreased and the pressure remained constant. This is called Charles' law, and it explains why, for example, if you leave an inflated balloon in a hot car all day it will expand.

One way in which Charles' law relates to diving is in how temperature affects the pressure in a scuba tank. As a general rule, for every change in temperature of 1 degree Fahrenheit, the pressure in a scuba tank changes about 5 psi. For every change in temperature of 1 degree Celsius, the pressure in a scuba tank changes about 9 psi. To do more precise calculations requires a little simple algebra, but at least you now understand why your tank's burst disc let go that time you forgot and left it in your trunk on a hot summer day.

Years later a researcher named Julius Mayer explained the phenomenon Charles and Gay-Lussac described. He suggested that heat is simply a result of molecular motion. Therefore, increasing the temperature was merely increasing the motion of the molecules. As the molecules increased in motion, they increased in their frequency of collision. This is measured as an increase in pressure. In 1843, the scientist James P. Joule proved Mayer's theory experimentally. Incidentally, if you're not terribly afraid of a little math, both Boyle's and Charles' laws can be integrated into what's called the general gas law. This lets us predict gas behavior regardless of whether the factors that vary are volume, pressure or temperature.

John Dalton

So far, nothing we've discussed considers what happens when different gases are mixed together. While this may seem a trivial matter, it's anything but. In fact, not knowing how gases behave in a mixture can get a diver killed. The first person to explore this phenomenon was an English scientist, John Dalton. (In addition to his work with gases, Dalton is famous for his work describing matter as being composed of atoms.)

Dalton found that even though a gas mixture is made up of several different constituents, each gas will continue to demonstrate its own behavior, as though the other gases didn't exist. Again, more common sense; if a gas mixture is made up of 80 percent nitrogen and 20 percent oxygen, then it stands to reason that 80 percent of the pressure is exerted by the nitrogen and 20 percent by the oxygen. Furthermore, he termed these individual pressures within mixtures partial pressures, and he found that each partial pressure is proportional to the number of molecules of that gas within the mixture. That may sound obvious to us today but this tidbit of common sense is so important, and its implications so profound, that it's called Dalton's law of partial pressures. Let's see how this concept applies to us as divers.

We'll return again to our gas mixture of 20 percent oxygen and 80 percent nitrogen, and we'll assume it's at a pressure of 15 psi. This is similar to our own air, but ignores the trace gases, and working in round numbers makes the concept easier to understand. According to Dalton's law, oxygen exerts 20 percent of the total pressure of the gas, while nitrogen exerts 80 percent. Another way of stating this is that of the 15-psi total pressure, the partial pressure of the oxygen exerts 3 psi (20 percent) while nitrogen partial pressure exerts the other 12 psi (80 percent).

Now let's double the total pressure to 30 psi and see what happens. (We'll assume the temperature remains constant at all times.) Each gas component continues to exert its partial pressure in proportion to the 80/20 mixture. Of the total 30 psi, nitrogen exerts 80 percent or 24 psi, and oxygen exerts 20 percent or 6 psi.

If the ambient pressure increases, the pressure inside the container (such as our lungs) also must increase for the container to maintain its original volume. This means more gas must be put in the container to increase the internal pressure. As we saw before, this is exactly what happens when a diver breathes from his regulator at depth; more gas molecules go into his lungs to maintain a constant lung volume.

Note that while the percentages of the gases that make up the mixture never change, the number of gas molecules increases to exert more pressure. This means more molecules of each gas reach the diver's lungs. For example, let's assume a lung volume at the surface contains 100 molecules of air. (Of course the real number would be vastly more than this, but a small number makes it easier to understand.) If we continue to assume an 80/20 nitrogen-oxygen mixture, then of the total 100 molecules, 80 will be nitrogen and 20 oxygen.

Now assume the diver descends to 132 feet (40 m) or 5 ATA. At that depth the ambient pressure is five times what it was at the surface. So, to maintain a normal lung volume, the diver takes in 500 molecules with each breath. This is five times the number he breathed at the surface. As this is still an 80/20 gas mixture, nitrogen accounts for 400 molecules or 4 ATA of pressure, while the oxygen component is responsible for 100 molecules or 1 ATA. Notice that breathing this air mixture at 132 feet is physiologically equivalent to breathing pure oxygen at the surface — 100 molecules at 1 ATA.

We can demonstrate the insidious nature of increasing partial pressures in yet another way. Suppose that while filling a scuba tank a 1 percent quantity of carbon monoxide enters the mixture. Using the previous example of 100 molecules to equal a full lung, carbon monoxide would now account for one of the 100 molecules inhaled with each breath while at the surface. But, if the diver descends to 99 feet (4 ATA), his lungs now require 400 molecules to fill — four times the surface quantity. Of those 400 molecules drawn from the tank with each breath, carbon monoxide will now account for four molecules. The problem is, breathing these four molecules of carbon monoxide at 99 feet has the same physiologic effect as breathing a gas mixture of 4 percent carbon monoxide at the surface (which is toxic).

Thus, we see why an air supply that might contain tolerable levels of contaminants at the surface can quickly become toxic at depth even though the gas inside the tank never changes. Once the tank is full, the proportion of gases in the mixture remains unchanged. The problem results purely from breathing the mixture under higher pressure; and it's all a result of the good Dr. Dalton's law.

William Henry

As a science educator, I see that one of the more difficult concepts for my students is understanding that gases can dissolve into liquids. The reason is that the concept seems to belie reality. For example, to the naked eye a liquid doesn't appear to have any "space" in it to allow gas to enter. However, we all know better; gases can dissolve into liquids. We're reminded of this every time we pour a can of soda into a glass of ice. The profuse formation of bubbles is merely carbon dioxide being released from the liquid. The gas, although not visible in its dissolved form, remains in solution until something acts on it to make it come out. The other important concept, besides the fact that gas can be held inside a liquid, is that the gas also continues to exert pressure while in solution. This internal pressure is called gas tension.

Exactly how much gas a liquid will absorb, and what factors affect this absorption, was first studied by a colleague of Dalton's named William Henry. His experiments proved that the amount of gas that dissolves into a liquid at a given temperature depends on the partial pressure of the gas. Yep, you guessed it. This concept is called Henry's law, and it's yet another phenomenon that we've all experienced. Why, for example, does a freshly tapped keg of beer taste better than the dregs at the end of the keg?

In almost every recreational diving class in the world, the good Doctor Jacques Charles is credited for any discussion involving pressure-temperature relationships. But in fairness, his law describes the relationship of pressure and volume, not temperature. The pressure-temperature insight was actually the work of the 18th-century scientist, Guillaume Amontons. Thus, it's really Amontons' law that describes "the pressure of a fixed mass of gas kept at a constant volume (like a scuba tank) is proportional to the temperature." He discovered this relationship while building an "air thermometer." Fair is fair.

Simple. Because of Henry's law. More gas — in this case, carbon dioxide — is dissolved in the liquid when it's first tapped. But over time, as the carbon dioxide dissipates, the contents "go flat." The decline in taste results from the reduced gas tension in the liquid.

Henry's law further tells us that both pressure and temperature affect how gas dissolves into liquids. Let's see how this might happen. Imagine you have a beaker of water with absolutely no gas dissolved in it. The beaker is also inside a chamber where a perfect vacuum exists. This means that absolutely no gas is in contact with the water. (These conditions are impossible to achieve except perhaps in outer space, but it makes the concept easier to understand.) If air enters the chamber and comes in contact with the water, air molecules begin dissolving into the water. The gas in the water then exerts a pressure, or gas tension. In addition, the gas tension will obey Dalton's law and each component gas continues exerting its own partial pressure.

Gas will attempt to dissolve into liquid until the gas tension equalizes with the air pressure in contact with the liquid. But this takes time. The difference between the air pressure in contact with the liquid and the gas tension within the liquid is called a pressure gradient. If the pressure gradient is high, gas will be absorbed into the liquid quickly. But, as the gas molecules continue to dissolve into the water, the gradient begins to decrease. Molecules dissolve into the water more slowly.

Over time the gas tension in the water equals the air pressure in contact with the liquid. Although molecules will continue to pass between the liquid/air interface, no net exchange of gas occurs. The water is now said to be saturated.

Let's now pressurize the vacuum chamber. This increases the pressure of the gas in contact with the water. This causes even more gas to dissolve into the water. Over time, gas will continue to enter the water until the gas tension in the liquid and the air pressure on the liquid are equal (saturation). As Henry's law predicted, the more pressure the gas exerts on the water, the more gas dissolves into the water.

As you might expect, if we release the pressure in the chamber the phenomenon is reversed. With less pressure on the water, the gas dissolved in it has a greater gas tension than the air in contact with the water. Now the water contains more gas than it can keep in solution at that pressure.

Gas transfers out of the liquid until the gas tension is equal to the air pressure. If air pressure is reduced very slowly, if it isn't shaken, or if no foreign particles are present in the water, the gas transfer is undetectable — no gas bubbles form. But if the air pressure decreases too quickly, or the water is vigorously shaken, or if foreign particles are added to the water, the gas begins to escape more rapidly. So quickly that — like a shaken bottle of soda — the gas molecules will form visible bubbles.

In addition to pressure (Boyle's law), temperature (Charles' law) also affects gas absorption into liquids. Heat makes the molecules of a liquid vibrate more activity. This rapid movement leaves less space in the liquid for gas molecules to occupy. Now fewer gas molecules can dissolve into or remain in the liquid. We see this take place any time we boil water. As the water begins to heat, small air bubbles form and collect at the bottom of the container. They're caused by the speeded-up molecules pushing dissolved gas out of the water. It makes sense, then, that cooler liquids can hold more dissolved gas than warmer liquids. A cooler liquid contains slower molecules, allowing room for more gas molecules to occupy.

If you haven't already figured out why this phenomenon is so important, it's because gas dissolves into our blood and other tissues — which are primarily liquid — just as it dissolved into the beaker of water. But absorption isn't as big of a concern as elimination; the real problem begins when pressure is reduced and the gas has to come out. Under certain circumstances, this could lead to significant bubble formation and decompression sickness. There are, however, some important differences between body tissues and a beaker of water, which makes understanding the mechanism of decompression sickness a bit more complicated than the oft-used "shaken bottle of soda" analogy. Still, whether it's carbon dioxide dissolving into soda water or nitrogen into the bloodstream, the physics is all the same.

So you see, you don't need to be a rocket scientist to understand physics. Like all science, it's fundamentally common sense. These gas laws govern us on every dive, so it's nice to know the rules and the folks who first discovered them. ☙

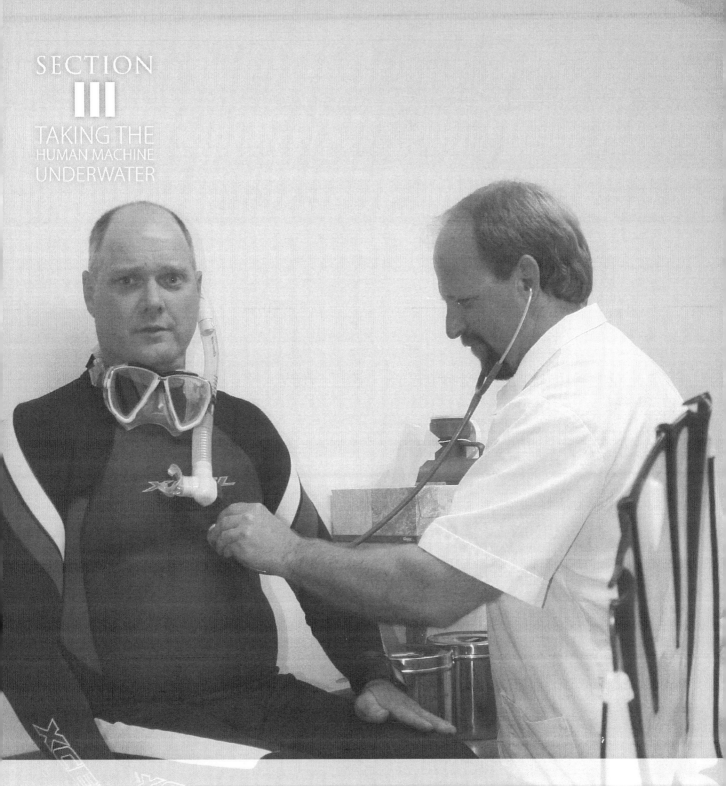

CHAPTER 7

The Doctor Will See You Now:
Diving Fitness and Medical Examinations

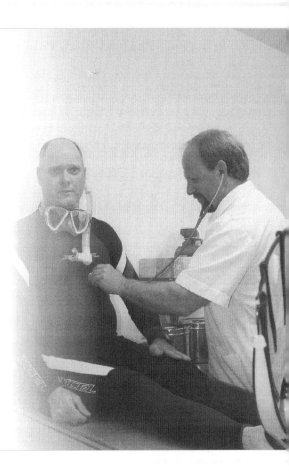

We Americans are

a fickle lot when it comes to our health. On one hand we have a cult-like obsession with fitness, yet more than a third of us are obese. We live in a time in which it has never been easier to make healthy dietary choices, yet each year nearly a half million of us die from heart disease, much of which is preventable. We have what is supposedly the best health care system in the world, yet our children may be the first generation ever to have a shorter life expectancy than their parents.

The disconnect between perception and reality, when it comes to fitness, also reaches into the realm of scuba diving. Compliments of the increasing notoriety of diving — thanks largely to the now more than 200 cable channels — most folks today know that diving is no longer limited to young, macho daredevils. In fact, on dive boats today, you're more likely to encounter a pudgy baby boomer than some tanned Adonis. From this, many have drawn a false and dangerous assumption that one needn't be any more fit to participate in sports than to watch them on TV. Of course reality shows up to bite us on the backside when we couch potatoes actually try to do something like play football or basketball. In short order, the ravages of time and laziness become painfully apparent.

But diving is different. As long as the conditions are benign, the physical challenges of diving can be minimal, so even those with poor physical fitness can be lulled into believing that, "I'm fit enough." That is, until the day things don't go as planned, and their level of fitness is what makes the difference between them going home to their family or not.

Regardless of how easy diving appears to have become, surviving underwater places our bodies under some pretty stressful and unforgiving conditions. But what exactly does it mean to be "fit to dive," and how can we assess that? Does determining our fitness always require the insight of a trained medical professional? And which medical conditions absolutely preclude diving, and which might just be a minor hindrance? These questions have been debated since the beginning of recreational diving; and as in most fields, opinions and practices have changed over the years. Even today, worldwide policies on prequalification medical exams and diving fitness are not universal.

Defining 'Fitness'

It's difficult, if not impossible, to come to a single definition of what fitness means to divers because it has many components. It's also context-specific; all diving isn't the same and, thus, what constitutes fitness for some forms of diving may be wholly inadequate for others. In addition, what might be considered a critical aspect of fitness for one type of diving might be relatively unimportant in another. Take strength, for example. The level of strength required to lug around a full technical diving rig clearly isn't necessary for the average shallow, warm-water recreational dive in which you're wearing not much more than a bathing suit and a tank. In fact, except in these "extended range" technical diving activities strength isn't really all that vital to the diving experience. But that wasn't always the case.

In the early days of diving, the limited and rudimentary equipment did place a premium on self-reliance and physical prowess, which meant a good deal of strength. But that hasn't been the case for many years. With more extensive and reliable equipment has come a shift from an emphasis on strength to one that stresses endurance. The problem is that many divers today lack even this essential condition. Some contend that, by choosing the right conditions, diving doesn't have to be all that demanding. But they forget that the conditions present at the beginning of a dive aren't always the same at the end. So, entering the water with only the level of fitness required to deal with ideal conditions is a recipe for disaster. Conditioning has always been, and will always remain, an important prerequisite for safe diving. Of course, that doesn't mean that divers need the stamina of a triathlete. But it does mean that you could quickly find yourself in a world of hurt if you have only the stamina of Homer Simpson.

Unfortunately, diving accident data seems to be pointing to fitness, or rather the lack thereof, as an increasingly significant role in why divers die. Rather than exotic pressure-related injuries emphasized in your training, like gas embolism or decompression sickness, what kills most divers appears to be preventable by simply being better prepared for the conditions that they encounter. And by "prepared" I mean physically capable of handling the conditions that Mother Nature doles out. As the average age of divers increases — it has for many years — factors involving fitness and heart disease are becoming more prevalent. Certainly, nothing can halt the aging process, but that's no excuse to ignore the role fitness can play in slowing it.

Another issue in the fitness debate is a misconception held by many divers that diving is an activity that can help develop it. Stated plainly, that's just not true. You cannot get into shape by diving, but instead must get in shape for diving. The exercise demands required for any training effect simply aren't sufficient in diving, at least not if you're diving properly. An elevated heart rate and associated demands on your respiratory system, when diving, are a sure sign that something is wrong, not a normal condition. So, if you find that you encounter significant physical challenges when you dive, that's a sure sign to re-evaluate your fitness level (and change the way or kind of diving you do until your fitness improves).

Assessing Your Fitness

Assessing your level of fitness for diving doesn't have to be a complicated process, but it does require some self-honesty. Start by thinking about the physical demands that you encounter during your average day, and how well you deal with — or avoid — them. For example, do you cringe at the thought of taking the stairs rather than the elevator? If you do have to climb stairs, what kind of shape are you in at the top? How much walking does your job involve, and do you do things that tend to minimize or promote this? Perhaps, most importantly, do you engage in any form of regular exercise, and if so for how long and — honestly — how many days per month? I think you know what answers put you in the "it's time to do something" category, and that's a good signal that you probably aren't fit for the rigors of diving.

All diving requires a modest degree of health and stamina, but in determining what fitness to dive means to you, you also need to understand that there's no single answer and, as stated earlier, it depends on what kind of diving you do. So, the next issue to consider in evaluating your fitness level is examining where and what type of diving you plan to do. Obviously, enjoying a shallow reef in the Florida Keys on a calm summer morning is far less demanding that braving 8-foot (2.4 m) seas to dive the wrecks off the New Jersey coast. Although this may seem obvious, it's amazing how many folks assume that their Florida Keys fitness is all they need when they one day do decide to tackle the rigors of New Jersey or California. Your well-being demands that you be honest about what it is you want from the diving experience, and make sure that you don't exceed the conditions on which you've based your fitness decision.

Personally, I'm seeing this situation more and more here in the Florida Keys, where the increasing number of wrecks has somewhat changed the nature of diving. Today, in every region of the Keys, artificial reefs have provided easily accessible but much deeper and more demanding dive sites. The danger is that some consider these wreck dives no more challenging than a 30-foot (9 m) plunge into the bathtub-like conditions of a reef. Frankly, sometimes diving the deeper wrecks is about as easy as diving the reefs. But that's a rare event, and one that you can never assume will be so. (This is why some dive operators do not allow their guests to dive deeper wrecks without advanced certification or supervision by staff members.)

Assessing your fitness also isn't a one-time event. When I started diving as a young teenager, there were few physical tasks a diver might encounter that I couldn't handle. But to assume that's still the case more than four decades later is not only kidding myself, it would mean endangering my own life. So, the next time you're filling out your log book, take a few minutes to ask yourself a few simple questions: Did I encounter conditions that were close to or beyond my physical capabilities? How likely is it that these conditions might occur again? Do I need to reconsider my "comfort envelop" and alter the way or type of diving I do, or try to improve my fitness? The answers require a great deal of self-honesty, but this thought process might be the best thing you'll ever do for your health and well-being.

Finding a clear method to assess and quantify your level of fitness isn't always easy, but there are some basics you can keep in mind. First, if you can't walk around the block without a rest — or if you've never even tried — diving at any level probably isn't something you should try (or continue). At least, not until you've improved your conditioning. A very minimal guideline for fitness is the ability to walk a mile within 12 minutes. If you can't do this, you should plan to exercise for at least 20 minutes four or five times per week, but only after you've obatined the approval of your doctor. And if possible, add swimming with fins to your routine. A useful measure that I've always given my own students, based on years of practical experience, is this: No one should consider themselves prepared for a certification course who cannot swim, using a mask and fins, for at least 200 yards (182 m) without stopping and/or becoming exhausted.

Medical Concerns

Aside from physical fitness, divers and would-be divers must also consider how any existing medical conditions can affect their health and safety. Surviving in an environment that's 800 times denser than the atmosphere can present problems that might never arise while sitting in your living room, or even engaging in moderate physical activity on terra firma.

First, let's consider temporary conditions such as colds, flu, injury or even pregnancy. All should be considered reasons to curtail diving until the effects have passed. Colds, flu or allergy attacks cause swelling or blockage in the sinuses and eustachian tubes, which means pressure equalization will be difficult or impossible. Injuries can leave you with restricted strength, stamina or mobility, and might even put you at a greater risk of decompression sickness due to alterations or restrictions in blood flow. Furthermore, when diving with an injury, the accompanying pain could mask symptoms of decompression sickness. So it's best to postpone diving until you're fully healed. Lastly, diving while you are or could be pregnant is considered a no-no for one simple reason: We just don't know enough about its effect on the developing fetus, so why take the chance? Can any hour spent underwater be worth the risk to a child's life or future quality of life?

It should be obvious that you must take into account the effect of any medications. This goes for both prescribed and over-the-counter (OTC) meds. Frankly, most medications have no effect on diving, but some definitely do. They may cause drowsiness or fatigue, which might make you more susceptible to nitrogen narcosis, or just impede your thinking at just the time thinking is most critical. Other medications, as well as illicit drugs, can affect heart rate even in those without heart problems. Clearly, if you plan to dive, it's especially important to read the warning labels before using any drugs. And it's just downright stupid to dive while taking any recreational drugs.

Another concern that's completely foreign to any landlubber taking meds is whether and how any drug can be affected by the increased pressure. There is always a possibility of such an unexpected reaction to medications, and some drugs are noted particularly for pressure-induced side effects. But the problem is that these reactions can vary from diver to diver, and even from day to day. So, the first step in preventing a dangerous situation is knowing well in advance what side effects any medication has on you before using it while diving. It isn't smart to pop a pill for the first time just as you're about to enter the water. This is true even of common OTC drugs like cold and allergy or seasickness medications.

The effect of diving on prescription medication can be a very complex issue, and requires a knowledgeable doctor's advice. Regardless, always remind your doctor that you're a diver when he or she prescribes a med. And, if your doc isn't up on how diving can affect your condition or medications, you should be prepared to provide some resources. (See the sidebar "Educating Your Doctor.")

Some medical conditions aren't temporary, and these can have major consequences for divers. Two of the more common concerns are asthma and diabetes. Both are becoming epidemic in many regions of the world, including North America, the Caribbean and the islands of the South Pacific; and many believe that this is the result of lifestyle and the degrading quality of our environment. This is a serious problem for all segments of society, but it poses special problems for the diving community. For decades there has been much debate about whether to allow those with either condition to dive; and at one time the answer was quite simple: no. But many have questioned such an absolute ban on diving, and today, after careful medication evaluation, some asthmatics are permitted to dive.

Diabetes, as well, is a chronic condition that's been recently reconsidered by diving medical experts. Today, rather than a blanket disqualification, divers and diving candidates with diabetes are evaluated on a case-by-case basis with an appropriate medical specialist. A similar situation exists for one of the most common disorders in almost every developed society: cardiovascular disease. Research and debate continue regarding these conditions, and it's not unlikely more issues and findings will appear.

Stick Out Your Tongue and Say 'Ahhh'

Whether you're a diver or not, the cornerstone of good health is a regular physical exam. Opinions on exactly how often this should happen seem to vary; and to be per-

As we all know, doctors are very busy people. Their medical school training is intense, and with continuing advances in medical research, they have to know more and more. So, it's no surprise that a subject like diving medicine doesn't receive much, if any attention, in either medical school or afterward. In fact, if a doctor doesn't take up diving personally, he may know less about diving medicine than a knowledgeable scuba instructor. This isn't intended as a slam; it's just that, in the scheme of things, scuba diving isn't a very common activity. So, most doctors only rarely deal with divers and would-be divers. As a result, when it comes time for a diving medical exam, you may find yourself in the delicate situation of having to educate your doctor.

But the situation isn't as daunting as it may sound. The RSTC "Diving Medical Statement and Questionnaire" contains a section designed just for this purpose, entitled, "Guidelines for Recreational Scuba Diver's Physical Examination." It includes three pages of detailed instructions with 16 medical references. So, when you show up to your doc's office, be sure that you take a copy of the entire six-page form, not just the part he or she has to sign.

The guidelines address areas of concern for divers, and what to look for in a medical assessment. Temporary, relative and severe risk conditions are listed for the neurological, pulmonary, gastrointestinal, orthopedic, hematological, metabolic /endocrinological and otolaryngological systems. There's also a segment on behavioral health. At a minimum, the examination should include these points. The list of conditions is not all-inclusive, but contains the most commonly encountered medical problems.

The guidelines define "temporary risks" as those that are responsive to treatment, allowing the student to dive safely after they have resolved. "Relative risks" refer to conditions that exist but, in the judgment of the physician, are not contraindicated for diving. Finally, "severe risk" implies that an individual is believed to be at substantially elevated risk of decompression sickness, pulmonary or otic (ear) barotrauma or altered consciousness with subsequent drowning, compared with the general population. In these cases, as the guidelines state, "The consultants involved in drafting this document would generally discourage a student with such medical problems from diving."

The guidelines conclude by informing physicians that medical professionals of the Divers Alert Network associated with Duke University Health System are available for consultation. If you find that your doc would like even more insights, here are some additional references:

• *Medical Examination of Sport Scuba Divers,* 3rd Edition, A.A. Bove, MD, PhD (ed.). Best Publishing Company, P.O. Box 30100, Flagstaff, Arizona, 86003-0100.

• *The Physician's Guide to Diving Medicine*, C.W. Shilling, C.B. Carlston and R.A. Mathias. Plenum Press, New York, New York, (available through the Undersea and Hyperbaric Medical Association, Bethesda, Maryland).

Educating Your Doctor

fectly honest, after graduating from college I didn't set foot in a doctor's office for almost 20 years. But that all changed when I hit the big 4-0, a milestone no one should ignore. Since then I've had regular annual checkups, along with the associated diagnostic, age-appropriate tests involving treadmills, CAT scans, endoscopes, rubber gloves and assorted other accoutrements of medical technology.

The issue of physical examinations for divers has undergone quite an evolution. Even today, policy varies from country to country. When I got certified back in the Dark Ages, everyone was required to first secure medical approval from a physician before being accepted into a class. But in North America, that hasn't been the case for a long time. As many of you no doubt know from your own experience, some of you had to have physical exams, while others didn't.

North American-based diver training organizations require that all candidates for instruction complete the Recreational Scuba Training Council's "Medical History Statement and Questionnaire." (A copy of the form can be downloaded from many sources; just type in the search term "RSTC medical form.") As the form explains, its purpose is to find out whether a prospective diving student should be examined by a doctor before participating in training. A "yes" response to any question doesn't necessarily disqualify someone from diving, but it does indicate that there could be a pre-existing condition that may affect safety. Therefore, the candidate must seek the advice of a physician before engaging in diving activities.

Some believe that this approach is inadequate, contending that everyone new to diving should first have medical clearance from a physician. In fact, some countries such as Australia require this. But is this additional expense and inconvenience really warranted? Some who have studied the matter don't think so. For instance, the UK Sport Diving

The 'Diving Medical Statement and Questionnaire' has been produced under the auspices of the Recreational Scuba Training Council and endorsed by the Undersea and Hyperbaric Medical Society, Divers Alert Network and more than two dozen of North America's top diving medical specialists. To assess whether an individual should have medical clearance to enroll in a scuba course, here are the areas it addresses:

First, the questionnaire addresses those more than 45 years of age. For this group, a positive response to smoking, high cholesterol, family history of heart attack or stroke, high blood pressure, diabetes (even if controlled by diet alone), or if they are receiving medical care means a trip to the doctor's office.

It then goes on to ask all applicants if they have or have ever had any of several medical conditions listed below; and if they are taking any prescribed medications for anything other than malaria prophylaxis or birth control. Female diving candidates are asked whether they are, could be or are attempting to become pregnant. Again, an affirmative response to any of these questions or conditions, and a doctor's approval is required for continuing with your wishes to become a certified diver.

- ☐ Asthma, or wheezing with breathing, or wheezing with exercise.
- ☐ Frequent or severe attacks of hayfever or allergy.
- ☐ Frequent colds, sinusitis or bronchitis.
- ☐ Any form of lung disease.
- ☐ Pneumothorax (collapsed lung).
- ☐ Other chest disease or chest surgery.
- ☐ Behavioral health, mental or psychological problems (panic attack, fear of closed or open spaces).
- ☐ Epilepsy, seizures, convulsions or take medications to prevent them.
- ☐ Recurring complicated migraine headaches or take medications to prevent them.
- ☐ Blackouts or fainting (full/partial loss of consciousness).
- ☐ Frequent or severe suffering from motion sickness (e.g., seasick or carsick).
- ☐ Dysentery or dehydration requiring medical intervention.
- ☐ Any dive accidents or decompression sickness.
- ☐ Inability to perform moderate exercise (example: walk one mile [1.6 km] within 12 minutes).
- ☐ Head injury with loss of consciousness in the past five years.
- ☐ Recurrent back problems.
- ☐ Back or spinal surgery.
- ☐ Diabetes.
- ☐ Back, arm or leg problems following surgery, injury or fracture.
- ☐ High blood pressure or take medicine to control blood pressure.
- ☐ Heart disease.
- ☐ Heart attack.
- ☐ Angina, heart surgery or blood vessel surgery.
- ☐ Sinus surgery.
- ☐ Ear disease or surgery, hearing loss or problems with balance.
- ☐ Recurrent ear problems.
- ☐ Bleeding or other blood disorders.
- ☐ Hernia.
- ☐ Ulcers or ulcer surgery.
- ☐ A colostomy or ileostomy.
- ☐ Recreational drug use or treatment for, or alcoholism in the past five years.

Medical Committee found that examination by a physician was largely unhelpful in identifying divers with significant medical conditions, and concluded that a health questionnaire — like the current medical history form — is perfectly sufficient. A similar result came from a study several years ago published in the *British Journal of Sports Medicine*.

However, this selective nature of medical exams does not apply to some divers. All commercial divers, including professionals such as divemasters, dive control specialists, assistant instructors and instructors, are required to have full medical clearance before they're accepted into training. Scientific divers, including most divers in university programs and those working under the guidelines of the American Academy of Underwater Sciences, also require a very extensive medical evaluation for qualification and to remain active.

For recreational divers, the current medical standard has been in effect for three decades. The aforementioned questionnaire was developed by the Undersea and Hyperbaric Medical Society (UHMS) and Divers Alert Network (DAN). (More information about the form is contained in "Assessing Your Medical Fitness to Dive" on Page 59.)

In the end, however, the final arbiter of who can enter a diving course — for medical reasons or otherwise — is that of the instructor. In fact, based solely on his or her judgment, an instructor may require anyone to secure medical approval from a physician, even if the candidate has indicated no affirmative answers on the questionnaire.

It's human nature to think the best of ourselves, but often our image doesn't reflect reality. Usually, this has little potential to do harm to anything but our ego. Fitness for diving, however, is an entirely different matter. When it comes to fitness, lying to yourself or others can put both you and your buddy at serious risk. Remember, no diver ever thought that they weren't coming back from their last dive.

The Rockport Walk Test

Step 1: Weigh yourself on a scale. The numbers on the scale aren't as important as your overall health and numbers like your cholesterol level and blood pressure, but they can help you determine where your weight should fall. Check out an accurate height and weight chart to find your healthy weight range and take your body frame and build into consideration as well.

Step 2: Determine your body composition by calculating your BMI. BMI stands for Body Mass Index and it can provide you with an overall assessment of your fitness and health level.

Step 3: Find your target heart rate. Your target heart rate is the heart rate you need to maintain while exercising. Determine your resting heart rate by finding your pulse on either your neck or wrist and counting it for 15 seconds. Use a calculator to multiply your result by 4. This is your resting heart rate. Calculate 220 minus your current age and the result is your maximum heart rate. Multiply your maximum heart rate by 60 percent and 85 percent and those numbers equal your target heart rate range to aim for each time you exercise.

Step 4: Test your aerobic fitness by doing a simple one-mile walk. Track your time and your heart rate at two different points during the walk: the middle and the end. Record your results.

Step 5: Determine your muscular fitness by doing as many repetitions of pushups or pullups as you can. Pullups tend to be harder to perform than pushups so take your current muscular fitness level into consideration. Record this number in your notebook.

Step 6: See how flexible you are by sitting on the floor with your legs outstretched in front of you. Lay a yardstick in front of you and make sure your heels land at the 15-inch (38 cm) mark. Reach your fingertips as far as you can toward your toes and record the number closest on the yardstick.

Step 7: Keep a fitness journal and test yourself as you journey through your fitness program. Seeing your fitness level improve can be motivation to keep working toward your fitness goals.

You can find out more about the Rockport Walk Test at **www.exrx.net/Calculators/Rockport.html.**

CHAPTER 8

Going Down?
The Big Squeeze of Descent

What diver hasn't envied

fish. Gills free them from any limits on bottom time, and millions of years of evolution have given them a pass on the great bane of divers, decompression illness. Those without gas bladders — the fishy form of a buoyancy compensator — can even thumb their nose (excuse me, fin) at problems the good Dr. Boyle explained to us about changing pressure and volume. If only we were so lucky.

In addition, lungs, sinuses and assorted other air spaces make taking the human body underwater a considerable challenge. Our inability to extract oxygen directly from water requires the elaborate and costly technology we call scuba. Sophisticated decompression models also are necessary to avoid the ravages of the bends. Our poor subaquatic design makes even descending more than a few feet a chore that, unless done properly, can be injurious. The medical literature has a name for these injuries: barotrauma (literally *pressure injury*).

Typically, most discussions of barotrauma address the more dramatic and life-threatening form experienced on ascent. These are the disorders that give rise to the cardinal rule of scuba diving: Never hold your breath. I can think of no other activity in which death can result merely from this simple and natural act. We certainly don't need to learn how to breathe, but we sure have to be trained to keep doing it when something goes wrong underwater. So it's hardly surprising that this represents a good portion of scuba training.

Far less time and attention is given to the more mundane, yet more common, injuries that result from descent.

Yet, although rarely serious, descent barotrauma is the overwhelming cause of most problems. So, an occasional revisit of the issue of descent barotrauma is worthwhile for any diver who wants to avoid a ruined dive or worse.

The Essence of Squeeze

In the parlance of diving, descent barotrauma is, for obvious reasons, more commonly referred to as squeeze. Pascal's principle tells us that, within a fluid, pressure will be distributed equally in all directions. Furthermore, as we're composed mostly of water, and it's incompressible, the issue of squeeze is irrelevant to most of our body structures. The problems result when that pressure transfers across tissues and into the gas-filled structures. The areas or structures primarily affected are the sinuses, ears and areas of the face (under the mask). The lungs, too, may be affected though this is rarely a problem.

Some of the gas-filled structures of our body, like our lungs and digestive tract, are flexible and can compress on descent. But others, like our sinuses, middle ear — as well as the air space added when we don a mask — cannot compress. The sinuses and middle ear also contain a delicate, blood-rich lining called the mucosa. If the pressure inside the sinuses and ears can't equalize as external pressure increases on descent, the body compensates by causing the mucosa to swell. If the pressure continues, the capillaries near the surface of the mucosa begin to leak fluid and bleed. If the blood and fluid remain trapped in the cavities, it will decrease the internal volume and help to increase the internal pressure. If it drains from the cavity, then the pressure differential will continue, as well as the bleeding.

While that might be an interesting lesson in physics, it's also very painful and can result in some serious problems. The trapped blood and fluid, which can take days or weeks to resolve, provides an excellent growth medium for bacteria. This is why infections are a common result of sinus and ear squeeze. On rare occasions the bony walls of the sinus may actually rupture, sending air into the eye socket (a condition called orbital emphysema) or into the brain cavity (called pneumocephalus). Both conditions are serious and the latter can be life-threatening.

In the case of our mask — the artificial air space we attach to our body — it works a little differently. As much of the mask is inflexible, it acts like a vacuum. The increasing external pressure pushes the glass plate against our face, and negative pressure develops within the mask. As the plate can't flex, but the tissue of our face can, the skin and eyes are sucked toward the negative pressure area inside. If this pressure isn't equalized by a simple exhalation from the nose, the pressure differential increases, blood vessels begin to engorge and eventually rupture, and a "mask squeeze" results. The effect is a bruise-like discoloration of the skin under the mask, and in severe cases rupture of the blood vessels in the sclera (white part of the eyeball). While a mask squeeze can be painful and appears horrifying, it's rarely a serious problem except in the most severe cases. Incidentally, in case you didn't already realize it, the need to equalize internal pressure via exhalation is why a diving mask must also enclose the nose. Without it — as is the case with swimming goggles — there is no way to equalize the air spaces, and this is why you can't wear goggles while scuba diving.

As you probably have realized, mask squeezes rarely happen. In more than 40 years of diving I can count the number that I've seen on one hand. The reason is because, under normal conditions, we unconsciously exhale into the mask through our nose, keeping the in-

ternal pressure equalized. The condition is seen most often in very inexperienced divers, or those who have restricted air passage through their nose due to a cold. By the way, this same phenomenon can happen to other parts of your body when you add a sealed air space in the form of a dry suit. Preventing this condition, called suit squeeze, is one reason you should seek professional training when purchasing a dry suit. As air is not trapped in a wet suit, suit squeeze is not an issue there.

Pinch and Blow

Barotrauma is completely and easily preventable because the air spaces in question all have some connection to the outside and, therefore, can be equalized. Yet, in some cases, equalization can be compromised in individuals who have chronic or congenital problems involving the passageways such as a deviated nasal septum, chronic sinusitis, severe allergies or unusually small eustachian tubes. Unfortunately, in a minority, these conditions can be so severe or persistent they are disqualified for diving. This is why questions relating to ears, sinuses and equalization are included in the standard diving medical history form that all diving candidates must complete prior to training.

The specific anatomy of the major sinuses goes like this: They are all connected to the nasopharynx via narrow openings called the ostium. The ears are connected to the nasopharynx via the eustachian tubes, which terminate at the rear of the throat. Normally, air and mucus pass freely in and out. But in cases in which the mucosa becomes inflamed because of sickness, irritation or allergic reaction, the passages can swell to a point at which the airway is partly or fully blocked. As divers we're all too aware of what that means: no diving.

While we're most familiar with sinus issues on descent, sometimes problems can arise during ascent. When sinuses don't equalize on the way up it's termed a "reverse block." This happens because, for some reason, the passageways close off while underwater. As a result, the higher-pressure air inside the cavity cannot escape. Often this is caused by medication (decongestants) that wears off during the dive, allowing the mucosa to re-swell. (Sometimes the swelling that results when a medication wears off is worse than the initial swelling, and is called a "rebound effect.") A reverse block can also occur when a diver elects to dive with a cold. In this case equalization on descent may be possible, although usually with difficulty. However, the forceful equalization can irritate the mucosa to the point of causing further inflammation, making it very difficult for air to evacuate the sinus or ear on ascent. The only alternative in this case is to remain below the depth at which you feel no pain, and wait for the air to work its way out gradually (and pray that you have enough air left in your tank to delay the ascent). The best advice is a lot simpler: Never dive with a cold and never, ever force equalization.

Normally, sinuses either clear or they don't. Period. But sometimes they need a bit of coaxing. Although it's never a good idea to force the issue, I have to admit that I've had chronic sinus problems my entire life, and sometimes I need to help the equalization process along. Here's what's worked for me over the years. First, give your sinuses a check before leaving the surface. A quick "pinch-and-blow" before you get in the water can tell you whether to expect problems once you're underwater.

Once in the water, if you do experience a problem, take it slow. Never descend so quickly that you actually experience pain. If that happens, ascend a few feet. There's also another trick that I've used for years when I encounter some resistance to equalization, and that's to remove my mask and give the old schnoz a good blow. I know it sounds crude — and I've grossed out more than one dive buddy — but it has worked for me time and again and saved countless dives over the years.

The other problematic air space beside sinuses is the ears. Equalization of the ears occurs in the eustachian tubes. Air exchange through these tubes is controlled by a muscle that, in most people, keeps them closed. Opening the tubes usually requires positive pressure. The ease with which it opens varies greatly among divers, and some lucky few need do nothing more than wiggle their jaw. Most of us, however, must take more active steps to "clear," and the most common method is the Valsalva maneuver (the formal name for the ubiquitous "pinch-and-blow" method).

As with sinuses, clearing your ears can be a problem — sometimes impossible — if you dive with a cold or too soon after having one. Most divers are smart enough to avoid this, so probably the more common reason for ear squeeze comes from trying to clear too late. In fact, like sinuses, some divers don't even begin the clearing process until they experience slight pain. Bad mistake! Pain means there's a problem. Studies have shown that pain normally begins when the differential between the ambient and middle ear pressure reaches only 60 mmHg

(millimeters of mercury). This is equal to a descent of only 2.5 feet (0.8 m). By the time the eustachian tubes reach a pressure differential of 90 mmHg (equal to a descent of less than 4 feet [1.2 m]), they will essentially "lock shut." Therefore, to be effective, clearing must begin before descending a mere 4 feet underwater. Waiting until you are deeper than 4 feet underwater will require you to exert substantially more force to open the eustachian tubes. The lesson here is that you shouldn't wait until you feel a pressure sensation to start clearing your ears. Instead, as mentioned earlier, begin clearing at the surface to ensure the eustachian tubes are open, and don't begin your descent unless they are open.

Another technique that many find effective involves tilting the head. The idea is to straighten the eustachian tube to facilitate airflow. You can accomplish this by tilting the head to the side such that the affected ear is up and the unaffected ear is down. Moving the jaw back and forth as you tilt your head also helps to open the eustachian tube.

Many divers believe, quite mistakenly, that the only consequence of an ear squeeze is a bad earache and perhaps an infection. Actually, certain forms of ear squeeze can have very serious long-term consequences. For example, a forceful Valsalva maneuver can create a pressure of more than 250 mmHg, and easily overpressurize the middle ear. This excessive pressure can cause tears in the inner ear (cochlea), which will require surgical repair. You can avoid excessive pressure by using an alternative to the Valsalva such as the Frenzel maneuver. This involves pinching the nose and using the tongue as a piston to increase the pressure of the nasopharynx, forcing air up the eustachian tubes. (Yes, it does takes some practice.) Another technique is called the Toynbee maneuver, and involves simply swallowing while pinching the nose and keeping the mouth closed.

When injury is caused by ambient pressure forcing the eardrum or tympanic membrane inward, it's called an internal ear squeeze. But there's also a phenomenon called an external ear squeeze, in which the drum is pushed outward. Until recently external ear squeezes in trained divers were quite rare. The most common cause was wearing earplugs, which is one of the first things you learn not to do in a diver training course. Wearing an earplug establishes an air space between the plug and the eardrum. On descent, as the pressure increases, the

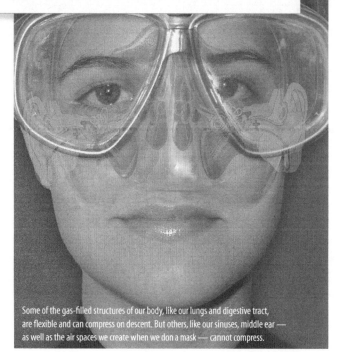

An excellent resource, **"The Diver's Complete Guide to the Ear,"** is available from the Divers Alert Network website at www.diversalertnetwork. org/medical/articles/article.asp?articleid=13.

Some of the gas-filled structures of our body, like our lungs and digestive tract, are flexible and can compress on descent. But others, like our sinuses, middle ear — as well as the air spaces we create when we don a mask — cannot compress.

When Things Go Wrong

Many divers who read this will have experienced equalization problems sometime in the past, so you probably know what it feels like. In case you are one of the lucky few who hasn't, victims of ear squeeze commonly experience pain, a sensation of fullness in the ear, decreased hearing and occasionally ringing in the ears (tinnitus) and even dizziness. To treat minor ear problems you should stop diving and attempt to decongest the middle ear. Other than just giving it time to heal, some otolaryngologists recommend using Afrin™ nasal spray for no longer than three days, twice a day, or Sudafed™ 60mg, three times a day.

Every diver will likely experience a problem with ear equalization at some time, but those with persistent cases should be examined by an otolaryngologist who is familiar with diving. The reason it's important to consult a diving-savvy doc is because they'll often prescribe treatments and offer advice that's outside the scope and experience of their nondiving colleagues.

Aside from knowing how to deal with an ear barotrauma, there's also the question of when it's OK to return to diving. Generally, it's safe to return when pain subsides, your ear clears easily when you pinch your nose and swallow, your hearing is fairly normal, and any factors that cause the problem — such as allergies or colds — have cleared up. There are also some hints for exactly how to return to diving after an ear problem. These include: Always descend feet-first, equalize your ears more often than normal, tilt your head so the problem ear is higher than the good ear as you equalize and avoid constant changes of depth in shallow water.

Human evolution never took into account that we'd one day spend time back in the sea from which we came; and in diving the structures we evolved to accommodate a land-based existence unfortunately get in the way. However, with a little training, practice and insight, the problems associated with descent can be overcome. Just remember not to force the issue of equalization and never attempt to dive when your ears or sinuses object. You can always dive another day, and no experience is worth the risk of long-term or permanent injury. Make sure the only thing you intentionally squeeze is your orange juice. ⌀

air inside the newly formed space has no way of equalizing. As you descend, higher-pressure air is forced up the eustachian tubes into the middle ear. Pressure is then exerted outward against the eardrum. If the descent continues, the eardrum will rupture in an outward direction, and the plug will be driven deep within the ear. On very rare occasions this has happened as a result of excessive build-up of earwax.

Unfortunately, external ear squeezes are increasing in frequency because of an increased use of dry suits — particular, the use of dry hoods. A dry hood can create a condition similar to the earplug scenario. Learning to avoid this problem is yet another reason for professional instruction when you buy a dry suit. It's also why many divers who use dry suits still opt to wear wet suit hoods. Furthermore, although far less common, an external ear squeeze is possible even with a tight-fitting wet suit hood. This rarely occurs because normally some of the air you exhale through your nose migrates under the hood, keeping the ear canal at ambient pressure.

CHAPTER 9

Gill Envy:
The Science of Breathing Underwater

Breathing is a symbol

of life second only to a beating heart. And like a beating heart, breathing is so much a part of what it means to be alive that we rarely think about it. To a healthy person who never ventures underwater, this oblivious attitude toward breathing is perfectly fine; but not so for scuba divers. Leaving our gills behind in the womb in favor of lungs has very significant implications. Of course, proper breathing is the very basis for the first rule of scuba: Breathe normally; never hold your breath. However, understanding the intricacies of breathing goes well beyond the need to merely avoid holding your breath.

In diving, improper breathing is often the first sign that something has gone wrong. In fact, a simple condition like exhaustion is responsible for far more accidents than other more exotic disorders like decompression sickness or lung expansion injuries. Yet, except for a cursory admonition to "stop, think and act" or "breathe deeply," there's scant attention paid in training to just how important proper breathing is to diver safety. That's a shame, because the subject of breathing is a lot more involved — and a lot more interesting — than one might expect.

How We Breathe

Until you took a scuba course, you probably thought that what triggers our urge to breathe is simply the need for oxygen. But if you have a c-card in your wallet, you probably know this intuitive assumption is wrong, or at least not entirely true. While there are chemical receptors in the walls of the aorta and carotid arteries that monitor the amount of oxygen in our blood, these sensors stimulate breathing only if the oxygen level falls dangerously low — below about 0.10 ATA (atmospheres absolute). Similarly, the urge to breathe is also controlled somewhat by stretch receptors in the *pleura*, the membrane that surrounds the lungs. At appropriate points in the breathing cycle, these receptors alternately signal the brain when the muscles of the rib cage should stop expanding or contracting.

But oxygen sensors and stretch receptors are minor league players in the game of breathing. The primary stimulus to breathe comes from the carbon dioxide content and acidity level of our blood, which is continually monitored by the reflex respiratory center of the *medulla* (located in the lower brain). These receptors are so sensitive that our breathing rate will double if they detect a mere 0.03 percent increase in the carbon dioxide level. Generally, our breathing rate and volume is controlled so that carbon dioxide is expired at the same rate that it's produced.

The mechanics work like this: Once we receive the stimulus to breathe, our body responds by causing the diaphragm to flex downward, creating a negative pressure within the lungs. Air rushes to fill the area of negative pressure and our lungs fill. When the diaphragm flexes upward the lungs empty. (In respiratory terminology, the word "empty" is relative because our lungs always retain a *residual volume* even if we exhale as hard as possible.) At rest, the action of the diaphragm alone is all that's necessary to maintain adequate breathing. As the oxygen demand increases, we can ventilate our lungs more efficiently by expansion and contraction of the rib cage.

It's also important to understand the pathway air travels in its journey to get to our bloodstream. From our mouth, air flows into the trachea (windpipe, for the uninitiated) that divides into the right and left bronchi. The bronchi then branch into smaller and smaller passageways, eventually becoming bronchioles. The bronchioles finally terminate at microscopically small air sacs called alveoli. A good way to imagine the structure of the lungs is to think of an oak tree turned upside down. The trunk is analogous to the trachea, which divides into increasingly smaller branches (bronchi and bronchioles). The branches terminate at the leaves, much like the bronchioles terminate at the alveoli.

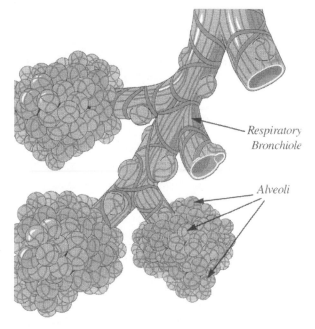

Respiratory Bronchiole

Alveoli

It's at the alveolar (leaf) level where all the action of gas exchange takes place. The alveoli are incredibly tiny structures, numbering around 300 million in an average adult. This provides an enormous surface area for gas exchange. So large that, if the total surface area of the alveoli were somehow laid flat, it would cover an area roughly the size of a tennis court.

Alveoli are so tiny that their walls are only one cell thick. They're so small, in fact, that according to the laws of physics they should collapse. The only reason they don't

is because a special soapy chemical called a surfactant coats their interior. This vital substance reduces their surface tension and, thus, their tendency to collapse. (One of the most severe problems associated with near drowning is when this surfactant is washed away by water in the lungs, causing the alveoli to collapse.)

Perhaps the most unbelievable part of the story is that, as small as the alveoli are, alveoli are actually surrounded by numerous capillaries that take up and give off gas. Amazingly, while the distance between the gas in the alveoli and the blood in the capillary is less than one-twentieth the thickness of this page, at no time is the blood in the capillaries directly exposed to air. Gas instead diffuses across the cell membranes.

Oxygen diffuses into the blood because the air in the alveoli has a higher oxygen partial pressure than the blood in the arterial capillaries. Some dissolves into the plasma directly, but not enough to sufficiently supply our metabolic needs. Most of the oxygen is carried in the hemoglobin of the red cells as a chemical called oxyhemoglobin.

After supplying some of its oxygen stores to the tissues as it makes its way around the circulatory system, the blood also takes up carbon dioxide. This is a waste product of the metabolic process. A small portion of this carbon dioxide simply dissolves in the plasma, and a slightly greater quantity bonds to the hemoglobin or other blood proteins. But the vast majority of carbon dioxide is carried off in a different way. When combined with water, carbon dioxide forms carbonic acid. This easily breaks down into a chemical called bicarbonate; and it's in this form that over 80 percent of carbon dioxide is carried away from the cells. Bicarbonate makes the blood more acidic, and is why acidity levels indicate the blood's level of carbon dioxide.

While at rest, the average adult needs only about 250 milliliters of oxygen per minute. But this can increase tenfold or more with exercise. As more carbon dioxide is produced, the chemoreceptors mentioned previously come into play. Sensing the increase in carbon dioxide, the body responds with an increased breathing rate in an attempt to keep the oxygen and carbon dioxide levels in line. With heavy exercise, the system may be unable to keep pace with the increased demand for oxygen.

Once the oxygen supply is used up, muscles can continue to function for a short time by two other methods referred to as anaerobic (without oxygen) metabolism. The first is to use the energy from a store of special phosphate compounds. This, however, is only a short-term solution. The second method provides a much larger energy reserve by breaking down glucose (a form of sugar) into lactic acid. In turn, lactic acid raises the blood's acidity level, which is picked up by the reflex respiratory center, and the respiration rate increases dramatically. While the energy produced by this process does not require oxygen, it will be needed later in the much slower process of eliminating the lactic acid. (Incidentally, it's the lactic acid that's also responsible for the burning sensation you often experience when you exercise a muscle to excess.)

If exertion proceeds to this point, however, you must reduce your oxygen requirements by reducing your activity level. If not, you'll either succumb to physical exhaustion when diving, or exceed your regulator's ability to deliver enough air. Attempting to get more air than the regulator is capable of delivering is often called "overbreathing" the regulator, and occurs when the diver tries to draw more air than can flow through the first- and second-stage orifices. This sensation is often interpreted as a malfunctioning regulator, or not being able to get enough air. Panic can often be the result, so maintaining a cool head and reducing your breathing rate is absolutely essential.

Your Lungs Underwater

It may not seem like it — particularly with a high-quality, well-adjusted regulator — but the mere act of breathing underwater requires that you expend way more energy than you do when breathing on land. Let's look at why this is so.

Even when you're not underwater, breathing resistance results for several reasons. One is overcoming the elastic forces that resist the inflation of the lungs. The second factor, which is relatively inconsequential, is resistance from the friction caused by air flowing through the passageways of your respiratory system.

This situation changes dramatically once you enter the water, even without scuba. First, immersion alone causes compression of the thorax (chest). This, in turn, causes a reduction in the tidal volume (the volume of air that moves in and out with each breath) by as much as 20 percent. Thus, merely by being in the water, your respiratory efficiency is reduced. And for scuba divers, the problems don't end there.

On descent, when breathing from a scuba tank, the pressure of the air we're breathing increases. This means that the density of the air also increases, causing further breathing resistance from friction. One study has shown that at 100 feet (30 m) in a chamber, air resistance doubles and maximum ventilation rate (the amount of air you can move in and out of your lungs) is reduced as much as 50 percent. And by the time you reach 150 feet (45 m), your maximum rate is down to only 33 percent of the surface rate. Noteworthy is that these tests were done under dry conditions using subjects who were at rest and using apparatus that's a lot more efficient than standard scuba equipment. One can only imagine what happens to breathing efficiency when we add the increased resistance of a typical scuba regulator, and the constriction of the chest and abdomen from a wet suit, buoyancy compensator and weight belt. There can be no better rationale for purchasing the best-quality regulator you can afford; and reviewing all technical data on performance such as flow rates, inhalation and exhalation effort before any purchase.

Unfortunately, the problem of breathing efficiency doesn't end with increased resistance. There's also the issue of increased dead air space. "Dead air" is defined as portions of the respiratory path in which no gas exchange takes place. For example, the mouth and trachea are considered dead air spaces. (Remember, gas exchange takes place only within the alveoli.) When diving, the regulator or snorkel adds more dead air space than normal, while chest compression by submersion decreases the diver's tidal volume. This increases the proportion of dead air to usable air, making the diver breathe more deeply to ventilate the dead air spaces. But, as your tidal volume has decreased, you can't ventilate the dead air space as efficiently as you could at the surface. The result is a rise in the carbon dioxide level that, in turn, leads to an increased respiratory rate. This is a dangerous cycle to initiate, and, once started, difficult to end. So, even a relaxed diver must exert considerably more energy than someone on land simply to breathe normally.

Interestingly, there are some indications that scuba divers may actually adapt to changes in carbon dioxide levels. One study has shown that some divers can develop a reduced response to carbon dioxide, and even tolerate a higher resting carbon dioxide level. However, this isn't necessarily a benefit. Someone who is relatively insensitive to carbon dioxide might not be stimulated to breathe as readily as someone with a normal response. And as the carbon dioxide level builds, that individual might be more prone to losing consciousness than normal. This is because his body may use up its oxygen store before there's a sufficient rise in the carbon dioxide level to trigger a response to increase his breathing rate. These so-called "CO_2 retainers" may also be at increased risk of decompression sickness, nitrogen narcosis and, when technical diving or using nitrox, oxygen toxicity.

Except for athletes, few of us give much thought to how we breathe; all that really matters is that we do. When it comes to diving, however, an awareness and insight into our breathing habits is essential. In fact, our very lives can depend on it. A good diver is aware of his breathing all the time, and continually adjusts his activity level to keep it under control. He also knows both his own physical limitations and those of his equipment. Still, sometimes it sure would be nice to have gills.

1. Use a good-quality regulator. Any regulator will probably do the job if you stay shallow, or don't get into trouble. But who's to say you won't someday dive deeper, or have a problem that requires placing great demands on your regulator? Therefore, buy the best unit you can afford; and it should, at the least, have a balanced first stage. Discuss your specific needs with your local dive center. Never buy this vital piece of life-support equipment via mail order.

2. When you feel your breathing rate increasing beyond a slow, comfortable rate, signal your buddy, slow down or stop all activity until your respiration returns to normal.

3. A lot of unnecessary air expenditure occurs because divers don't control their buoyancy properly. Your buoyancy compensator (BC) should do the work of keeping you comfortably in the water column, not the effort of kicking.

4. Most of your energy is expended by overcoming the resistance of the water as you swim. To make swimming as efficient as possible, be sure you're as streamlined as possible. Don't overweight yourself; wear only the amount of weight you need, no more and no less. Secure all straps and hoses against your body. Learn to trim your buoyancy so you swim in a position that's parallel to the bottom. And underwater, your arms are useless for swimming. Keep them at your side.

5. Get in the habit of paying attention to your breathing rate. This will let you know that you should make adjustments to your activity level long before you reach a point of exhaustion. Maximum efficiency comes from slow, deep breathing. To ensure relaxed, efficient breathing, some find it helpful to exhale slightly longer then they inhale, i.e., inhale for three seconds, then exhale for four.

6. Once you've regained a comfortable breathing rate, continue the dive only if the conditions that caused the problem don't persist. In other words, if you caused the problem by swimming too fast, then slowing down will solve the problem. But, if the problem was caused by environmental conditions, such as severe current, then it's probably time to head home.

7. If you experience exhaustion while at the surface, inflate your BC, rest and don't try to fight the current. The current can't kill you, but exhaustion can. Once your breathing rate is back to normal, signal "OK" to the boat so they know you're not in any danger, and wait for assistance. If seas are rough, keep your snorkel in your mouth. This allows you to save energy by keeping most of your head underwater. There's also less resistance breathing from a snorkel than from a regulator.

CHAPTER 10

When Things Go Bust:
A Close-up Look at Lung Expansion Injuries

As a child of the '50s, I was

a big fan of the hallmark TV series *Sea Hunt* and its indomitable hero, Mike Nelson, played by the late actor Lloyd Bridges. One episode I particularly remember involved the kidnapping of a scientist. As this was the era of Sputnik, it was implied — though never overtly stated — that the culprits were a group of "stinking Commies." The scientist was being held in a cave on an island. Central to the story line was the fact — seemingly unknown to the bad guys — that the cave could be entered from underwater.

Of course, Mike Nelson knew all about the underwater entryway, and planned a highly sophisticated escape: He swam into the cave, distracted the guards, gave the scientist a 30-second scuba lesson, dodged a few bullets on the way out and — fade to black — the world was once again a safe place for mom, apple pie and clean-cut capitalists.

For years, I thought that the episode was pretty bogus. Even as a kid I knew that becoming a scuba diver required hours of arduous training. I never gave the show much thought until years later when, following in my hero's footsteps I, too, became a scuba instructor. Hey, even back then, everyone wanted to be like Mike. I soon came to realize that my hero hadn't let me down after all. In fact, his 30-second lesson was brilliant in its cut-to-the-chase elegance, and certainly could have been enough training given the dire circumstance and high motivation of the unlucky victim. I don't remember the dialogue verbatim, but it went something like this: "You see this thing? [Pointing to the regulator mouthpiece] You put it in your mouth and breathe. Whatever you do, keep breathing; don't ever hold your breath or your lungs will burst and you'll die!"

End of lesson. Any questions?

It was one of the few instances in which Hollywood actually got the facts straight. If you had but 30 seconds to teach someone to scuba dive, what would you tell them? The same thing Mike did — the Golden Rule of scuba diving — breathe normally; never hold your breath. The rest is pretty much details.

Of course, if you're learning to dive without the distraction of gunfire, and your instructor has a bit more time to explain the nuances and importance of breathing, you probably would be subjected to either an illustration or an actual example of the most commonly used prop in diver training — the ubiquitous balloon. And the explanation, though lacking the dramatic effect that Lloyd Bridges could bring to the lesson, would be something like, if a flexible, gas-filled container — like a lung — can't vent excess pressure as it rises in the water column, its volume will expand until it bursts. Of course, today you might have sophisticated video or computer-based graphics, but the essence of what Mike told the scientist remains the same.

Unfortunately, the balloon-aided explanation is about all that most divers ever learn. Now, there's nothing really wrong with the balloon analogy. It's just a bit oversimplified, especially if you really want to fully understand the nasty consequences of forgetting what Mike Nelson so succinctly told the scientist. For one thing, our lungs bear little resemblance to balloons (if anything, they're more akin to a sponge). And due to the intricate and delicate nature of their anatomy, severe problems occur from lung expansion long before, as Mike so aptly put it, "your lungs burst and you die."

Lung Anatomy 101

If you didn't read the previous chapter, here's what you need to know regarding the lungs. The human lungs are amazing structures that are made up of microscopically small air sacs called *alveoli*. While incredibly tiny, the massive number of alveoli — numbering in the hundreds of millions — provide an enormous surface area for gas exchange. How large, you say? If the total surface area of the alveoli were somehow laid flat, it would cover an area two-thirds the size of a tennis court. (Albeit a bloody, squishy tennis court.)

And talk about delicate — alveoli redefine the term; their walls are only one cell thick. Yet, as small as they are, each alveolus (that's singular for alveoli, for those of you whose native tongue isn't Latin) is surrounded by numerous capillaries, which take up oxygen and give off carbon dioxide. And how about this for amazing: These capillaries are so small that red blood cells pass through in single file. Equally incredible is that while the distance between the gas in the alveoli and the blood in the capillary is less than one-twentieth the thickness of this page, at no time is the blood in the capillaries directly exposed to air.

The fact that alveoli are so delicate might be interesting, but it's also at the root of the problem when it comes to lung expansion injuries. Unlike the highly elastic balloon you probably heard about in your Open Water course, the alveoli of the human lungs can't quite take the same licking and keep on ticking. In fact, in shallow water, alveolar rupture can occur with an increase in internal pressure of a mere 70 mmHg (millimeters of mercury) — in English that translates to about 2 psi — over the external pressure. Why's that important? It means that if you hold a full breath in shallow water, an ascent of only four feet (a little over a meter) could ruin your day.

This brings up the first of many interesting contrasts between lung expansion injuries and decompression sickness (DCS). Unlike DCS, in which the risk increases with depth, lung expansion problems are more likely in *shallow* water (above 2 atmospheres) because of the greater change in volume. (To understand this, think back to the trusty old balloon. If brought from 33 feet [10 m] to the surface, it will show a 100 percent increase in volume; but bringing the same balloon from 66 feet [20 m] to 33 [10] will result in only a 50 percent volume increase, and only a 33 percent increase from 99 feet [30 m] to 66 feet [20 m]. One should need no more rationale than this to explain to your untrained friends why it's not safe to "play around" with your tanks even in the seemingly innocuous environment of a swimming pool.

The Bubbles Go Round and Round

Lung expansion injuries can be divided into at least three types, depending on where the bubbles go once they leave from the alveolus. The most critical injury happens when air escapes directly into the tiny capillaries surrounding the lung, and the mechanism involved is very interesting (except perhaps if you're the victim). First, overpressurization of the alveolus forces air into the surrounding blood vessels. This often results from a tear in the alveolar wall. But believe it or not, because of the tiny size and delicate structure of the alveoli, in some cases gas can escape without actually tearing lung tissue.

Regardless of how the air gets out of the alveoli, it can't begin its trip to the brain just yet. At first, expansion of the overstretched alveoli compresses the blood vessels, preventing air bubbles from entering the bloodstream. Only when the alveolar expansion is relieved through exhalation can the air bubbles make their way into circulation. Another interesting tidbit is that only a very small amount of air is required to produce catastrophic effects. It's estimated, for example, that gas bubbles as small as 30 microns — that's 30 millionths of a millimeter — are sufficient to cause symptoms.

Once in the capillaries, air bubbles flow into the pulmonary veins, which lead to the heart. From there they merge onto the superhighway of the body's blood vessels and enter the arterial circulation. While in a head-up position, as in the case of an ascending diver, the tendency is for the bubbles to travel to the brain. (In a head-down or vertical position, they're more likely to enter the coronary circulation, causing a heart attack.)

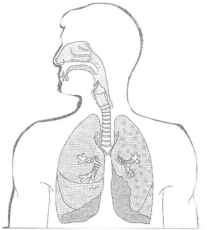

Pneumothorax is a condition in which expanding air escapes from the lungs into the inner layer of the membrane surrounding the lungs (visceral pleura). The trapped air exerts pressure on the lungs and heart, which may interfere with breathing and circulation.

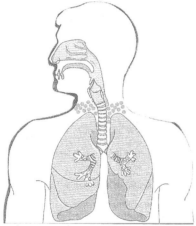

Subcutaneous emphysema is the term for air bubbles that become trapped under the skin in the area around the victim's neck.

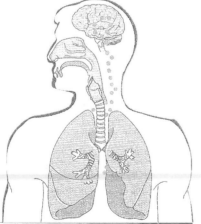

When bubbles enter the circulatory system, they may migrate into the brain, where they can block off blood circulation. Such a condition is termed a cerebral arterial gas embolism, or CAGE.

Like the tiny balloon your instructor told you about, the bubbles continue to expand as the ascent progresses. And as the bubbles continue on their journey, the circulatory system branches into smaller and smaller vessels. At some point the bubbles become larger than the diameter of the vessel containing them, and a blockage occurs. Medically such a blockage is called an embolus, and in this case is caused by air or gas. Furthermore, in divers the condition normally occurs in the brain. (Another example of an embolus would be dislodged plaque from an artery that causes a stroke.) Thus, the term in medical parlance for this condition is cerebral arterial gas embolism or simply CAGE. In nonmedical parlance it's termed up the proverbial creek; a place you definitely don't want to go.

As no more blood can flow to affected regions due to the blockage, the tissues served by the vessel are starved for oxygen. The brain is the body's control center, and as the blockage can occur virtually anywhere in the brain, the signs and symptoms of air embolism are highly variable. In most cases, however, the onset of symptoms is sudden (within one minute of surfacing), dramatic and might appear strokelike. Specifically, victims might experience dizziness, blurred vision, disorientation, personality change or decreased level of consciousness, paralysis or weakness, bloody froth from the mouth or nose, convulsions, shock, unconsciousness and respiratory arrest. And you think you had a bad day.

Some version of what was just explained is about all that most divers know about lung expansion. But there's a lot more. For example, the gas escaping from an alveolar rupture doesn't necessarily have to enter the circulatory system. Instead, the bubbles can escape and lodge between the lung tissue and capillaries, and track along the loose tissue plates surrounding the airways and blood vessels. From there the gas might continue to travel into the mediastinum (the medical term for the space containing all the organs of the chest except the lungs), into the region surrounding the heart (pericardium) or up to the base of the neck. In the case of the air in the mediastinum, the condition is called a pneumomediastinum or mediastinal emphysema. Involvement of the pericardium is called pneumopericardium, and air under the region of the neck is dubbed subcutaneous emphysema.

Like decompression sickness, one can never completely eliminate the risk of a lung expansion injury. But you can reduce your chances of injury. Here's how:

1. Ascend slowly. Even if you're breathing normally, a rapid ascent rate could lead to a lung over-pressurization injury through gas trapping.

2. Use a high-quality regulator and have it serviced regularly. It's believed by some that excessive inhalation effort might cause edema (fluid damage) to tissues surrounding the alveoli, thus reducing the size and impeding flow into and out of the airway.

3. Avoid diving too soon after a chest cold or respiratory infection. This means that no matter how good you feel, no diving if you are coughing up mucus, or if your breathing produces any abnormal noise or resistance. To reduce the tendency for mucus obstruction after a chest cold, drink plenty of water before diving.

4. Running out of air is the major cause of lung expansion problems, so practice good air management techniques. Have enough air to make the dive you're planning — plus some reserve. And monitor your own and your buddy's gauges frequently.

5. Forget what you were told about a 60-feet-per-minute ascent rate being OK. Slow down to half that. It will help you avoid both lung expansion injuries and DCS.

6. Don't smoke, and if you do, stop. Smoking causes the buildup of mucus, which can obstruct airways.

In severe cases, symptoms of these disorders might appear immediately, but in less severe cases can take several hours. For pneumomediastinum or mediastinal emphysema, the symptoms might include chest pain (usually under the breastbone), breathing difficulty or discomfort, fainting, shock or a change in voice. In subcutaneous emphysema, symptoms are swelling or feeling of fullness around the neck, significant voice change, difficulty swallowing and a crackling sensation when the skin is pressed. The formal medical term for this is crepitus, but it's sometimes described as fondling Rice Krispies® (something I'm sure the Kellogg's company wouldn't be real happy to advertise).

Finally, the air might escape by rupturing the visceral pleura — the inner layer of the membrane surrounding the lungs — and enter the pleural cavity. This condition is called a pneumothorax (literally, air in the chest). As there is no tissue connecting the lungs to the chest wall, any air introduced into the pleural cavity causes the lung to collapse. If the air space does not expand, the condition is called a simple pneumothorax. If the air space does expand, it puts tension on the heart and interferes with breathing and circulation. This condition is known as a tension pneumothorax, and can result from expansion of the air space in the chest on ascent, or even after the diver has surfaced with a simple pneumothorax. A tension pneumothorax is a very severe, life-threatening problem requiring immediate medical intervention. Symptoms of both types of pneumothorax include sudden unilateral chest pain with movement, breathing difficulty or very rapid breathing rate, and blue skin, lips or nailbeds.

Breathing Normally Doesn't Always Work

You, as well as your instructor, have probably always assumed that lung expansion problems happen only to divers who hold their breath because of some distraction, lack of training or panic situation. Well, I hate to burst your balloon — I couldn't resist that one — but I've got some bad news for you; lung expansion injuries can and do occur when divers follow all the rules. Yeah, like lots of stuff in life, it ain't fair, but it still happens. How it happens, assuming you're not the victim, is a fascinating twist of human anatomy. The answer lies in how air can remain trapped in the lungs even when the diver exhales. Some of the factors that can promote air trapping include asthma, bronchitis, cysts, tumors, scar tissue from surgery or radiation therapy, and obstructions from inflammation or mucus caused by smoking, and even recent colds or infection. This is why candidates for diving must be free of any serious pulmonary disease or other chronic problems involving the lungs. (See, that medical history form you had to fill out before class wasn't just a bunch of legalese nonsense.)

Another startling — and depressing — fact about lung expansion injuries is that many cases occur in divers who have neither held their breath nor have any of the conditions just mentioned. That's right, they did absolutely nothing wrong and had none of the conditions I just outlined. In fact, one Australian study showed that nearly half the cases of lung expansion injuries studied fell into this category. The $64,000 question is, of course, how can divers die or become so severely injured if they did nothing wrong? The answer, according to the study, was that the injured divers all had a reduced lung compliance (a measure of tissue elasticity). In essence, their lungs were stiffer than normal, and when distended, were subjected to more stress than those of other divers. For this reason some medical authorities advocate chest X-rays and other pulmonary tests for all diving candidates. In fact, in Australia, where this study was conducted, full medical exams including chest X-rays are required for anyone who enrolls in a scuba course. While not required here in North America, many diving physicians do recommend a baseline chest X-ray before beginning a scuba course, and based on the Australian experience, that appears to be sound advice.

Yet, even thorough medical screening can't prevent all lung-related problems. Like DCS, divers are never fully immune to the possibility of a lung expansion injury even if they have no predisposing factors. Again, the answer lies in the nuances of human anatomy and the fact that we evolved on land, not underwater. When diving, a combination of factors such as blood shift due to immersion, constriction of the wet suit and pooling of fluids in the lower lungs cause a reduction in lung volume. There's nothing we can do about it; it just happens. This might lead to airway obstruction even though the diver is breathing normally and is otherwise completely healthy.

In still another example of what seems like Alice-in-Wonderland logic, evidence also points to a risk of em-

bolism due to exhalation. That's right, exhalation. Physiologists theorize that an extremely forceful exhalation can cause small airways deep in the lungs to collapse. This, in turn, would trap air, causing overpressurization. (This is one of the reasons you were taught to make a continuous "ah" sound when doing an emergency swimming ascent, and not merely to exhale fully and ascend.) Luckily, under normal circumstances divers aren't likely to encounter conditions in which such a forceful exhalation might occur.

AGE to DCS: And Never the Twain Shall Meet?

Because both conditions are caused by bubbles, divers are often confused by the differences between air embolism and decompression sickness. On the surface, the distinction seems clear: An air embolism is a traumatic injury resulting from a mechanical rupture of the alveoli that introduces air bubbles into the arterial circulation. DCS is caused by supersaturating of inert gas and results when dissolved nitrogen comes out of solution to form gas bubbles. In fact, to emphasize their distinct causation, instructors often place great stress on the differences between air embolism and DCS.

More recently, however, this delineation has become blurred and has caused many to rethink how divers should be trained and how medical authorities should describe the disorders. In fact, it's now believed that while they're caused in fundamentally different ways, the disorders nonetheless could have significant interaction. For example, some physiologists believe that many unexplained cases of DCS actually begin as subtle air embolism events. The mechanism works as follows: What could be termed a "micro air embolism" occurs, introducing tiny amounts of air into the bloodstream. Then, the high level of supersaturated nitrogen begins dissolving into the bubbles, causing them to grow. Without the air bubbles to act as "seeds" for further bubble growth, DCS would probably not have occurred. But is such an event a case of air embolism or DCS? The answer is, probably a little of both. So, in an attempt to merge these complicated, interrelated and speculative processes, scientists and clinicians now use the term decompression illness (DCI) to identify what have classically been described separately as air embolism or decompression sickness.

While the differences in symptomology between DCS and lung overpressurization injuries can be subtle, this is of no concern to divers on the scene of an accident. Regardless of which disorder is actually present (and sometimes both are), the first-aid measures are the same. The information below was excerpted from Divers Alert Network's (DAN) Underwater Diving Accident and Oxygen First Aid Manual.

1. Administer CPR if required, with victim lying flat (supine).

2. Keep airway open and prevent aspiration of vomitus.
Unconscious victims should be intubated by trained personnel.

3. Administer oxygen by tight-fitting, transparent, double-seal mask at the highest possible oxygen concentration.
Do not remove oxygen except to reopen the airway or if victim shows signs of convulsions.

4. Keep victim in the horizontal left-side-down position
if symptoms occurred within 10 minutes of surfacing and steps 1 through 3 have been completed.

5. If convulsion occurs, do not forcefully restrain. Turn victim on side (supporting head and neck), maintain airway and sweep away any vomitus. Hold diver loosely to prevent self-injury and do not forcefully insert an airway or tongue blade. Resume oxygen administration when convulsions cease.

6. Protect the victim from excessive heat, cold, wetness or noxious fumes.

7. For Conscious Victims Only —
Give nonalcoholic liquids orally such as water or fruit juices.

8. Transport the diver to the nearest emergency room
to be evaluated and stabilized in preparation for transport to a recompression chamber.

9. Call DAN at 919-684-8111. State that you have an emergency, and ask for the person on call.
(If necessary, call collect in an emergency.)

10. If air evacuation will be used, it is critical that the victim not be further injured by exposure to decreased barometric pressure at altitude.
Flight crews must maintain cabin pressure at sea level or fly at the lowest safe altitude in unpressurized aircraft.

11. Contact hyperbaric trauma center or chamber before transporting the victim.

12. If available, send a copy of DAN's Underwater Diving Accident and Oxygen First Aid Manual, and record history (dive profile, diver's complaints, medical history and first aid) with the victim.

13. Send all diving equipment with the victim for examination.
If that's not possible, arrange for local examination and gas analysis.

What Happens When It Happens

Perhaps the most important practical reason for downplaying the differences between air embolism and DCS in diver training has to do with first-aid measures. While the differences between the two disorders might be interesting in an academic sense, from the standpoint of how you assist an injured diver, such differences are irrelevant. Anyone suspected of having decompression illness — regardless of whether the condition is caused by mechanical injury or supersaturation — is treated the same way at the scene of an accident.

One aspect of managing a diving casualty that still evokes some confusion and even controversy is the issue of head position. For many years divers were taught to use a left-side-down, head-low position for treating diving accident victims. Most often this was accomplished by putting the entire body on an incline (called the Trendelenburg position). The idea was that in such a position, the buoyant force of the bubbles would resist moving in a downward path, thus reducing the tendency for bubbles to travel toward the brain or heart and make the condition worse. But practical experience has shown the T-position to be of no use to victims of DCS, and to have little if any positive effect on most air embolism victims. Moreover, in some cases it actually caused complications, such as breathing difficulty and edema of the brain. And without a backboard, placing and keeping a victim in such a position is very difficult. So, a few years ago the guidelines changed to simply keeping the victim in a left-side-down position, with no head tilt or incline.

Still, there are those who believe that a slight head-low position could be beneficial for a victim who is likely suffering from air embolism; and advocates point to both animal studies and anecdotal experience to support their opinion. Currently, the advice from medical authorities is that if a head-low position is used, it should only be done for a short period (20 minutes or less) and only if it does not impair breathing or interfere with other first-aid measures such as CPR. Under no circumstance, whether the victim is in a head-low position or merely lying flat, should he or she be allowed to raise their head.

Although air embolism commonly accompanies the various other forms of emphysema and pneumothorax, that's not always the case. But as embolism is the most serious disorder, it's important that it's ruled out even in cases in which only the other disorders are suspected.

These are, of course, medical decisions that can be made only by a qualified physician.

Cases involving emphysema only are most often managed solely by observation and having the patient breathe pure oxygen. Treatment for pneumothorax alone depends on the severity of injury. Minor cases (fewer than 20 percent collapse) might require nothing more than medical observation. In more severe cases, the air must be extracted surgically. In either case, rarely is recompression used.

Air embolism is a completely different matter. Immediate recompression is absolutely essential, and treatment has historically involved compressing the victim in a chamber to 6 atmospheres, an equivalent depth of 165 feet (50 m). (This is far deeper than the maximum depth of 60 feet [18 m] used to treat DCS.) The extreme pressure reduces gas bubbles to one-sixth of their surface volume. This helps restore blood flow and promotes reabsorption of the bubbles. More recently, however, some clinicians have revised this treatment procedure, and first take the patient down to 60 feet for observation. If he responds, then the descent is halted and treatment continues at that depth. (One reason this method is beneficial is that many chambers don't have the capability of going to 6 atmospheres.)

The ironic part about lung expansion problems is that while they are the most serious injuries divers face, they're also the easiest to prevent. Accident data also has provided two important lessons. First, as one might expect, lung expansion injuries occur primarily — though not exclusively — to novices and less experienced divers. And second is some good news: Recent accident analyses show the frequency of such injuries is declining. This is partly attributed to the increased awareness of the value of slow ascent in preventing DCS, and to the increased popularity of dive computers (all have ascent rate monitors, often with audible alarms). I wonder what Mike Nelson would have to say about all this? 🐬

CHAPTER 11

The Heart of the Matter:
Diving and the Cardiovascular System

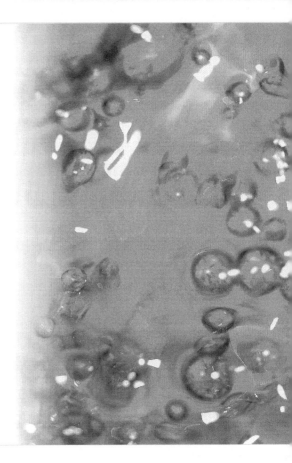

Like a lot of my fellow baby boomers, I like to deceive myself into thinking that I'm the same immortal adolescent that I was in high school. But, invariably, there's always a mirror somewhere nearby to yank me back into reality. Indeed, it's a delusion. That thickening, balding guy looking back at me in the morning as I shave is, unfortunately, me.

Although vanity might be the immediate cause of that deflated feeling when I look into that mirror each morning, the issue that's of much greater concern to me is health. While my ego can accept not looking like a hunky heartthrob (as if I ever did), the prospects of succumbing to the physical ravages of middle age are another matter. I also have to consider that, as a diver, I regularly place my aging body in situations in which my physical condition could determine whether I come home in a car or a coffin.

In the United States, and many other developed countries, probably the first thing that springs to mind when we hear of anything health-related is cardiovascular disease (CVD). The reason is simple. It's America's No. 1 killer. Each year CVD kills about a million of us here in the States and countless more elsewhere. A quarter million of us die of heart attacks before even reaching the hospital. Today, more than 1 in 5 suffer from some form of CVD; and it's estimated that more than 2 of every 5 Americans will die of some form of it. In fact, each and every day, more than 2,500 adults die from heart disease. And unlike the common assumption,

CVD is not a "guy thing." While the hormone estrogen makes women less prone to most coronary artery disease, this protection lasts only until menopause. After that, men and women are about equal in their risk of coronary artery disease. Fully 48 percent of CVD victims are women.

The leading contributor to CVD is hypertension or high blood pressure, a condition that is estimated to plague more than 50 million in the United States alone. But perhaps the most startling statistic is that one-third of those 50 million don't even know they have it.

From the perspective of a diver, CVD is no small issue. In fact, the most likely cause of death for a diver over the age of 40 is heart attack. According to diving accident statistics published by Divers Alert Network (DAN), heart disease accounts for or contributes to about a quarter of all diving fatalities. By comparison, air embolism and decompression sickness accounted for only 8 percent and 1 percent, respectively. In a review of autopsies on recreational scuba divers between 1989 and 1992, another DAN report showed that of 33 cases of sudden death while diving, 31 were attributed to coronary disease. In yet another study of divers, the autopsies of more than 50 percent of the subjects showed a narrowing of the arties (stenosis) around the heart, with some showing a complete blockage and evidence of heart attack. And even those without signs of stenosis often had pre-existing hypertension. This leads one to believe that many diving fatalities, otherwise attributed to "drowning," could have actually resulted from CVD, making heart disease responsible for killing far more divers than we realize.

A Real Heartthrob

Understanding the human heart has occupied the minds and careers of many. From a scientific perspective, a medical doctor, Sir William Harvey (1578–1657), is credited with first correctly describing how this vital pump circulates blood around the body. But like a lot of history, the truth is a matter of perspective. Many believe that Harvey merely rediscovered and extended work done by earlier Muslim physicians.

Heart problems can begin when the old ticker's demand for oxygen exceeds its supply. This can result in abnormal heart rhythms or even death of heart muscle (heart attack).

Interestingly, as the exercise demand of the heart increases, there is no great increase in the extraction of oxygen from the blood. (Typically, the increase is only about 2 ml of oxygen per 100 ml of blood from a baseline of 10.) Whether it's diving or any other form of activity, exercise causes an immediate response in the cardiovascular system. There are changes in local blood flow, which in turn initiate signals to increase how much blood the heart pumps out. Yet diving does present some unique problems; adding submersion and breathing compressed air to the equation makes things more complicated. First, immersion alone — without even breathing compressed air — increases blood flowing into the heart. Next, breathing a high-density gas mixture increases the pressure within the heart itself. The increased pressure of the surrounding water, which is transferred through the body, can also alter electrical conduction in the heart. Furthermore, the higher-than-normal oxygen concentration caused by breathing air under pressure can, in some individuals, slow the heart rate. The heart rate can also slow as a result of hypothermia. Finally, decompression issues make the picture even more complex because of a minor heart de-

fect that's completely harmless to nondivers. With all of this going on, there's little question that diving can alter cardiac function, and expose those with CVD to an even higher risk of problems.

Divers are at a further disadvantage when it comes to strain on the heart. When exercise demand creates an increased cardiac output, the workload is eased on the heart by blood vessel dilation in the peripheral circulation. This reduces the resistance to blood flow, making it easier for the heart to pump. But water immersion throws a monkey wrench into this mechanism. In all but the warmest water, the vessels in a diver's skin do not dilate. This is an important physiological response to conserve heat. Therefore, a diver's heart must pump against the increased resistance of the undilated vessels, making it work harder than it would for equal effort on land.

Ironically, there's yet another heart-related downside to exercising underwater. On land, one way we know that we've exercised too much is because our bodies overheat, and it's just too darned uncomfortable to continue. But because of immersion in water, this might not happen. Lacking the "hot and sweaty" warning signal, it's entirely possible for a diver to overload the heart without much or any warning.

Of course, our bodies are designed to deal with the extra load placed on the system when we exercise. At rest, the heart works at only a small fraction of its maximum capacity. What's important when we exercise is how well the heart's backup or functional reserve can perform. And measuring exactly how hard our "blood pump" can perform is essential in determining if we might have any limitations due to heart disease. This requires testing the heart's ability to pump enough blood to meet maximum needs, and is a primary reason all diving candidates over the age of 40 — and anyone with a significant medical history — is required to have medical clearance before learning to dive.

A common way of assessing cardiac health is by exercise stress testing, which can accurately measure the cardiovascular reserve. In general, a diver should be able to exercise on the treadmill without chest pain, severe shortness of breath, or blood pressure changes.

A Hole In the Heart

For divers a common and normally harmless heart defect, called a patent foramen ovale (PFO), might produce very serious, and sometimes deadly, consequences.

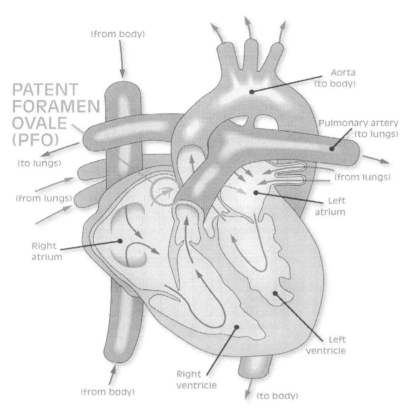

PATENT
FORAMEN
OVALE
(PFO)

(from body)

(to lungs)

(from lungs)

Right
atrium

(from body)

Right
ventricle

(to body)

Aorta
(to body)

Pulmonary artery
(to lungs)

(from lungs)

Left
atrium

Left
ventricle

eventually make their way back to the heart. Under normal conditions, these bubbles are trapped by the minute blood vessels of the lungs. There, the trapped bubbles then defuse into the lungs, and the gas is expired in the normal respiratory process.

Under some circumstances, like when you equalize your ears, the pressure in the right atrium can increase slightly over the left atrium. If a PFO is present, then blood can shunt from the right to left heart. This provides a pathway for not only small amounts of venous blood to bypass the lungs, but the silent bubbles contained in the blood as well.

Once in the left atrium, these microbubbles go directly into arterial circulation. Several studies have documented this phenomenon. Yet, as research is still limited on this subject, it's impossible to draw any solid conclusions about the implications of PFO. Nonetheless, while the PFO does not cause decompression sickness, additional bubbles entering the arterial blood flow in this manner might hasten the onset of symptoms or cause more severe forms of DCS. It could perhaps even cause arterial gas embolism.

One intriguing study comes from England where a researcher examined more than 100 cases of DCS. Of the test subjects who experienced symptoms of DCS within 30 minutes of surfacing, 66 percent had a PFO. In subjects experiencing symptoms later than 30 minutes, only 26 percent had a PFO. This data suggests that a PFO might contribute to the early onset and severity of DCS.

Understand, however, that researchers caution against drawing any definitive conclusions about the implications of PFO in divers, as the phenomenon requires far more study. While certainly far from conclusive, the PFO issue provides yet another reason why we should dive conservatively. The PFO issue also offers one more example of how much science has yet to learn about the mechanism of DCS.

To understand a PFO, and how it affects divers, we must review some basic anatomy and human development. While in the womb, a fetus has no use for its lungs. It receives oxygen directly from the mother's blood supply. Thus, in fetal circulation, blood bypasses the lungs. One way this bypass occurs is by shunting the blood entering the right atrium directly into the left atrium through an opening called the *foramen ovale*. The foramen ovale is similar to a one-way "flapper valve."

At birth, when the newborn takes its first breath, the pressure in the left atrium increases and causes the flapper valve to close. Over time the valve normally seals shut. However, in perhaps as many as 25 percent to 30 percent of the population, the valve remains partially open (the medical term is "patent"). This allows small amounts of blood from the right atrium to seep into the left atrium. Under normal circumstances, this condition is of no consequence because the pressure in the left atrium is higher than the right. This tends to keep the valve closed.

However, this defect can have significant consequences in decompression sickness. Asymptomatic or "silent bubbles" — a topic we'll address in Section 4 — that develop in the venous circulation of every diver

What If There's a Problem?

Whether a diver or not, we're all subject to the diseases of aging; and as we age, we tend to lead a more sedentary lifestyle. This sometimes results in CVD. As the diving community has matured, there has been a marked increase in heart-related issues and health. Therefore, having at least a rudimentary understanding of the disease process enables divers and would-be divers to make more informed decisions.

Let's look first at what's commonly called "hardening of the arteries" or, more properly, atherosclerosis. The disorder causes a narrowing, and sometimes blockage, of the arteries supplying the heart. The process that actually causes the damage to lining of the heart vessels is still poorly understood. But to understand its effects, think of the classic Drano® commercial; picture a drain pipe that's been gradually clogged over time by someone pouring grease down the sink. The "grease" in our arteries is another fat-based substance called plaque. When the plaque ("grease") finally closes off the artery ("pipe") the result is a heart attack, and it can cause you more problems than the most expensive plumber in the world.

Of course, the key is to detect CVD before it clogs your arterial drain, and this, as mentioned before, is accomplished by stressing the heart. For this a treadmill test is most often used. The goal is to detect any loss or abnormality in blood flow before it presents symptoms. When there's a decrease in the oxygen flow to the heart, electrocardiogram abnormalities and changes in blood pressure can also be detected. By injecting a small amount of radioactive isotope, doctors can get a highly detailed picture of the internal workings of your coronary circulation. By reproducing workloads similar to those that you'll encounter while diving, they can determine if your heart is capable of handling the increased exercise load. An abnormal test doesn't necessarily disqualify you from diving, but it does require further analysis and assessment by a specialist before approval.

An Ounce of Prevention

Diving often takes place in remote locales far from advanced medical care. So, obviously, it's better to prevent a problem rather than risk the consequences of a delayed response to emergency treatment. And prevention begins with understanding the risk factors. These include high cholesterol, smoking, high blood pressure, obesity and age (over 45 for men and 55 for women) and diabetes. While most CVD factors are controllable by appropriate choices and behavior, family history can be a clue that you might be at risk. For example, if a close relative (sibling or parent) had a heart attack before the age of 55, you're probably at increased risk of CVD. The first preventive measure is having your blood lipids (cholesterol, triglycerides, HDL, LDL) checked. If they're abnormal, you should then begin some treatment program to get the numbers back within the normal range (cholesterol: less than 200; triglycerides: less than 120; LDL: less than 130). And as you've no doubt heard time and again, it's a good idea to reduce your weight and limit your intake of saturated fat. Smoking is a terribly bad thing to do from a health perspective, and stopping it is the single most important way you can decrease your CVD risk. A wide range of drugs are also available to help reduce blood lipids. Anyone who either meets the age criteria, or who has two or more of the other risk factors, should have a complete physical evaluation — including a stress test — prior to beginning or continuing diving.

Exercise is vitally important in maintaining cardiovascular health; and keep in mind that diving, alone, isn't enough to make or keep you fit. You don't need to train for the Olympics; just do some moderate activity. Even walking has been proven to lower the risk for CVD. Moderate and consistent activity helps to maintain — or achieve — a normal blood pressure, keeps your weight down, and raises the so-called "good" cholesterol (HDL).

Diving With a Less-Than-Perfect Pump

Some are surprised to learn that a diagnosis of CVD doesn't necessarily bar one from diving. However, there are some very important caveats and considerations. First, don't consider diving if you've done nothing to help correct or mitigate a cardiac condition. A partially blocked artery, combined with the extra demand of exercise and stress of being underwater, can increase the risk of sudden death dramatically. Even if you don't have a heart attack, unconsciousness due to arrhythmia can occur. And, without immediate assistance, unconsciousness underwater means drowning.

In general, those who have had cardiac surgery, such as a bypass or angioplasty, can be approved for diving, provided they perform satisfactorily on a stress test. However, some medical authorities restrict such individuals to diving in less stressful warm-water conditions.

Dr. Fred Bove, a renowned diving medical authority and cardiologist, has provided a number of insights into heart-related issues involving diving. He was one of the first to contend that structural abnormalities of the heart shouldn't necessarily exclude someone from diving. Due to its anatomy and the way the heart forms before birth, certain structural abnormalities sometimes occur that can allow blood to transfer or "shunt" from one chamber to another. Examples include an open hole between the upper chambers of the heart — atrial septal defect, or lower chambers — ventricular septal defect. (This should not be confused with the PFO explained previously.) Because of the potential in divers for bubbles to shunt along with the blood from the right (venous) side of the heart and pass directly to the left (arterial) side of the heart, no one with an atrial septal defect should dive. On the other hand, a minor ventricular septal defect is of less concern, as the large pressure difference between the high-pressure left ventricle and the low-pressure right ventricle prevents any shunting of bubbles from the right side to the left side of the heart. Although severe leaks from the ventricular defect are very serious and will prevent diving, most cases are not severe enough to disqualify someone from diving. Obviously, only a thorough medical evaluation can determine the nature and severity of the problem.

Even heart valve problems shouldn't be considered an automatic disqualification from diving. There is, however, the special concern for the mitral valve. This valve connects the left atrium to the left ventricle, and abnormalities in it sometimes cause a condition called mitral valve prolapse or MVP. In an MVP, structural abnormalities of the valve allow it to bulge or "prolapse" back into the atrium as the heart beats. This is a hereditary condition caused by excess tissue. Quite often physicians disqualify individuals with an MVP from diving. According to Dr. Bove, however, unless this condition is accompanied by other factors, such as arrhythmia or chest pain, disqualification of diving candidates simply because of the presence of an MVP is unnecessary.

Even artificial heart valves don't warrant an unconditional exclusion from diving. According to Bove, if the heart is otherwise disease-free, there's no reason to disqualify a person from diving for simply having an artificial valve. The real issue is not the valve, but that those with artificial valves are usually on blood-thinning drugs. Because these drugs reduce the blood's ability to clot quickly, anyone taking them has an increased risk of hemorrhage if they're injured. But, as long as they understand and accept the potential complication should they suffer an injury, there's no reason to disqualify a person from diving solely because they're on blood-thinning agents, either.

On the subject of heart rhythm irregularities, Bove emphasizes that abnormal heart rhythms are not uncommon even in highly conditioned athletes; they commonly disappear as soon as the individual begins exercising. Provided they do respond to exercise, these types of abnormalities are of no consequence in one's qualification to dive. Furthermore, minor tachycardia (rapid heart rate) is also common in young individuals, and results from many factors. Contributing factors can include alcohol consumption, lack of sleep and excessive exercise. Normally, minor tachycardia is of no consequence unless other factors are also present. Of course, the only way to determine the exact nature and form of any arrhythmia is by proper medical evaluation. Therefore, individuals experiencing any type of irregular heartbeat should see their physician for proper evaluation before diving.

As the diving population ages, it's no surprise that there are a growing number of divers, and would-be divers, who have electronic pacemakers. Bove and many others say that there's no reason why a pacemaker should automatically disqualify anyone from recreational diving. The real issue is *why* the patient needs a pacemaker. If the device was implanted solely to correct a problem with the rhythm of the heart, then the candidate can dive. Pacemakers are all tested under pressure by their manufacturers so it would be prudent to check with the manufacturer for the pacemaker's "depth rating" prior to diving. Additionally, special consideration should be taken for patients who are "pacemaker dependent," meaning that they have no underlying heart rhythm capable of sustaining life without the pacemaker. It would be prudent for these patients not to dive, as any pressure-related malfunction of the device could have serious, and possibly life-threatening, consequences. Because of these issues, all pacemaker patients should see their cardiologist before beginning or resuming diving.

Get That Chicken Fat Out!

Taking your level of fitness into account is an important aspect of dive planning that's, unfortunately, often ignored. No prudent diver should ever knowingly get into situations requiring exertion beyond their physical capabilities. But what exactly is an acceptable level of physical fitness for diving? There's no easily quantifiable, one-size-fits-all answer, but there are some guidelines. One relates to you and the other to your buddy. First, you must be able to swim a reasonable distance in full diving gear without getting too short of breath. What exactly "reasonable" and "too short" mean depends on the kind of diving you do or plan to do. Only you can answer that. Second, because it's not just your life on the line, you must be able to help a buddy who might require assistance.

To stay fit for diving, strive for a workout program of four to five times per week, for at least 20-30 minutes. Many feel that swimming, especially with mask and fins, is the best exercise for diving. But if you don't have access to a pool, or it's too darn cold to consider jumping in, jogging, walking, biking or rowing will do — anything that increases and sustains your heart beating to a reasonable level. The idea is to get your heart pumping to an optimal level — not too high or too low. To put some numbers to this, here's Dr. Kenneth Cooper's classic "aerobic conditioning" formula to determine what's termed your "target heart rate" or THR. To calculate your THR, subtract your age from 220. Now multiply that by 70 percent. For instance, in the case of someone who's 53 years old, that's 220 minus 53 (167) times 0.70 for 117 beats per minute. If you're achieving less than that when you exercise, then you aren't getting much aerobic benefit from your workout. But there's also no need (and there could be some harm) to do more. A good guide is to do your exercise at the THR for 20 minutes, but add five to warm up and another five to cool down. And don't expect immediate results; it takes time to build up to your THR and sustain it.

A Warning Even to the Healthy

One unsettling phenomenon that has been studied among scientists — yet receives little attention in the recreational diving community — is something called the "sudden death syndrome." Several years ago, kinesiologist and UCLA Professor Emeritus Dr. Glen Egstrom presented an interesting paper on the subject, which provided a sobering overview. In it he noted that as early as 1956, an article on sudden death in recreational scuba divers appeared in a medical journal. The article identified the most common scenario for a sudden death incident, and it has remained unchanged. Typically, a sudden death incident occurs to a seemingly healthy, alert diver at the conclusion of the dive as he is swimming back to the dive boat or shore. Death occurs without any signs of distress or other warning signals. The diver is merely conscious and alert one minute, and dead the next. Overwhelmingly, the victims of sudden death have been males in their 40s.

Researchers who have examined the sudden death syndrome in divers vary in their opinion of its causes. Historically, studies have concentrated on some form of heart disease as the culprit. Yet, autopsies have shown that many sudden death victims have had no signs of heart disease.

Some have theorized that the cause of sudden death in disease-free victims is a complex interaction of several physiologic factors. A number of mechanisms have been proposed, most involving irregularities in the heartbeat caused by physical activity or some form of stress.

In one study, 20 percent to 25 percent of the victims had no prior indication of any CVD; and the first indication of any heart problem was sudden death. To prevent this, researchers suggest avoiding conditions in which the blood supply to the heart is reduced. These conditions include fright, dehydration, physical stress, poor nourishment, obesity and arrhythmia (irregularities in the heartbeat). Research has shown factors that can cause arrhythmia are psychological stress, fatigue, exercise, carotid sinus reflex from a tight-fitting hood or dry suit neck seal, drugs and cold. Most importantly, no single factor appears to cause sudden death by itself. Rather, it's a combination of factors. The paper also concluded that the idea that sudden death syndrome is strictly a cold-water phenomenon is a myth. In fact, a number of incidents have occurred in Florida and the tropics.

As you see, the subject of diving and the heart is a serious matter, and not exclusively the concern of males, those with graying hair or with CVD. Every diver needs to be aware that, when we take the plunge, there might be much more than excitement responsible for that heart-pounding experience.

CHAPTER 12

Take a Deep Breath:
A Gas Guide to Diving

Gas. Believe it or not, it's an interesting topic.

Actually, gas isn't as much a substance as it is a description; like a solid or liquid, the term describes a substance's state of matter. Specifically, a "gas" describes any matter in a highly compressible, fluid and normally invisible state like the constituents of our own atmosphere. Some substances occur in a gaseous state under normal temperature and pressures. Others become gases only when heated beyond a particular temperature. Gases are, of course, ubiquitous. Even though we never actually see most of the atmosphere's components — experiencing them mostly as the blowing wind — we take for granted that we spend our lives beneath a sea of gases, including oxygen, nitrogen, carbon dioxide and a few other trace elements.

Folks who never venture underwater can live their entire lives assuming that gas is nothing more than the product of a meal that didn't agree wwith them. In fact, few pay any attention to even the most precious gas — air — as long as there's enough of it to breathe.

But as soon as you put a c-card in your wallet, or strap a scuba tank on your back, your nonchalance toward gas ends abruptly. When we combine its high compressibility with the fickle nature of human physiology, gases begin to do some seemingly strange things to us. They can make the unwary and uninformed diver as high as a kite or as dead as a doornail. Under some circumstances, gases can leave us writhing in pain or convulsions, yet under other conditions prevent or alleviate these very same effects. To a diver, gases can become either welcome and essential friends or insidious, mortal enemies. So, understanding the gases we breathe is as vital a part of safe diving as its cardinal rule: remembering always to breathe.

More recently, however, the gas picture has become more complicated as many divers today no longer limit the contents of their tanks to regular air. Enriched-air nitrox has become as common a feature in the modern diving ex-

perience as the tanks in which it's contained. At the same time more and more "technical" divers breathe mixtures of exotic gases that Mother Nature never intended for land-bound humans. But before we delve into the world of enriched, mixed or exotic gases, we need to understand the basic components of air and their effects on us as divers.

Our Old Friend and New Enemy

Let's first address that most important of all gases, oxygen. I've always viewed this essential life-giving substance as the Dr. Jeykll/Mr. Hyde gas. Without it, most life on Earth cannot exist. Yet many are surprised to learn that this "elixir of life," so defined by Michael Sendivogius, the alchemist who discovered it in 1604, can be deadly. (Sorry, all you Joseph Priestley fans, but recent evidence shows that he was way late with his oxygen experiments.) When breathed in its pure form for too long a time or at too high a pressure, it becomes a wicked monster. Yes, oxygen becomes poisonous. The disorder that arises when breathing oxygen for prolonged periods is called low-pressure or pulmonary oxygen toxicity (it's also termed the "Lorraine Smith effect"). The primary symptoms are lung irritation, coughing, wheezing and breathing difficulty. Unless you're a diver breathing an oxygen-enriched gas mixture, breathing oxygen for too long usually isn't a concern. It typically only becomes an issue for patients who have to spend many hours in an oxygen tent. Most divers, too, have little to worry about from chronic oxygen poisoning unless they're being treated in a recompression chamber. (One of the treatment procedures is to monitor and prevent the patient from breathing oxygen for too long.)

The problem that oxygen poses for divers results from breathing it at a higher-than-normal pressure. In this case, the issue is a disorder sometimes called high-pressure oxygen poisoning, but more commonly and correctly termed central nervous system (CNS) oxygen toxicity. (Historical note: The famed 19th-century physician Paul Bert was the first to discover the noxious effect of high-pressure oxygen, and as a result it's also termed the "Paul Bert effect.") It's not that humans can't breathe oxygen under pressure; it's that we can do so for only a limited amount of time and pressure. The real problem is that science still doesn't agree on what the limit is; and making matters worse, the limit varies dramatically between individuals.

What we do know is that when oxygen is breathed at a pressure somewhere above 1.3 ATA (atmospheres absolute), serious problems can result. The actual cause of CNS oxygen toxicity is uncertain. Some believe that it's induced by free oxygen radicals which, through an interaction with iron, cause neurons to fire uncontrollably. The more popular view is that the high partial pressure of oxygen inhibits the production of a Gamma-aminobutyric acid (GABA). This is a neurotransmitter that inhibits muscle reaction, so without it, the neurons fire uncontrollably.

Furthermore, the problem with CNS oxygen toxicity isn't that it will, in and of itself, kill you. It's that the most common and serious symptom is a grand mal-like seizure; and if this happens underwater drowning is a virtual certainty. (A way to reduce the probabilty of drowning from a seizure is not to use a standard scuba second stage, but to wear a full-face mask; this is one reason why full-face systems are so common in technical and commercial diving.)

Complicating matters even further is that there are two ways in which someone can end up breathing oxygen at high pressure. If you were to breathe pure oxygen, this 1.3 ATA limit occurs as the pressure reaches a mere 19.11 psi — just 4.41 psi above atmospheric pressure. That's why scuba systems that use pure oxygen, like rebreathers, can be so dangerous, and why specialized training beyond what

an open-circuit diver receives is absolutely essential. Luckily, recreational divers are rarely exposed to situations that could result in breathing pure oxygen. However, the insidious nature of CNS oxygen poisoning is why all divers who use nitrox must be certain about the oxygen content of the nitrox mixture in their tank.

The other way all divers breathe high levels of oxygen is through the seeming slight-of-hand of Dalton's law of partial pressures. (If you skipped Chapter 6 on the gas laws, it might be a good idea to give that a read before proceeding here.) Since this can happen to anyone breathing regular compressed air, understanding the mechanism is important. A diver breathing air alone will reach the 1.3 ATA limit simply by descending to a depth of 172 feet (172 fsw = 6.21 ATA, of which, for all practical purposes, 4.91 ATA is accounted for by nitrogen and 1.3 ATA is accounted for by oxygen). In case you didn't notice, this is just 50 feet (15 m) beyond the maximum limit of recreational diving, and within easy reach of most divers wearing even a single tank. Remember that nothing within the tank changes; the disorder arises merely from breathing the higher concentration of air — and therefore oxygen — at depth. Of course, if using an enriched-air mixture, one reaches the 1.3 ATA at a much shallower depth, which is the rationale for the designation of an MOD (maximum operating depth) for any nitrox mixture.

Nitrogen: The Inert Scourge of Divers

Most folks are surprised to learn that almost 80 percent of each breath we take contains a gas for which our bodies have no direct use. In essence, it's a "filler gas," and it's called nitrogen. It's ironic that nitrogen gas is useless to us given we are nitrogenous materials, such as proteins, which make up a big portion of what we are. But our bodies have no way of processing the gaseous raw form of nitrogen that we breathe. Atmospheric nitrogen must first be "fixed" (converted into a useful form) by various essential microbes before it's usable. And that's the heart of the problem. Because we cannot process atmospheric nitrogen, whatever goes into our body via respiration must come out via respiration. (While it's common in diving to call nitrogen inert, anyone with a basic knowledge of chemistry knows better; it's more accurate to call it "physiologically nonreactive.") And just like the oxygen issue, this fact is of utterly no consequence to anyone unless they're a fighter pilot, an astronaut or a diver. (All of whom are susceptible to decompression sickness.) In the case of divers, as we descend, the pressure of the air we breathe, which includes the nitrogen component, increases and the more nitrogen we absorb. This increased nitrogen level has two significant and dramatic effects on us as divers: One effect occurs at depth, while the other happens once we get back to the surface. We'll examine how nitrogen affects us in much more depth in Chapter 16 and Section 4, but for now here's the "quick and dirty."

On the way down, nitrogen begins weaving its web of problems through its insidious ability to depress mental and motor functions. We know this condition as nitrogen narcosis. Exactly how this happens is still largely a mystery to science, but the most widely accepted explanation involves the solubility of nitrogen — and other inert or nonreactive gases — in fatty tissues. Here's the theory: Nerve impulses are transmitted throughout the body via cells called neurons, which are made primarily of lipid (fat) tissue. Neurons transmit electrical signals to other neurons at junctions called synapses. It has long been known that the narcotic potency of any inert gas is a function of its solubility in fat tissue — those that dissolve more easily into fat are more narcotic. The theory holds that anesthesia occurs because the inert or nonreactive gas — in this case nitrogen — causes the synaptic membrane to expand. In turn, impairment is caused by the slowed or halted transmission of electrical impulses. A portion of the brain called the reticular center, which is responsible for receiving and distributing nerve impulses throughout the body, is particularly susceptible to this anesthetic effect.

The double-edged sword of nitrogen is that it can create problems for us coming up as well as going down. A seemingly safe ascent doesn't necessarily mean that you're free from nitrogen's talons. If a diver is lucky enough to avoid the narcotic effects of nitrogen on descent, he gets a second chance on the way back to the surface in the form of decompression sickness (DCS). As it has taken no part in the metabolic process, whatever excess nitrogen enters the blood and tissues must eventually make its exit. In most cases, if we follow our dive tables or computer — along with other appropriate practices such as slow ascents and safety stops — the gas remains in solution and the process is uneventful. However, in some cases — usually by violating safe diving practices — the gas escapes so quickly that it comes out of solution to form the pesky little bubbles responsible for DCS. Yet a fact that divers often forget, or

never learn in the first place, is that DCS can occur even when no diving commandment is violated. The take-home message is clear: Regardless of how well planned and executed, all dives carry with them some degree of DCS risk. The only way to totally avoid the possibility of getting the bends is not to dive.

Carbon Dioxide: More Than a Greenhouse Gas

Most recreational divers are taught little more about carbon dioxide than to "avoid excess levels." While that's good advice, an informed diver probably should know a bit more about the problems that gas, made famous for carbonating beverages and warming the atmosphere, can have on your well-being.

As you learned in elementary school, carbon dioxide is a byproduct of our respiratory process, and the atmosphere contains a concentration of the gas of about 0.04 percent. You'd think that the level is so small that it would be of no concern. Well, think again. Higher-than-normal concentrations of carbon dioxide can cause symptoms ranging from headache to dizziness to unconsciousness. And unconsciousness underwater, without prompt assistance, means death. This elevated level of carbon dioxide is known as hypercapnia.

Because divers learn relatively little about carbon dioxide during open-water training, myths and misconceptions abound. On one side, many believe that open-circuit scuba, unlike rebreathers or surface-supplied systems, doesn't provide enough dead air space (areas where air doesn't circulate) to allow the buildup of carbon dioxide. The counter-belief is that the increased workload caused by factors such as submersion and breathing denser air means that divers typically retain far more carbon dioxide than those performing an equal workload at the surface.

Indeed, the standard design of a second stage provides for little dead air space, but there are still ways a recreational diver can retain higher-than-normal levels of carbon dioxide. This happens, however, not for the reasons some assume. First, more carbon dioxide is not produced merely by being at depth; and an increase in exertion doesn't usually cause an increase in retention, either. If the same amount of work is done at depth as at the surface, exactly the same amount of carbon dioxide is produced regardless of the diver's depth. Our bodies have highly efficient mechanisms to expel carbon dioxide. The increased production is handled primarily by an increase in the breathing rate, which, in essence, "blows off" the excess.

Still, by exerting heavily, particularly when using a poorly maintained regulator, wearing an exposure suit that's too tight or deliberately "skip breathing" (taking a breath only occasionally to conserve air), you could eventually exceed the body's ability to sufficiently eliminate carbon dioxide. Moreover, the reason some people tend to retain carbon dioxide appears to be a matter of individual variation; some just do.

Numerous studies of military and commercial divers have documented that, during heavy exertion, certain individuals do not increase their breathing rates enough to rid their body of all the excess carbon dioxide they manufacture. These people, often termed "carbon dioxide retainers," are simply less sensitive to the stimulus that, in most others, causes them to breathe more as their carbon dioxide level increases. This has not been studied extensively in recreational divers, but common sense leads us to believe that the same phenomenon probably occurs. There is also a question as to whether reduced sensitivity to carbon dioxide is an adaptive response to diving, or if this condition arises regardless of whether the individual is a diver. While there is no quick way of identifying these unique individuals, some researchers suspect that those who show low air consumption rates and repeated post-dive headache to be good candidates as carbon dioxide retainers. If you fall into this category, it might be wise to take the warnings about carbon dioxide very seriously.

The signs and symptoms of carbon dioxide toxicity depend on both the rate of buildup and the amount of gas present. Although unlikely to happen to a recreational diver using standard open-circuit scuba equipment, a rapid buildup may cause sudden unconsciousness with little or no warning. The more likely occurrence is a gradual buildup, which should allow time for noticeable symptoms before any loss of consciousness. The first sign is often shortness of breath followed by rapid, deep breathing. If the buildup continues, blood vessels dilate, causing the pulse and blood pressure to rise. Often a throbbing headache is reported, which might last for many hours after a dive. Should the carbon dioxide level rise even more, dizziness, nausea, confusion, disorientation and restlessness might occur. Eventually, if the level isn't reduced, muscle twitching, blurred vision, convulsions and unconsciousness might occur. In other words, it's something that you want no part of.

And there's more bad news. Hypercapnia is also believed to increase a diver's susceptibility to DCS, nitrogen narcosis, oxygen toxicity and hypothermia. In the case of DCS, carbon dioxide retention is thought to cause the blood vessels to dilate. This increases tissue blood flow, resulting in increased nitrogen uptake. It's also believed that the excess carbon dioxide can rapidly diffuse into any existing bubbles, enlarging their size.

Studies have also found that hypercapnia might increase the narcotic effect of nitrogen and greatly increase a diver's susceptibility to oxygen toxicity. How it affects narcosis is not understood, but carbon dioxide might affect susceptibility to oxygen toxicity because of its ability, through vasodilation, to increase the amount of oxygen delivered to the brain. Finally, carbon dioxide accumulation affects the body's thermoregulatory mechanism. Studies have shown hypercapnia impairs heat production and promotes heat loss due to the increased perfusion to the skin and limbs.

While too much carbon dioxide (hypercapnia) can lead to serious consequences, so too can too little carbon dioxide (hypocapnia). This is because carbon dioxide is the primary trigger regulating our body's urge to breathe. Another concern with hypocapnia is that, unlike hypercapnia, it can occur with relative ease. This has led some freedivers to use voluntary hyperventilation as a way to extend breath-hold time. We'll examine hyperventilation a bit more closely in later chapters, but here is the "Cliff's Notes" version. Deep, rapid breathing reduces the level of carbon dioxide. This lower level delays the breathing stimulus — allowing one to hold his breath for a long period — but also allows blood oxygen levels to fall dangerously low before breathing is triggered. But, as most divers are aware, if excessive, this practice can lead to a condition known as shallow-water blackout. What scuba divers sometime fail to realize is that hypocapnia can also occur involuntarily when breathing is excessively stimulated because of panic, anxiety or other factors. Symptoms of hypocapnia include limb tingling, dizziness, lightheadedness and headache. Should these signs occur, it's imperative that you relax, calm down and take slow, deep breaths to allow the carbon dioxide level to return to normal.

While there are other "trace gases" that occur naturally in the atmosphere, they're of no concern to the average recreational diver. But they can enter the discussion of safety when we, in any way, alter the gas mixture that we breathe. And as using enriched and alternative gas mixtures is becoming a more common practice, every diver should know a little about these more exotic gases and mixtures. ♺

CHAPTER 13

Just Say No:
Alcohol, Nicotine and Divers

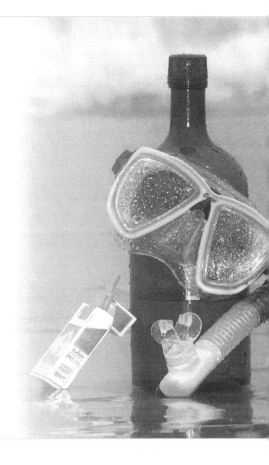

The last thing you probably want to read

is another tirade on the dangers of drinking and smoking. Besides, what can I say that's new? Although some recent evidence points to drinking alcohol in moderation as a health benefit, no one doubts the dire consequences of imbibing in excess. And no informed person on Earth doubts that smoking is merely a form of protracted suicide. But while we've known about these dangers for decades, many of us still drink — at least occasionally — and a quarter of us still smoke.

Smoking and alcohol are so much a part of our society that we no longer even consider that both are essentially a form of self-prescribed drug administration. In fact, we describe drug use, smoking and alcohol as if they were distinct and unrelated activities. In reality, all that's different is the substance in question, its effect and the form of administration. I won't delude myself into believing that this article will make any significant dent in the statistics on alcohol or tobacco use. I believe that in a free society, people should be able to do what they wish, provided it doesn't hurt anyone else. But there is one important proviso in the decision-making process that many ignore, and that is that the consequences of our choices can vary according to the circumstance in which we find ourselves. For example, it might be OK to drink, but not drink and drive. Diving is another case in point.

For us, the effects of alcohol and smoking go far beyond the normal concerns of heart attacks, cancer or some other so-called "lifestyle disease." Those who venture underwater have special concerns when our mental or physical capabilities are impaired. We also must consider special factors irrelevant to nondivers such as heat loss and decompression. So, to make a responsible and informed decision about drinking and smoking, divers must first understand the unique effects that alcohol and nicotine present to us.

Staying Warm

Diving requires surviving in a medium where heat is pulled from our bodies about 25 times faster than it is in air. So, no matter what the water temperature, heat loss is almost always a concern. It's just a matter of degree. And who hasn't been told that a great way to fend off the cold is with a good stiff drink? After all, alcohol feels so warm going down that it certainly must rekindle the internal fire, and give us that essential extra burst of energy. While it might sound logical, it's just not true. Pharmacologically, alcohol is a peripheral vasodilator, meaning that it causes blood vessels in the skin to open up more than normal. As blood flow increases to fill the expanding vessels, we experience that warm, flushed feeling. But this momentary sensation is misleading because it masks a more sinister effect.

The blood flow responsible for that "warm and fuzzy" feeling is diverted from the body core. This loss of blood saps heat from a more vital area of our body and makes us more — not less — prone to hypothermia. Moreover, alcohol depresses shivering, the major symptom warning us of the onset of significant heat loss. There's also a possible double whammy because some research out of Canada has shown that nitrogen narcosis also delays the body's shiver response. That means a predive drink or two compounds the heat loss problem, and post-dive alcohol consumption can impede the rewarming process. How much sense does it make to spend hundreds of dollars for an exposure suit only to reduce its effect by taking "a couple 'a belts"?

Bad as it is, problems don't end with increased peripheral blood flow. Ironically, the blood vessels supplying our muscles do not dilate but *constrict*. This causes an increase in blood pressure, and is one reason those with hypertension are advised not to drink excessively. As muscle accounts for the greatest tissue mass in our body, this elevated blood pressure can place significant stress on the heart. Some believe this stress could be a contributing factor in the increasing number of diving accidents involving those with underlying heart disease.

Alcohol might also play a role in accidents blamed on poor physical conditioning. How so? Think back to the last time you had a few drinks. You probably didn't feel a lot like exercising. This is partly due to mental impairment, but there's another more direct reason for the feeling of fatigue; alcohol actually drains energy. One of the body's primary fuels is a molecule called glycogen, a substance produced primarily by the liver and within muscles. Glycogen provide an energy reserve that can be quickly mobilized to meet a sudden need for glucose. Alcohol consumption impedes the breakdown of glycogen to produce glucose, thus reducing our exercise ability far below normal. So, regardless of how you feel, an imbibing diver might be incapable of making the extra effort required to keep an unexpected situation from turning into an emergency. Alcohol also increases the likelihood of vomiting which, especially when diving, can easily lead to asphyxiation. So, whether it's from aggravating an underlying heart condition or sapping our energy when it's most needed, alcohol might be the final straw that tips the balance against us.

A Toast to Decompression

No one has ever established a direct relationship between drinking and any increased risk of decompression sickness. But prudent judgment tells us that, at least theoretically, such a relationship might exist. Researchers who study the subject think it might work like this: We already know that alcohol consumption increases peripheral circulation. If you drink before diving, the increased blood flow could cause greater nitrogen absorption than that predicted by your computer (or tables). Therefore, this might increase your susceptibility to decompression sickness even if you are within the no-decompression limits. Some also believe that drinking could promote DCS in other ways, and point to alcohol's diuretic (makes you pee) property. The loss of fluid through urination contributes to dehydration. The decreased fluid volume, in turn, makes the blood "thicker," reducing its circulatory efficiency and further altering the absorption and elimination of nitrogen.

Although dehydration is discussed in more detail in Chapter 24, it's worth noting here how this might put divers at risk of Type II decompression sickness, the most serious form. This is because the brain is especially susceptible to dehydration from alcohol consumption, and explains why a headache is the most common symptom of a hangover. It's also worthy of note that the effect of dehydration lasts even longer than the headache. This is why it's particularly vital that anyone drinking alcohol the night before, even if they feel well the next morning, drink plenty of water prior to diving. Some researchers even argue that changes in blood flow caused by drinking *after* a dive could accelerate the release of nitrogen and indirectly enhance bubble formation. So it's wise to avoid excessive drinking even after diving.

Other research suggested that alcohol might contribute directly to DCS bubble formation. This, the theory goes, might be possible because of alcohol's ability to reduce surface tension. Surface tension refers to the tendency for a substance, such as a bubble, to exhibit properties resembling those of a stretched elastic membrane. The phenomenon is what's responsible for the "skin" that seemingly arises on the surface of a pond or swimming pool, allowing a bug to literally walk on water. But surface tension is also important to divers from a physiologic perspective. It helps resist bubble growth in decompression sickness. So, anything that reduces the surface tension of a bubble could encourage the growth of bubbles that might otherwise remain too small to cause symptoms.

Indeed, this is all theory, but it might have an important role nonetheless. For example, several studies have shown that silent or asymptomatic bubbles are a relatively common occurrence in divers (even after profiles nowhere near the normal no-decompression limits). This seems especially so in multiday repetitive diving, like when on a diving holiday. Common sense tells us, then, that at even the theoretical possibility that drinking might push these silent bubbles to symptomatic bubbles shouldn't be ignored. While the whole issue of alcohol's contribution to decompression sickness is speculative, it's still based on sound physiologic principles. If you do decide to consume alcohol, play it safe by following the guidelines contained in the sidebar on Page 102.

I'll Have Tee Martoonis, Please

A fact probably known only to scuba divers and anesthesiologists is that alcohol shares a property with the atmosphere's most abundant gas, nitrogen. Both substances have the ability to sedate. In fact, the similarity between the symptoms of alcohol intoxication and nitrogen narcosis was, in the early days of diving instruction, the rationale for what was termed "Martini's law." This "law" — actually a rough estimation, at best — stated that for every 50 feet (15 m) a diver descends, his impairment from nitrogen is the same as drinking one martini at the surface. So, accordingly, a trip to 150 feet (45 m) is equivalent to a three-martini lunch, without the sobering benefit of the food. Of course, if even a slight amount of real alcohol is added to the formula by predive drinking, the effect would be magnified (though by how much no one knows). Even diving accident reports appear to support the premise that alcohol and depth are an especially dangerous combination. Data from the Divers Alert Network has long shown that 30 percent to 40 percent of injured divers admitted to consuming alcohol the night before, and 2 percent to 3 percent report drinking just before diving or between dives.

The Nicotine Fit

There's no need here to relate the dangers of smoking. Only tradition, and a strong lobby, would allow the legal sale of a product that kills people when it's used as intended. Clearly, if its effects were immediate rather than long term, the sale of tobacco would be as illegal as heroin, and tobacco executives would be the bunkmates of imprisoned cocaine dealers. Indeed, cigarette smoke contains some pretty remarkable bad stuff.

Aside from causing diseases such as cancer and emphysema, nicotine itself is a poison. It's even sold commercially in the form of a pesticide, which is its role naturally in the tobacco plant. It takes only about 60 milligrams or 0.002 of an ounce of nicotine to kill an adult. In fact, if all the nicotine of a cigarette was absorbed, it would take only three or four to do the job. The reason nicotine toxicity does not occur in smokers is that only about one or two milligrams are absorbed from smoking a single cigarette.

Nicotine, like caffeine, is a naturally occurring alkaloid, an organic compound made out of carbon, hydrogen, nitrogen and sometimes oxygen. It's also only one of the more than 4,000 chemicals found in tobacco smoke and smokeless tobacco products, but it's the primary component that acts on the brain. The addictive nature of nicotine was suspected as early as the 1940s, and regardless of the lies told by tobacco executives, it has been proven so conclusively. In fact, its addictive prowess is on par with drugs like heroine and barbiturates.

Nicotine changes how the brain and body functions, and its effects are paradoxical — it can act as both a stimulant and a sedative — depending on how much and how often it's taken. Nicotine can be delivered to the brain with incredible speed, within 10 seconds of inhaling tobacco smoke. Once in the bloodstream, there is a "kick" caused, partly, by the drug's stimulating the adrenal glands to release the "fight-or-flight" hormone epinephrine (adrenaline). This, in turn, causes an increase in both heart rate and blood pressure along with rapid, shallow breathing. The adrenaline rush also causes a sudden release of glucose. Furthermore, nicotine suppresses insulin output from the pancreas. Because this is the hormone that tells your cells to take up excess glucose from your blood, smokers are in almost a continuous state of slight hyperglycemia. Maintaining more sugar in the blood is one reason some might find smoking an appetite suppressant.

Nicotine also indirectly causes a release of the neurotransmitter dopamine in the brain regions that control pleasure and motivation. This is a reaction similar to what's seen with other addictive drugs such as cocaine and heroin; and it's what's thought to underlie the pleasurable sensation of smoking.

Another effect of nicotine is that it appears to slightly increase the basal metabolic rate. In other words, it makes you burn more calories than normal when you're at rest. But before you go take up smoking to lose weight consid-

- Avoid drinking to excess anytime, but particularly before diving or while on a diving vacation.

- Avoid alcohol completely for at least eight hours before diving.

- If you have been drinking the night before, avoid diving if you feel hung over, as you're likely to be significantly dehydrated.

- If you have been drinking the night before, you might still be dehydrated even though you don't feel hung over. So, drink plenty of noncarbonated liquids — ideally, water.

- Avoid alcohol completely for <u>at</u> <u>least</u> one hour after diving, and even longer if you were diving deep (below 80 feet [24 m]) or near a no-decompression limit. Avoid excessive intake even after the hour has passed.

- Of course, try to stop smoking completely. But if you can't, try to abstain from smoking as long as possible before diving; and don't smoke during a surface interval between dives.

er this: Nicotine also increases the level of "bad" (LDL) cholesterol, which increases your risk of heart disease and stroke (to say nothing of the risk of cancer and other diseases from the other compounds contained in tobacco smoke). Studies have also documented that nicotine causes hardening of the arteries (atherosclerosis) in mice.

Of course, the problem with tobacco is not just nicotine but the other insults to the body created by smoking. Smoking is unquestionably a bad thing for anyone to do, but for divers it's especially foolish. First, tobacco smoke contains significant amounts of a gas that we go to great lengths to avoid — carbon monoxide. Smoking just prior to diving results in reduced tissue oxygenation because the carbon monoxide in the smoke binds with hemoglobin more than 200 times more readily than does oxygen. The result: By smoking you intentionally reduce your body's ability to process oxygen. This means that smokers must work harder simply to maintain a normal level of activity. And just before entering the water seems an odd time for a diver to willingly lessen his ability to function at a peak level.

Smoking also has many complex effects on the lungs, which are of no small interest to divers. First, it temporarily paralyzes the ciliary hair cells lining the airways for about one hour after smoking, and can even destroy the cells in chronic smokers. These cells function to remove mucous, dust and other particles in the air we breathe. In addition, smoking causes the production of more mucous than normal. Thus, the added mucus, combined with the decreased ability to rid it, increases the likelihood that a mucous plug could partially or fully block an airway, trapping the gas beyond the blockage. This is unlikely to be a critical issue for most people, but for a diver it can be life-threatening. Any trapped gas would greatly increase the risk of a lung expansion injury such as an air embolism even if the diver is breathing normally and ascending at the correct rate. And this risk isn't theoretical; it has been proven in retrospective studies of divers who've suffered lung expansion injuries after normal dives.

Another factor involving smoking is that at least one study has shown it to cause constriction of airways in the lungs. In fact, only 35 minutes after one cigarette a threefold increase in breathing resistance was documented. It was also demonstrated that a smoker's breathing performance is measurably increased even after as little as 24 hours of *not* smoking, a good incentive to stop smoking at least the day prior to diving.

Lastly, chronic smoking causes widespread lung damage, reducing the surface area where gas exchange takes place. Especially relevant to divers is that this causes a breakdown of the walls between the alveoli, and can give rise to the formation of air sacs termed bulla. These regions of trapped gas can present a significant risk of lung expansion injury for divers who smoke. So, the conclusion is obvious: Don't do it.

Repeal of the 18th Amendment proved how unlikely it is that we'll ever put a stop to alcohol use. Smoking is perhaps an even greater challenge because its active agent — nicotine — is one of the most addictive substances ever discovered. Yet what sets us apart from other animals is our capacity to learn, and change our behavior when we know something could hurt us. Mixing diving with either alcohol or nicotine can be a recipe for disaster, but if you still insist on rolling the dice, at least do so with your eyes fully open.

CHAPTER 14

The Big Chill:
The Truth About Heat Loss

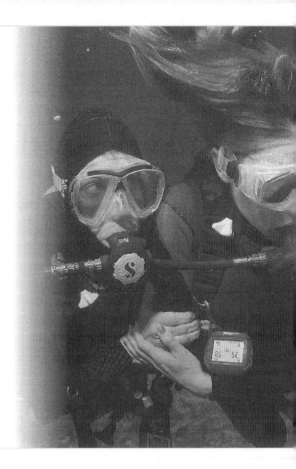

I freely admit that I

hate being cold more than almost anything else in the world. I need an exceptionally good reason to jump into water below 70 degrees Fahrenheit (21 degrees Celsius), and sometimes hesitate when it's below 80 (26 C). My loathing of cold is the main reason I live as close to the equator as is practical. So, as I avoid "cold water" like the plague, one might assume that I care little about the subject of heat loss. The truth is that I care a great deal; and so should you.

Unfortunately, getting cold is tough to avoid as a diver. As anyone who has experienced it long enough knows, we can get cold even when conditions are as warm as bath water. Thus, whether you're a warm-water wimp like me, or one of the odd folks who actually enjoy diving when the water gets hard, an understanding of heat loss is important to everyone who ventures underwater.

Our body temperature is generated largely by cellular processes. We can maintain and even increase our core temperature through muscular activity, or by increasing the ambient temperature. So under normal environmental and health conditions, we manage to maintain a delicate Goldilocks balance between not too hot and not too cold.

While it might be hard to believe as you swim nearly naked through tepid tropical water, the plain truth is that rarely, if ever, do divers encounter conditions in which heat *doesn't* drain from our bodies. In fact, for someone not wearing exposure protection, the optimal temperature range for heat loss to match heat production — the point at which you could remain in the water comfortably for an extended period of hours — is between 91 F (33 C) and 95 F (35 C). However, the metabolic heat production from swimming might balance heat loss at around 74 F (24 C). (Still a bit chilly for my liking.) This interaction between water temperature, exposure suit protection and the amount of exercise performed while diving, makes predicting heat loss difficult, yet a basic understanding of how it occurs is essential to our safety and enjoyment.

Into the Wild Cool Yonder

Whether it's a human body or the water in your bath tub, heat loss happens because of one or a combination of four phenomena: 1) radiation — the emission of heat via infrared energy; 2) evaporation — the transfer of heat via conversion of liquid to vapor; 3) conduction — the transfer of heat via direct contact between two surfaces; and 4) convection — the transfer of heat via fluid motion. For divers, radiation is irrelevant. Evaporative heat loss is also relatively minor, but does explain why you get cold during your surface interval if you're wearing a wet wet suit. It contributes somewhat to heat loss through respiration, which I'll address later.

It's mainly conduction and convection that we have to worry about. And it all starts with a fact that's taught in every scuba course under the sun — the ability for water to conduct heat about 20-25 times faster than air.

Conductive heat loss occurs by direct contact, like heat transfer between skin and water or, more relevantly to divers, between the surface of an exposure suit and water. The rate of heat loss is proportional to the temperature difference between the two points of contact. Convective heat loss is due to the movement of fluid (air or water). If the water is moving, the heated water next to the skin is continuously replaced with new, cold water and the rate of heat loss is much faster.

Contrary to popular belief, tissue damage from cold doesn't require frostbite. The cold-induced vasodilation addressed in the main article occurs at a threshold of 50-54 F (10-12 C). Prolonged exposure (normally more than six hours) of limbs in water below this temperature can cause permanent damage to nerves and muscles. In less severe cases, rewarming often returns blood flow and limbs become hot, red, swollen and painful. Subsequently, limbs become very temperature sensitive with intense vasoconstriction in cold, and intense dilation and profuse sweating in heat. In severe cases blood flow does not return, causing gangrene and extensive nerve damage.

Upon immersion, a diver begins losing heat via conduction, but the rate of loss depends on the amount and type of exposure suit worn. In recreational diving, even the best exposure suits won't stop heat loss; only reduce it to a tolerable rate. The only effective way to actually stop heat loss is through the type of exposure suits worn by some commercial divers in which warm water is continually pumped through the suit via the diver's umbilical. In a poorly fitting standard wet suit, heat loss is accelerated by the continual flushing of new water through the suit. But even the best-fitting suit doesn't completely eliminate the problem. On descent, neoprene compresses, and the resulting thinner material is less effective as an insulator. (Think of 12 inches [30.5 cm] of insulation in your attic versus 2 inches [5.1 cm].) For example, a neoprene wet suit can lose as much as 50 percent of its insulating value by the time a diver reaches 60 feet (18 m), and up to 75 percent upon reaching 100 feet (30 m).

A dry suit has several advantages over a wet suit, of course. As virtually no water enters the garment, you needn't worry about the "flushing" problem of a wet suit. More importantly, it uses air and undergarments as insulation, which are far more efficient than trapping and retaining a layer of water. And, as the suit is inflated to maintain adequate insulation at depth, the thickness of the waterproof shell is less of an issue.

The Physiology of Cold

Our body's response to decreased core temperature is a complex process. Control of body temperature begins with sensory input from deep receptors within the spinal cord, abdomen and other organs, along with superficial temperature receptors in our skin. Signals from these receptors are integrated in the hypothalamus from which messages are sent to regulate heat loss and heat production via the control of sweat glands, muscle tone and shivering (thermogenesis). While it might not seem all that significant, shivering can actually increase metabolic heat production in the body up to five times normal.

The hypothalamus also controls blood flow from the core to peripheral regions via vasoconstriction (a decrease in the diameter of the blood vessels) and other mechanisms. This prevents the conduction of heat from internal portions of the body to the skin. In this way, heat must be conducted through layers of subcutaneous fat, slowing the rate of loss. Also, as the skin cools, the temperature difference between the body and the environment is reduced, also reducing conductive heat loss.

Humans also have a crude "countercurrent" system similar to a more highly developed mechanism in species of so-called "warm-blooded" fishes like tuna, billfish and some sharks (a mechanism called the *rete mirabile*). The configuration works like an anatomical heat exchanger. Arteries in the extremities run beside large veins carrying blood back to the heart. Heat loss is reduced by the arterial blood giving off some of its heat to the returning venous blood. Some studies have indicated that our physiology might adapt to cold, improving our ability to conserve heat markedly, but this adaptation seems to be lost in only a few weeks once you're no longer exposed to cold conditions.

In humans, the areas of greatest heat loss are at the base of the neck, armpits, groin and the head. The reason for this is simple: Major arteries in these regions are near the surface.

The head requires special mention because common wisdom is that 30 to 40 percent—and according to some sources even 70 percent—of heat loss occurs through the human dome. This traces back to reference in an old a US Army survival manual. However, A recent British study totally contradicts this common assumption.

It appears that the misconception arose through a flawed interpretation of a vaguely scientific experiment conducted by the U.S. military in the 1950s. The study had volunteers dressed in Arctic survival suits and exposed to bitterly cold conditions. Because it was the only part of their bodies left uncovered, most of their heat was —surprise, surprise — lost through their heads. Actually, the head comprises only about 10 percent of the body's surface area. Although much of the head does not vasodilate in the same way as the rest of the body, if the experiment had been performed with volunteers wearing only swimming trunks, heat loss would be much closer to 10 percent than the oft-quoted 30 percent or more. Indeed, the face, head and chest are more sensitive to changes in temperature than the rest of the body, which makes it *feel* as if covering these areas does more to prevent heat loss.

In one lab study with subjects in cool-water tanks, researchers compared the rate of heat lost by monitoring core temperature through different body parts and quantities of skin exposed. At rest, they found that the rate of heat loss only depended upon the amount of skin surface area exposed, and the percentage of heat lost through the head was the same as the rest of the body. Subjects did show a temporary increase in heat loss through the scalp that returned to the baseline of about 7 percent as they continued to exercise.

There is one situation in which special protection for the head is warranted, and that's when dealing with hypothermia. When a hypothermia victim is not shivering — at rest — the heat loss through the head remains about 7 percent to 10 percent. But things change dramatically when they are shivering, at which time heat loss via the scalp can increase substantially. This is because a shivering hypothermia patient does not vasodilate the peripheral circulation like someone who is exercising. But the shivering muscles do increase cardiac output, and therefore increase cerebral circulation. So, protecting the head well under these circumstances is a very important part of treating someone in hypothermia.

The Cold Continuum

As our core temperature drops, our body responds most noticeably in the extremities. This is often accompanied by numbness in the hands and feet. As the core temperature continues to fall, things get worse. You first experience difficulty in fine motor movement, which progresses to impairment of even gross movement. Shivering usually occurs as an early symptom only if you're not engaging in heavy physical activity. If symptoms progress to *any* level of mental confusion or impairment, the condition has probably progressed to a point at which you must take action. Most importantly, abort the dive and get warm.

If your core temperature were to dip below 95 F (35 C), then you pass from simply being cold to the realm of mild hypothermia. Of course, as your temperature continues to plummet, the condition worsens to include a wide range of increasingly debilitating effects.

At about 91 F (33 C) you'll experience a profound loss of muscular coordination. Shivering, however, can slow or even stop altogether; and you're likely to demonstrate a varying degree of weakness, apathy, drowsiness, confusion and slurred speech.

Below 90 F (32 C) we enter the realm of true severe hypothermia, with symptoms including cessation of shivering, increased muscle tone, loss of consciousness, absence of detectable vital signs and heart arrhythmias. Eventually, cardiac and respiratory arrest occur. It's true that some people have survived after suffering a drop in core temperatures as low as 61 F (16 C), but those are rare exceptions; the envelope for survival is typically much narrower.

While discussions of cold and heat loss often focus on hypothermia, that's not the primary concern in diving. In most cases, divers will abort a dive long before hypothermia occurs. The real problem is that cold water causes physical incapacitation by draining energy from the body to a point at which a diver can no longer function. In extreme cases the muscles no longer function adequately, so the victim doesn't succumb to hypothermia, but drowns. This is sometimes called "swimming failure."

Of course, while you're losing heat, your body is also responding by generating more. Body heat is produced in several ways. First there's your basal metabolism, the heat engine of normal cellular processes. Next, there's the heat produced by muscular activity, including that produced by shivering. (Incidentally, while shivering can produce five times more heat than when you're not shivering, the act of simply tensing

In dealing with any case of severe cold stress the most important first-aid measure when dealing with any suspected occurrence is preventing further heat loss. This means getting out of the water and restoring body heat.

Once out of the water, the most important step is getting the diver into shelter, out of his or her exposure suit and into warm, dry clothing. If that isn't immediately possible, at least have the diver cover up with a windproof garment, space blanket or even a sheet of plastic to prevent rapid evaporative cooling from his exposure suit. It's also important, especially in cases of clinical hypothermia, that you handle the victim very gently, as the cold heart is susceptible to arrhythmias.

If the diver can swallow and has a normal state of alertness, give him plenty of warm, sweet liquids. Never, under any circumstance, give the diver alcoholic beverages. Even though they might "feel warm," this is only the effect of the alcohol making its way to your stomach, and the initial vasodilatation of your blood vessels.

Traditional methods of actively rewarming the victim have been shown to be generally ineffective. Hypothermia victims are fully capable of rewarming themselves solely through metabolic heat production, provided they're well insulated. Mild hypothermia victims can rewarm by exercises, provided they're comfortable in doing so. However, exercise should not be used in more severe cases. Be certain that the areas of highest heat loss — head, neck, arm pits and groin — are especially well insulated; and don't forget to insulate under the victim if he's lying down. Eventually, the victim will begin to feel warm, but don't stop the rewarming effort too early (and don't let them start removing insulation because they start feeling too warm). Sweating is the only sign that the victim has restored sufficient heat, and the rewarming effort must continue until this occurs.

If the diver doesn't seem to improve, or if symptoms worsen after rewarming attempts, consider this a serious medical emergency that requires medical intervention. Seek emergency medical assistance immediately, and be sure to exercise extreme caution in handling the victim. If possible, keep them in a prone position. Remember, rough treatment can cause heart arrhythmia. If CPR is necessary, assess vital signs for at least two minutes before administration, as breathing and pulse may be significantly depressed.

the muscles can increase heat output by 50 percent.) There's also a minor contribution through chemical thermogenesis via secretion of the hormones norepinephrine and epinephrine.

One final issue worthy of note is the common belief that women are more susceptible to hypothermia than are men. The usual rationale for this is that females supposedly have a larger surface area-to-mass ratio than men. Actually, this isn't necessarily true. First, unless you compare extremely small and large people, in an individual basis this ratio actually differs very little between the sexes. However, the mechanism of how male and female bodies respond to heat loss does appear to differ. In general, women can preserve more heat in their core, while men tend to be able to produce more heat to offset loss. There are gender differences that can clearly affect risk, such as total body mass and muscle mass available for heat generation through shivering. However, in general most studies have failed to find any evidence that women are at significantly greater risk of hypothermia than men.

Heat Loss In Divers

In diving, the mere act of breathing leads to heat loss. At issue here is that the air we often breathe is cold air from our tank; and even in warm-water conditions, our air is almost always going to be much colder than ambient due to expansion from a pressurized source. Regardless, once inhaled, our lungs warm the air, thereby expending more heat. The situation is magnified even further as you go deeper because as depth increases so does the density of your breathing gas. Denser air, in turn, means more molecules to heat, thus even more heat is drained away. Worst of all, none of the regulatory responses that our body normally makes to conserve heat are activated by loss through respiration. In short, there's little that we can do about it (although, over the years, a few devices have appeared that were designed to warm a diver's air as it's inhaled).

Research has also shed light on another diver-specific issue involving heat loss. Studies from Canada have found that nitrogen narcosis — the subject of chapter 16 — can inhibit the shivering response, eliminating one possible warning sign of hypothermia. This could mean that, due to narcosis, you might not recognize your true state of thermal distress,

making you more likely to extend your dive beyond the point of safety. Conversely, cold stress has also been shown to increase the effect of narcosis. And due to reduced off-gassing of nitrogen, cold stress might increase the risk of decompression sickness.

Furthermore, the phenomenon of vasoconstriction, addressed earlier, causes another response that increases heat loss. When submerged, shifting blood

Wear more exposure protection than you think you'll need. Probably the wisest investment a tropical water diver can make to avoid heat loss is to buy a hood.

Make sure your wet suit fits well to avoid water exchange and convective heat loss.

Bring sufficient clothing for when you get out of the water. It should be warm and windproof. Again, the guideline is to bring more than you think you'll need.

In the air, a wet wet suit works like a refrigerator. So, if you'll be wearing your wet suit between dives, or on your ride back to the dock, bring a windproof jacket or overgarment to cover your exposure suit. This will prevent heat loss through rapid evaporation.

Get out of the water when you feel cold. Don't wait for shivering to occur, as it could be delayed by a number of factors such as heavy exercise, alcohol consumption and even nitrogen narcosis. Avoid alcohol before diving and, if you're cold, even after. It might make you feel warm, but that's deceptive; it actually accelerates heat loss.

If you do begin to shiver, exit the water immediately and rewarm. While shivering helps the body rewarm, this works only on land. Shivering in the water only promotes further heat loss.

from the outer regions of our body into the core is interpreted by the brain as a state of overhydration — too much fluid. This shuts off production of antidiuretic hormones, causing you to urinate more frequently. As the urine is at body temperature, significant heat is lost along with the fluid.

Divers battle heat loss on virtually every dive we make. Yet, it is amazing how we can manage to stay relatively comfortable and, more importantly, functionally safe, over a wide range of environments. While for a variety of reasons Mother Nature didn't design us well to function underwater, our ability to manage heat loss is testament to modern technology and the adaptability of the human machine.

CHAPTER 15

Fear Factor:
A Physiological Perspective

Both popular and scientific literature are full of examples of people who, when under the extreme stress generated by fear, do things that are seemingly impossible, like soldiers in combat surviving wounds that any ER doc would write off as mortal. My own experience with fear bears out that it can be a powerful motivator. I remember quite clearly one windy day out in the middle of the Bahamas Bank. Bouncing around in rough seas in a 17-foot (5 m) tender meant that I might be seeing my lunch for a second time if I didn't get in the water quickly.

So, long before anyone else was ready, I made a backroll into the water. We were on a shallow patch reef that I thought would offer a relaxing way to end a busy day of diving. As the bubbles cleared, a blurred image appeared of what was obviously a fish about the same size as the Boston Whaler I'd just vacated. And much to my distress, it was only a few boat lengths away. As if that wasn't enough, I quickly recognized the distinctive striped pattern of a tiger shark, and the next thing I remember I was back in the tender, shaken. Although I have hardly any recollection of it, I had climbed over the gunwale — wearing full scuba gear — and back into the boat with absolutely no assistance from anyone. Once I stopped shaking, I rinsed out my wet suit.

One aspect shared by these and similar events is that they all involved fearful situations. According to Webster's, fear is "an unpleasant emotion caused by the belief that someone or something is dangerous, likely to cause pain, or a threat." Indeed, we all think of fear as an emotion — a state of mind — not as a physiologic state, like being cold. Yet, in learning to deal with fearful situa-

tions, which can easily lead to panic, it's vital to consider not only what fear can do to the mind, but also the body.

Of course, we're all aware that fear has physical effects like increasing our heart rate and making our palms sweat, but these physiologic aspects go much deeper than what we're consciously aware of during, or even after, a fearful event. So, exactly what is our body's physiologic reaction to fear?

The Fearful Brain

As fear is, at its root, an emotion, it makes sense to start with what happens in our brain when we're exposed to a fearful event. Imagine this scenario: A diver is swimming along a beautiful coral reef and suddenly confronts a 5-foot (1.5 m) bull shark. Immediately, he swims into the shelter of a nearby cavern to hide from what he recognizes as a potentially aggressive creature. A few minutes later he decides to resume his dive, keeping a watchful eye out for the shark.

The diver's actions seem like a logical, considered response based on a knowledgeable individual's assessment of risk. However, new research into the workings of the human brain bring this assumption into question. Neuropsychologists (don't worry if you've never heard of such a thing before, it's a relatively new field) now believe that even before a situation is evaluated via the conscious mind, a split-second unconscious decision has already been made. The internal processing goes like this: Information about a dangerous situation reaches the amygdala — a part of the brain in a primitive region called the limbic system — which is active in processing emotional responses. This information travels down two different pathways. One is termed "direct" while the other is "indirect."

The direct pathway carries information unconsciously from the eye to another part of the brain, the thalamus, and on to the amygdala, passing under the cortex. The cortex is the "thinking" part of the brain. Because this is a shorter pathway, it registers any perceived danger more rapidly and responds far more quickly than the indirect pathway that's processed in the cortex. This has both advantages and disadvantages. The disadvantage is that we sometimes react quickly to perceived danger, which is groundless, like jumping at the sound of an engine's backfire. However, the advantage is that this system allows us to react with great speed — and without having to think — when it's necessary to avoid genuinely dangerous situations.

The indirect or cortical pathway is slower than the direct pathway. Here, information travels from the eye to the thalamus through the visual cortex to the amygdala. This is the pathway used to assess the situation after the initial rapid response. It's this thoughtful, conscious response that allows us to consider whether it is or isn't necessary to react to a loud noise.

Now let's return to the shark scenario. On witnessing the animal, the direct pathway may have manifested an immediate reaction even before the situation had consciously registered. However, once inside the cavern, the indirect pathway came into play. There, information consciously began to register, and the diver was able to draw on his prior knowledge and experience. Based on that assessment, his decision was to resume the dive.

Should I Stay or Should I Go?

Mother Nature is amazing for many reasons, not the least of which is how she's programmed us for self-preservation. When reacting to a fearful situation, the first decision at hand is whether to flee or stand your ground. This is the well-known "fight or flight" response. It was first studied extensively, and so named, in the 1930s by two researchers, Cannon and Selye, to describe a pattern of physiological responses that prepare higher animals, like us, for emergencies. Whether

---

Scientists have recently discovered a gene that appears to control whether fear reactions to impending danger are appropriate or not. Mice lacking the gene stathmin appeared fearless in conditions that should instinctively inspire fear. The gene is expressed in particularly high levels in the amygdala of the brain. Its discovery may lead to a new understanding and important new advances in the treatment of anxiety disorders.

The same researchers identified a similar gene a few years ago, called GPR, that appeared to be important in the process of "learned fear." This is where animals, including humans, learn over time that something is a threat or danger, as opposed to the instinctive fear that animals are born with. GPR appeared to block the action of circuitry in the amygdala of the brain that learns fear. Conversely, the recently discovered gene, stathmin, appears to help this circuitry.

Mice bred to lack stathmin showed abnormally low levels of anxiety in situations that would normally make a mouse very afraid, such as being in large open spaces. They also reacted less to learned fear. In the study, this learned fear was a neutral tone that was played while the animals were delivered a mild electric shock.

The mice showed a decreased memory for the fearful situations and had difficulty recognizing dangerous environments. Their memory for things other than fear was not impaired, however.

Source: BBC News

---

it's humans or any other animal, we are hardwired to use as many resources as needed, and as much energy as possible, to deal with a threat. Faced with danger, whether real or imagined, our body changes its inner-balance and priorities to enable either fight or flight.

As we saw in the earlier explanation of the brain, exactly what happens inside our body when we sense danger is both complex and interesting. Aside from what was already mentioned, the brain activates another player — the autonomic nervous system or ANS. The ANS has two branches: the sympathetic nervous system (SNS) and the parasympathetic nervous system (PNS). These control the body's energy level so we can prepare for action. The SNS is an all-or-none system, meaning that when it's activated it quickly turns on all of its component parts. This is exactly what we want in an emergency response system. The all-or-none nature of the SNS also explains why panic symptoms tend to be numerous. The SNS controls our fight-or-flight response and releases the energy needed for action. The PNS is the body's relaxation and recovery system; it returns our body to a normal state when the danger is over, but more on this later.

Once an alarm reaction is triggered, as we all know, both our heart and breathing rates increase. At the same time, the blood supply is prioritized according to need. For example, more blood is pumped to the muscles and vital areas of the brain to increase both the oxygen supply and the amount of sugar (fuel). This ensures that our muscles and brain will have sufficient resources for response. Likewise, the fear response causes the blood to thicken, increasing the number of oxygen-carrying red cells per volume. This also increases the number of both white cells and platelets, enhancing our body's ability to fight infection and more quickly stop bleeding. Blood supply is also reduced to the digestive system and irrelevant brain regions, such as the areas responsible for speech.

At the same time, blood flow to nonvital areas like the skin, peripheral organs and feet decreases. This reduces blood loss if we are injured. This, along with an increase in platelets, explains in part why many soldiers survive combat wounds that in other circumstances, such as a car accident, would be fatal.

Furthermore, a stress response triggers changes in our glands. Sweating will increase, which helps to cool the body during exertion. In fact, the familiar phenomenon of "cold sweat" is what we feel when sweating occurs at the same time blood flow to the skin decreases. This, of course, goes totally unnoticed underwater. On the other hand, saliva production decreases, giving us the quintessential sign of a fearful situation — a dry mouth.

The SNS also tells the body to breathe more rapidly and deeply. The upside to this is more rapid and efficient breathing, which enables the muscles and all other tissues to work better. But there's also a down side. Hyperventilation occurs when rapid breathing is not accompanied by increased muscle action. It's like revving a car while holding down the brake. As any breath-hold diver knows, the decrease in blood carbon dioxide levels caused by hyperventilation can result in tingling and numbness, and ultimately leads to passing out. What is less known is that hyperventilation can also result in chest pain and, when under stress, even choking. This happens because rapid chest breathing and muscle tension are occurring at the same time. Learning breath control is perhaps the best coping strategy for dealing with fearful situations. Along with the chest, other muscle groups tense up for activation, which compound feelings of tension and — once the situation is over — aches and pains. Recognizing and taking steps to counteract these physical sensations allows you to calm down and think more clearly.

Other physiologic responses to stress can include nausea, diarrhea and involuntary urination. This is because digestion isn't needed during times of danger, so the sympathetic nervous system shuts down this nonessential function. This often leads to an upset stomach. Diarrhea is the result of both the shutdown of digestion and an attempt, believe it or not, for our body to eliminate excess weight to assist in flight. Similarly, uncontrolled urination lightens the body in case there's a need to flee.

A not-so-obvious sign of extreme fear is pupil dilation. The upside here is that the additional light improves night vision; but during the day it can mean blurred vision. Furthermore, these changes in visual perception, when combined with the aforementioned sensations, can contribute to the feelings of unreality often reported after an incident of high anxiety or panic.

The Real Adrenaline Rush

The brain and nervous and immune systems aren't the only actors in the response to fear. So, too, is the endocrine system. All so-called "stress hormones" — a collective term for all hormones that affect parts of the brain where attention and responding actions are controlled — are produced and secreted by the adrenal gland located on top of the kidneys. As everyone knows, adrenaline — the first hormone ever discovered — is secreted as a direct reaction to stressful situations, and its powerful effects are similar to those manifested by the SNS.

Many health professionals now believe that stress-induced immunosuppression is not only responsible for some infections, but also for the growth of tumors. Some researchers even believe that certain people who are especially susceptible to stress may be likewise more prone to cancer than those who are better able to handle stress. Psychologists even have a name for this personality, the "Type C" person.

In a well-known and respected textbook, Health Psychology, the authors define the characteristics of the Type C personality: "The first includes a tendency to keep in resentment and anger rather than express it and a marked inability to forgive. In addition, research suggests that cancer victims are ineffective in forming and/or maintaining close, long-term relationships with other people. They are more likely to be loners without extensive social support systems. Third, they engage in more self-pity than what may be considered normal. And these people tend to have poor self-images. Thus the cancer-prone individual 'puts on a happy face' and denies any sense of loss, anger, distress, disappointment, or despair while living an inner life of self-pity, insecurity, and a certain degree of loneliness."

Like adrenalin, noradrenalin is released from the adrenal glands as a hormone into the blood. But unlike adrenalin, it's also released from noradrenergic neurons during synaptic transmission of the SNS. Along with adrenalin, noradrenalin underlies the fight-or-flight response, directly increasing heart rate, triggering the release of glucose from energy stores, and increasing skeletal muscle readiness.

Although it reacts somewhat slower than the almost instant response of the ANS, hormones produced by the endocrine system actually have a wider effect on the body than the ANS. The effects of adrenalin and noradrenalin are also felt long after the PNS begins calming us down. Secretion of stress hormones increases both the sensitivity and the strength of other relevant systems. At the same time, secretion of powerful natural painkillers called endorphins provide an instant defense against pain.

Immune System Response

Until recently it was believed that the brain and immune systems were separate and incapable of influencing each other; but that view has undergone a radical change based on groundbreaking new research. Scientists are finding many connections between the two. For example, nerve endings have been found in tissues that produce, develop and store immune system cells; and the thymus (an endocrine organ located just behind the sternum), lymph nodes, spleen, and even bone marrow — all vital components of the immune systems — have been shown to respond to signals from the brain. What has resulted is a new field called psychoneuroimmunology, which specializes in understanding the new-found relationship between stress and illness. A key assumption among psychoneuroimmunologists is that psychological distress can suppress the immune system to the point of inducing physical illness.

Several studies have documented how physical stress and fear can suppress the immune system. One early study showed clear immunosuppression in animals exposed to mild electric shock. Over prolonged periods these subjects became ill. The study also showed that the same stress response occurred when the animals weren't shocked, but were presented with some stimuli previously paired with the shocking, like turning on a light. Thus, not only does physical stress produce a weakened immune system, but the mere anticipation of a fearful situation triggers a similar effect.

Clear evidence now exists that the same mechanism is at work in humans. When we're stressed, or placed in any state of fear, our bodies go into a state of immunosuppression. As a result, we are much more likely to be affected by infection-based illnesses.

Importantly, stress is not the cause of the disease, but rather sets the stage for illness.

Psychologist Dr. Sheldon Cohen has applied these ideas to humans. In a landmark study, Cohen injected volunteers with a known cold virus, and then waited to see who came down with a cold. Amazingly, there was a clear correlation between subjects who did catch a cold and levels of stress experienced during the past year. Additional human research has shown declines in immune system cells in medical students taking final exams, people caring for loved ones with Alzheimer's disease, and women who recently had experienced a nasty divorce. One working theory is that stress may reduce the ability of leukocytes and other immune cells to identify and successfully destroy their targets. It is now clear that chronic stress without adequate coping promotes disease and other illnesses through immunosuppression.

Once the fearful situation is over, the PNS kicks in with a built-in recovery system, quickly stopping the sympathetic nervous responses. Although it's connected to the same part of the brain as the sympathetic nervous system, it's a bit more cautious. Its effect takes hold more slowly than the SNS response, just in case danger returns. In addition, other chemicals in the body begin to neutralize adrenaline and noradrenalin. But, as adrenaline and noradrenalin can take some time to be neutralized one may still feel apprehensive even after the PNS has relaxed the body. There are also effects from the heightened muscular tension and alert status of other vital systems. Muscle soreness and a general state of fatigue can set in once the fearful situation has resolved.

So it's abundantly clear that fear isn't just an emotional state but a physiological state as well. Its manifestations are unconscious, but understanding exactly what happens inside our body when we experience fear can go a long way to controlling and reacting appropriately when responding to danger. To paraphrase FDR, there's nothing to fear but not understanding fear itself.

How Your Body Responds and Recovers From Fear

Area of Body	Emergency Response System (Sympathetic Nervous System)	Recovery System (Parasympathetic Nervous System)
Heart	beats faster & stronger	beats slower & normally
Lungs	breathe faster & more shallow	breathe slower & deeper
Muscles	tighter, more tense	more loose & relaxed
Stomach	decreases digestion	increases digestion
Sweat Glands	increase perspiration	decrease perspiration
Adrenal Glands	increase adrenaline	decrease adrenaline
Immune System	becomes suppressed	functions normally

CHAPTER 16

Rapture of the Deep:
Drunk as a Hoot Owl

In the October 1952 issue of *National Geographic* appeared an article, "Fish Men Explore a New World Undersea." It was written by a former French naval officer whom the world would come to know quite well. His names was Jacques-Yves Cousteau. In that article (and later in his hallmark book, *The Silent World*) he recounted personal experiences involving a mysterious diver's disease, which he termed *l'ivresse des grandes profondeurs* ("rapture of the deep"). He wrote, "The chief symptom of this phenomenon is, to put it bluntly, the sensation of becoming as drunk as a hoot owl."

Captain Cousteau brought to the public eye for the first time something that divers and scientists had known about for more than 150 years. His romantic phrasing survived long into the future; and in the early days of diver training "rapture of the deep" was a far more common way for an instructor to explain the effects of this enigmatic condition than the dry, clinical term *nitrogen narcosis*.

Without exception, every scuba training course covers nitrogen narcosis, but usually addresses it in a cursory way. Divers normally are told only that: 1) it's caused by breathing nitrogen at high pressure; 2) its effects increase with depth, normally becoming quite noticeable around 100 feet (30 m); and 3) ascending to a shallower depth will relieve the symptoms.

Case closed.

While these are certainly the highlights, this is far from an adequate explanation given that the consequences of being "narked" can be life-threatening. Additionally, the current popularity of technical diving has made recreational divers more aware and curious about diving to much greater depths than our own limit of 130 feet (39 m). But whether you're interested in learning more about the challenges of deep diving as a bridge to technical diving, or just want a better understanding of what goes on inside your body at any depth, all divers should possess a more thorough insight into narcosis than they're given in most open water — or even advanced — certification courses.

While we call it *nitrogen* narcosis, many gases, including oxygen, can have a narcotic effect when breathed under enough pressure. The condition produces a state similar to alcohol intoxication or breathing nitrous oxide ("laughing gas") at surface pressure. The good news is that, unlike decompression sickness, the effects of narcosis are completely resolved by ascending to a shallower depth, and with no long-term consequences. Therefore, provided a diver is aware of its symptoms and ascends to manage it, narcosis rarely develops into a serious problem.

Early Insights

We've known about nitrogen narcosis for about as long as technology has enabled people to breathe air under pressure. In 1834 a French researcher, Victor Junod, was the first to describe it, noting "the functions of the brain are activated, imagination is lively, thoughts have a peculiar charm and, in some persons, symptoms of intoxication are present." As a cause, he proposed that narcosis resulted from high-pressure gas causing increased blood flow, therefore stimulating nerve centers.

A bit later, in 1881, a physician named Walter Moxon proposed that pressure forced blood to inaccessible parts of the body and the stagnant blood somehow caused emotional changes. Others believed it was a result of psychological factors, such as latent claustrophobia.

It wasn't until 1935 that a diving physiologist named Albert Behnke — the father figure of the U.S. Navy's diving program — suggested that it was the nitrogen component of air responsible for the narcotic symptoms. In 1939, Behnke and his colleagues were also the first to demonstrate that gases other than nitrogen, such as helium, could cause narcosis.

That year was also auspicious for yet another reason. On May 23, 1939, the U.S. Navy submarine, *Squalus*, suffered a catastrophic valve failure during a test dive off New Hampshire's Isle of Shoals. Fortunately it came to rest in just 240 feet (73 m) of water, rather than the crushing depths just offshore. Only a quick salvage-and-rescue operation would save the lives aboard, but the depth made air diving operations less than ideal due to the effects of narcosis. The rescue operation gave the Navy its first opportunity to try the then-experimental gas mixture heliox (helium-oxygen); and the recovery of the *Squalus* crew went down as one of the most famous and successful in U.S. Naval history.

What's Up With That?

To understand the current theory for what causes nitrogen narcosis, you must first know a bit about how the nervous system works. Electrical nerve impulses are transmitted throughout the body via nerve cells called *neurons*. These neurons, which are made partially of lipid (fat) tissue, transmit electrical signals to other neurons at junctions called *synapses*. The narcotic potency of an inert gas is a function of its solubility in fat tissue — those that dissolve more easily into fat are more narcotic. The greater the solubility, the less partial pressure needed to induce narcosis. Sedation occurs, it's thought, because the inert gas causes the synaptic membrane to expand, which slows or stops transmission of electrical impulses.

By the 1960s an alternative to the nitrogen theory was proposed, suggesting that narcosis was caused by high levels of carbon dioxide resulting from reduced respiratory efficiency. Although researchers have refuted the carbon dioxide theory, it has been shown that high levels of carbon dioxide will enhance the onset and severity of nitrogen narcosis. More recently, scientists have been looking at neurotransmitter receptor protein mechanisms as a possible cause of narcosis.

Regardless of the mechanism involved, the result is a slowing of our mental processes and reaction time. Essentially, information cannot be processed as fast as the input is received; and our performance of tasks, ranging from reasoning to manual dexterity, suffers.

A portion of the brain called the *reticular center*, which is responsible for receiving and distributing nerve impulses throughout the body, is particularly susceptible to this anesthetic effect. It's interesting to note, however, that although this theory is based on solid evidence, to this day no one is absolutely certain about what causes nitrogen narcosis.

What Are the Effects?

Most divers are taught that the symptoms of narcosis usually don't occur until a depth of around 100 feet (30 m). But that's really the depth at which symptoms become noticeable in most divers; subtle impairment starts in as little as half that depth. In fact, studies done by the U.S. Navy have documented that some highly susceptible individuals are affected by nitrogen narcosis at pressures as low as 2 atmospheres (33 feet [10 m]). Studies also show that, in virtually every diver, by the time they reach 3 atmospheres (66 feet [20 m]) there's a measurable slowing of mental processing, although at this depth you're usually unaware of any change. By 4 atmospheres (99 feet [30 m]) most are aware of some impairment. In the depth range of 4-5 atmospheres (99-165 feet [30-50 m]), divers can experience a wide variety of debilitating symptoms.

The effects of narcosis are also highly variable among individuals, and even with the same individual on different days. Some divers even believe they're virtually immune to the disorder, citing their ability to function well below 100 feet (30 m) without any apparent effect. But the truth is, no one is immune. Everyone is affected; the only questions are when, how and to what degree.

How Do Divers React?

In divers, the effects of narcosis generally start with some form of impairment of mental function. This might include loss of memory, reasoning ability, or a reduced ability to concentrate or to make sound judgments. These symptoms are especially dangerous because they often occur at times when divers need their wits about them the most; yet the victim might not even be aware that anything is wrong. As these symptoms can cause lapses in judgment, a "narked" diver can easily run out of air or overstay his allowable bottom time. It also makes a breakdown of the buddy system much more likely.

As depth increases, the symptoms can progress to impaired motor coordination and in some divers, a reduced or delayed response to sound and visual stimuli. This, combined with decreased mental capability, puts the diver at great risk. In extreme depths — beyond 165 feet — symptoms can become quite severe, and include extreme confusion, sleepiness and even hallucinations.

Most textbooks caution divers about the sudden and abrupt onset of symptoms, but many experienced technical divers disagree. They contend that the onset of narcosis, while subtle, can be detected in its very early stages. Symptoms they often point to include a reduced ability to read one's gauges, and an increased awareness and sensitivity to sound. "Perceptual narrowing," a condition akin to tunnel vision, is also a very common early symptom. It's important to note, however, that only those who are highly experienced at deep diving are likely to recognize such subtle symptoms. It's also not uncommon for victims of narcosis to have amnesia, reporting no recollection at all of events that took place at depth.

Both research and practical experience indicate that the effects of narcosis can be enhanced by several factors. Two such factors are the environment you're diving in and your mental state. For example, some studies have shown that divers in warm, clear-water environments — conditions likely to evoke a sense of comfort and control — are more likely to experience a sense of overconfidence, well-being and euphoria. But, in a less secure environment — such as cold, dark water — or in a less secure state of mind, symptoms of anxiety are more likely. In some cases, even terror and panic have been noted. This is a very important consideration because, as your diving environment and your mental state change, you can never assume that your susceptibility or response to nitrogen narcosis will always be the same.

There's also evidence of the importance of psychological factors, and how the onset of nitrogen narcosis could be influenced by what's termed "negative modeling," a form of self-fulfilling prophecy. One such study of anticipatory behavior modeling conducted back in 1965 resulted in some very interesting findings. The study involved three groups. The first group was taught that virtually all divers succumb to narcosis at 130 feet (39 m), and that symptoms would be severe. The second group was taught about narcosis, but was told that it was far from certain to occur and its severity was downplayed. The final group was given a three-hour lecture on narcosis, including a review of all known research, and

told that strong willpower could greatly reduce its effect. Each group was then given a series of cognitive exercises in a recompression chamber at depths ranging from 100 feet (30 m) to 240 feet (73 m).

The results showed an apparent correlation between how the divers were trained and their ability to deal with narcosis. For example, no members of the first group could perform past the 200-foot (61 m) level, and two subjects from the second group were also unable to perform. Amazingly, however, members from the third group actually showed better performance at 200 feet than at their surface test, and all but one subject continued to function well to the final depth of 240 feet. While one single study is far too little to determine any solid conclusions, instructors might do well to keep these results in mind the next time they teach their students about narcosis.

Another contributing factor is alcohol consumption or taking drugs that block nerve transmission. The drugs in question include not only prescription medications, but also over-the-counter remedies for conditions such as seasickness, diarrhea and nasal congestion. Besides drugs, high levels of carbon dioxide, exertion and fatigue can also contribute to the onset and severity of symptoms. There's even some evidence that an increase in oxygen partial pressure might influence the early onset of symptoms.

What Can I Do?

While no one is immune to nitrogen narcosis, there are some things you can do that might reduce its effects. First, be very careful about exceeding depths deeper than you're used to unless you have advanced training or are

Depth	Signs & Symptoms
33-100 feet (10-30 meters)	• Mild impairment of performance of unpracticed tasks. • Mildly impaired reasoning. • Mild euphoria possible.
100-165 feet (30-50 m)	• Delayed response to visual and auditory stimuli. • Reasoning and immediate memory affected more than motor coordination. • Calculation errors and wrong choices. • Idea fixation. • Overconfidence and sense of well-being. • Laughter and loquacity (in chambers) which may be overcome by self-control. • Anxiety (common in cold murky water).
165-230 feet (50-70 m)	• Sleepiness, impaired judgment, confusion. • Hallucinations. • Severe delay in response to signals, instructions and other stimuli. • Occasional dizziness. • Uncontrolled laughter, hysteria (in chamber). • Terror in some.
230-300 feet (70-90 m)	• Poor concentration and mental confusion. • Stupefaction with some decrease in dexterity and judgment. • Loss of memory, increased excitability.
300-plus feet (90-plus m)	• Hallucinations. • Increased intensity of vision and hearing. • Sense of impending blackout, euphoria, dizziness, manic or depressive states, a sense of levitation, disorganization of the sense of time, changes in facial appearance. • Unconsciousness. • Death.

Source: NOAA Diving Manual

under supervision of more experienced divers. Be sure to practice the tasks you'll perform on the deep dive, too.

Often, especially when on a holiday, we can't always choose our buddy; and even if we can, we aren't always that discerning. However, when deep diving, it's important that you both know and trust your buddy. Prior experience with an individual gives you a "baseline" for what constitutes normal behavior. This insight will make it easier for you to recognize signs of nitrogen narcosis sooner than you might with a buddy you don't know well.

It might seem obvious, but deep diving requires use of a high-quality, well-maintained regulator. A poor-performing regulator can cause stress that, in turn, can exacerbate narcosis. So, make sure that your equipment is in top working order, and has been serviced within a reasonable period of time. One way you can get optimal performance is by remaining relaxed and moving in a slow, deliberate manner.

Another common-sense guideline is to avoid drinking alcohol or taking any drugs for at least eight hours before diving. If you must take drugs, never take them for the first time before diving. Always know what effect a drug has beforehand. If the drug has a psycho-active effect or gives you a dry mouth, don't take it before making a deep dive. It could greatly increase the likelihood or effects of nitrogen narcosis.

Remember the KISS principle: Keep It Simple, Stupid. A simple dive plan means that you won't overload yourself with too many tasks. When deep diving you can't help but be impaired to some degree. Trying to accomplish too much will only increase the likelihood of poor performance or forgetting something.

Always try to begin a deep dive in a calm, relaxed frame of mind. Consider using the mental rehearsal techniques detailed later, and — most importantly — never be hesitant to call off the dive if for any reason it just doesn't "feel right."

Deeper water almost always means colder water, so wear adequate exposure protection. Remember, your wet suit will lose some of its effectiveness on a deep dive because of compression. Studies have documented that nitrogen narcosis can suppress the shivering response. This could lead to a false sense of your true state of thermal stress. In turn, moderate hypothermia can exacerbate the mental impairment caused by nitrogen narcosis.

Heed the advice and insights from more seasoned deep divers. Experienced deep divers often report that narcosis is at its worst when first arriving on the bottom. Therefore, don't be too quick to get on with the dive; take a minute or two to acclimate once you're on the bottom. Stop, relax, check your air supply and equipment and confirm that your buddy is alright before proceeding.

Deep diving is not something you want to learn by trial and error. It's strongly advised that you take a formal deep diving course from an experienced instructor. In addition, most courses will have you perform a timed task — such as solving an arithmetic problem or opening a combination lock — at the surface, and then compare it with the time it takes you to do the same task at a depth of 100 feet (30 m) or more. Interestingly, some divers can perform the task better at depth than at the surface, then mistakenly conclude that they're immune or not very susceptible to narcosis. That's a dangerous and false assumption because, as numerous studies have shown, the reality is that their improved performance is merely the effect of practice, not any indication of reduced sensitivity to nitrogen.

When deep diving, especially, be sure to keep a vigilant eye on your buddy. Ideally, never let more than three or four breaths go by without visually confirming their location, and verifying his or her mental state.

Finally, there's the issue of descent rate. Researchers have evidence that correlates a rapid descent with an increased likelihood of nitrogen narcosis. Logically, then, to reduce your risk, you should avoid descending too rapidly. But it's not quite that simple. On the other side of the issue, evidence also exists showing that a rapid descent might be helpful in avoiding decompression sickness by crushing gas micronuclei. As this issue is still under debate, the best advice is probably to descend at a deliberate, but comfortable, rate. Another way to perhaps prevent or control narcosis is to use a reference line to provide a constant visual orientation during the descent.

What Can We Learn From Technical Divers?

While scientists remain divided on the issue, experienced technical divers are adamant that divers can stave off some of the effects of narcosis by continued and frequent deep diving. This is probably due to both physiological adaptation, and because the seasoned diver develops coping skills, such as concentrating more intently on the task at hand. The adaptation is only temporary, however, and decays over a matter of days or weeks once diving ceases. The coping skills might last longer. A high motivation to complete the task appears to help reduce symptoms, as well.

Applying these ideas, technical divers often use special techniques to prepare for a deep dive. The first is to acclimate to the planned depth through a series of "rehearsal dives." These are dives made over several days, in progressively deeper water, where divers engage in tasks similar to what they'll do on the final dive.

The second preparation technique used by technical divers is *mental imagery*. Before entering the water, the diver sits quietly with eyes closed and imagines, as vividly as possible, making the dive. This lets the diver anticipate what's likely to happen, and deal with any problems in a calm, considered and deliberate manner. Should any of these problems actually occur during the dive, he'll be better able to handle the situation as he has, in a sense, practiced overcoming the problem before the dive. In addition, the imaging technique might help avoid the common problem of "task fixation," where-in concentrating so hard on overcoming one problem, the diver forgets about something else. An example might be fixating on adjusting a buckle, but forgetting to check your air supply. Mental imagery is also an aid to relaxation, and helps prevent starting your dive in an overly anxious mental state.

The effects of nitrogen narcosis are insidious. The early stages are virtually imperceptible; and by the time signs do become obvious to a buddy, the victim can be beyond the point of helping him or herself. Proper planning, preparation and awareness can prepare you to deal with the condition, and might even somewhat help you stave off the effects. But no matter what anyone tells you, everyone is affected. It's just a matter of when and where.

CHAPTER 17

Every Breath You Take:
Asthma and Diving

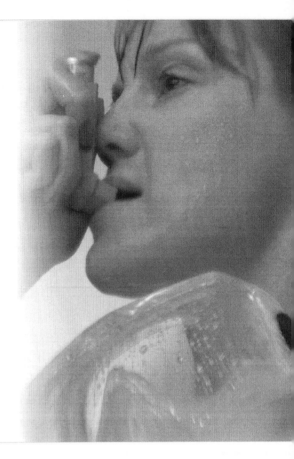

When I was a kid in the 1950s,

I had a friend who lived a few doors down from me who seemed always to be sick. Certainly, he missed more school than anyone I knew, and he was rarely able to take part in the daily baseball or football game that sprung up on the vacant lot behind my house every afternoon.

I asked my mom once why Allen was sick so much, and she explained that he had something called asthma. As a result, asthma was to me a very serious but rare condition, because in my entire childhood experience, poor old Allen was the only kid who I knew who had the disorder. Well, if you're the parents of children today, you know that that's no longer the case; asthma is now a very common disease, though more so in some communities than others. The statistics are nothing short of alarming. Asthma is one of the most prevalent medical conditions in existence, affecting more than 300 million people worldwide. In the United States it has increased by more than 75 percent since 1980 alone, and today more than 10 percent of all children in America have it. In many economically disadvantaged communities, the number more than doubles. Annually it accounts for about 5,000 deaths, a half-million hospitalizations and 2 million emergency room visits. And it costs our national economy more than $14 billion annually.

Of course, with such a large portion of the population affected by the disease, it's inevitable that some of these folks are divers or interested in becoming certified. And, indeed, diving and asthma has been at the center of diving medical discussions and debate for decades. But what, exactly, are the issues when it comes to diving? What are the special concerns for diving? Should asthmatics even dive at all? These are but a few of the questions the dive community has wrestled with as what some have described as the "asthma crisis" continues to rage throughout society.

Some Background

Asthma is a complex disease that's influenced by genetics, as well as a multitude of interacting developmental and environmental factors. It's a chronic or recurring inflammatory condition in which the airways develop increased responsiveness to various stimuli, characterized by bronchial hyper-responsiveness, inflammation, increased mucus production, and intermittent airway obstruction. The symptoms of asthma, which can range from mild to life-threatening, normally can be controlled with a combination of drugs and lifestyle changes.

Regardless of the current seeming epidemic, asthma has been with us for a very long time. The word asthma, from the Greek *aazein* ("sharp breath") first appeared in Homer's Iliad. The father of medicine, Hippocrates, was

Recommendations From the Undersea and Hyperbaric Medical Society

■ Exercise or cold-induced asthmatics should not dive.

■ Asthmatics requiring "rescue or reliever" medication should not dive. Asthmatics on chronic maintenance bronchodilation ("controller") and inhaled steroids are thought to be able to dive.

■ Mild to moderate asthmatics with normal screening spirometry can be considered candidates for diving. (FEV1/FVC ratio above 85 percent of predicted)

■ If an asthmatic has an attack, screening spirometry should be done and the individual should not dive until his airway function returns to normal.

Finally, it might be that our fears about the dangers of asthmatics diving have been overstated and that there is a sizable group of asthmatics who can dive at an acceptable level of risk.

A copy of the workshop on asthma and diving, "Are Asthmatics Fit to Dive?" can be obtained from the Undersea and Hyperbaric Medical Society, 10531 Metropolitan Ave., Kensington, MD 20895. The cost is $20 plus $2.50 additional for postage and handling.

Recommendations From the United Kingdom Sport Diving Medical Committee

■ Asthma may predispose to air-trapping leading to pulmonary barotrauma and air embolism, which may be fatal. An acute asthma attack can also cause severe dyspnoea (difficult or labored breathing), which may be hazardous or fatal during diving. These theoretical risks should be explained fully to the asthmatic diver. There is little if any evidence that the mild controlled asthmatic who follows the guidelines below is at more risk.

■ Asthmatics may dive if they have allergic asthma but not if they have cold, exercise or emotion-induced asthma.

■ All asthmatics should be managed in accordance with British Thoracic Society Guidelines.

■ Only well-controlled asthmatics may dive.

■ Asthmatics should not dive if he/she has needed a therapeutic bronchodilator in the last 48 hours or has had any other chest symptoms.

Control of the Condition:

■ The asthmatic should not need more than occasional bronchodilators, i.e., daily usage would be a disqualifying factor, but inhaled steroids/cromoglycate/nedocromil are permissible. During the diving season he/she should take twice-daily peak flow measurements. A deviation of 10 percent from best values should exclude diving until within 10 percent of best values for at least 48 hours before diving.

■ The medical examiner should perform an exercise test such as the 18-inch (43 cm) step test for three minutes, or running outside (not a bicycle ergometer) to increase the heart rate to 80 percent (210-age). A decrease in PEFR (peak respiratory flow rate) of 15 percent at three minutes post-exercise should be taken as evidence of exercise-induced bronchoconstriction and hence disbars.

■ The patient should be off all bronchodilators for 24 hours before the test.

■ A beta-2 agonist may be taken prediving as a preventive but not to relieve bronchospasm at the time.

the first person to use it in reference to the medical condition. Hippocrates even noted that *aazein* seemed to be associated with one's occupation, observing it mostly in tailors, fishermen and metalworkers. Six centuries later, another famed Greek physician of the Roman era, Galen, wrote that it was caused by partial or complete bronchial obstruction. In the 17th century, an Italian doctor named Bernardino Ramazzini noted a connection between asthma and organic dust, but there was no treatment for the disease until the 20th century. And, in fact, not until the 1960s was the mechanism of the disease understood well enough to enable the development of medications to treat it.

As Galen noted, asthma is characterized by blocked or narrowed airways causing breathing difficulty. But it occurs in two forms: allergic (extrinsic) asthma and nonallergic (intrinsic). The allergic form is triggered by an immune reaction, and is partially reversible with medication. This is the most common form, affecting more than half of the 20 million asthma sufferers in the United States. The nonallergic form presents many of the same symptoms as the allergic form, such as coughing, wheezing, shortness of breath or rapid breathing, and chest tightness. The difference is what triggers the attacks. The triggers for the allergic form is an inhaled allergen. Triggers can include common household insect droppings from pests such as dust mites and cockroaches, grass pollen, mold spores and pet dander. Air pollution is also a trigger, particularly ozone, nitrogen dioxide and sulfur dioxide. In fact, air pollution is what's currently believed responsible for the high prevalence of asthma in urban areas. There are also other chemical triggers such as sulfites, and various byproducts of chlorinated swimming pools.

The nonallergic form is triggered by factors not related to allergies such as anxiety, stress, exercise, cold air, dry air, hyperventilation, smoke, viruses or other irritants. Nor is there an immune system involvement in nonallergic asthma.

Exercise-induced asthma, or EIA, is a poorly understood condition characterized by shortness of breath induced by sustained aerobic exercise. It shows many of the same features as other types of asthma, and also responds to many common asthma medications. However, it does not appear to be caused by the same inflammatory reaction as the other types. While science doesn't yet have a full insight into EIA, it usually occurs after sustained and vigorous aerobic exercise, which demands that normal nasal breathing be supplemented by mouth breathing.

This is important because researchers believe that EIA is initiated by air inhaled through the mouth, which hasn't been warmed and humidified by the nasal passages. This, it's hypothesized, generates increased blood flow to the linings of the bronchial tree, resulting in edema (excess fluid collecting in tissues of the body). Then, as constriction of the bronchial vessels worsens, the degree of airway obstruction increases. EIA can be especially insidious in the way it can reoccur. For reasons not yet understood, 6-10 hours after an initial attack, a rebound attack with milder symptoms often develops without precipitating exertion.

What About Diving?

Clearly, the triggers for some forms of asthma, such as heavy exercise and breathing cold air, cannot be ignored, as they're commonly encountered conditions in diving. Furthermore, the symptoms of asthma, such as breathing difficulty and airway obstruction, can be life-threatening to divers, even at shallow depths. While asthmatics might experience broncho-constriction due to more than one trigger, many will experience a measurable increase in breathing resistance after exposure to any one or several. In addition, increased breathing resistance caused by bronchial narrowing can be compounded by mucus accumulation within the airways. All of these conditions are potential triggers for a lung expansion injury such as an arterial gas embolism.

The issue of reduced breathing capacity is no small concern for asthmatics. Even completely healthy and fit divers experience a reduction in breathing capacity due simply to the effects of immersion, and an increase in breathing resistance from compressed air. For example, at 33 feet (10 m), the maximum breathing capacity of a healthy scuba diver is only 70 percent of the surface value. At 100 feet (30 m), this is reduced to only about 50 percent. Of course, if a diver's breathing capacity is already reduced due to asthma, there's a very real danger that there might not be a sufficient reserve to accommodate the increase in breathing demanded caused by exertion. So, it's no surprise that for many years asthma was considered an absolute contraindication to scuba diving; if you had asthma, or at least admitted it on your medical history form, you could not become a diver.

However, in the late 1980s this attitude began to change. Medical authorities, advocacy organizations and even world-class athletes who had asthma began to seriously question the complete exclusion of asthmatics from diving. They pointed to essentially three issues as to why a simply blanket prohibition wasn't justified. First, asthma is a condition with a wide range in both the frequency and severity of symptoms. So, when used without precise definition or description, the term "asthma" might mean different things to different people. Second, despite sound theoretical objections to allowing asthmatics to dive, there was no empirical evidence that asthmatic scuba divers had an increased accident rate over nonasthmatic divers. And lastly, there are legitimate differences in philosophy among physicians and scuba professionals about personal risk taking. What constitutes "too much" risk is largely a subjective issue.

It is important to note that asthma severity can wax and wane. Symptoms might worsen for four to six weeks

For More Information

Wolf SL, Twarog F, Weiler JM, Barron RJ, Lang DM, Wells JH, Zitt M, Virant FS, Katz RM, Banyash LW, et al. "Discussion of risk of scuba diving in individuals with allergic and respiratory diseases: SCUBA Subcommittee." *Journal of Allergy and Clinical Immunology*. 1995 Dec: 96 (6, Pt. 1): 871-3

after a cold or during certain seasons (for example, in response to high levels of pollen in the air). Therefore, even if a person with asthma fits within the acceptable range, diving is not recommended unless the diver is free of respiratory symptoms before each dive.

One diving medical expert who agrees that asthmatics deserve more than a blanket "no diving" is pulmonologist Dr. Lawrence Martin. "Such a broad prohibition flies in the face of reality," Martin says in his book *Scuba Diving Explained*, "since it includes a large group of people with a history of asthma who, in fact, dive often and without any problem." On the other hand, Martin says, any asthmatic who is constantly wheezing and coughing should obviously not scuba dive. So where should we draw the line between a remote history of asthma and active disease? Not, according to Martin, at some arbitrary point based on, for example, the need for medication. "If there is a line to draw somewhere, it should be based on individual evaluation as opposed to something as arbitrary as five years or two days without symptoms. There can be no rule about diving that fits all asthmatics, except for the no-brainer that if you never dive you'll never have a diving accident. Ultimately the 'line' for diving vs. no diving should be based on a thorough evaluation of the individual, and not on any arbitrary and unproven criteria." These are, indeed, powerful words coming from a physician who specializes in lung disorders.

Martin is correct in stating that there's little evidence to support a blanket restriction for asthmatics, as there's been no statistically valid, published study that definitively shows that the accident rate for asthmatic divers is any higher than for the rest of the diving population. An informal reader survey, done in 1990 by a British dive magazine, did show some intriguing results. For example, 89 of the 104 asthmatic divers who responded indicated that they'd had the disorder since childhood; 70 reported wheezing spells fewer than 12 times a year, but 22 said that they wheezed daily. The cumulative experience level for the entire group was 12,864 dives, and none had suffered any lung expansion injury. Just one diver reported decompression sickness. Interestingly, 96 of the divers reported using an asthma inhaler just before diving, and some were also using preventive medication such as steroids.

Another informal survey conducted in Diver Alert Network's *Alert Diver* magazine had responses from 279 asthmatic divers. Of these, 88.7 percent reported taking some medication for the condition, and 55.8 percent took medication just prior to diving. Of this group, just over 26 percent had a history of hospitalization for asthma. The cumulative experience for this group was 56,334 dives. However, 11 cases of decompression illness (AGE or DCS) were reported in eight individuals, or 1 in 5,100 dives. According to the report, this "significantly exceeded" the estimated risk for recreational divers by a factor of 4.16. Thus, it concluded that "the risk of decompression illness is higher in the surveyed asthmatics than in an unselected recreational diving population."

However, one shouldn't take too much stock in informal surveys such as these, as they are fraught with validity problems. Bias creeps in by many routes. For example, they include only asthmatics who continue to dive and maintain enough interest to read scuba magazines, making the studies underrepresent asthma-related problems because they don't count asthmatics who stop diving. Additionally, many asthmatic divers do not admit that they have the disorder, which means this population is also under-represented. Finally, reader surveys such as these do not permit comparisons such as divers who have or have not had accidents, the severity of their asthma, level of control with medication, and reason for any predive medication (prevention vs. treatment of symptoms). And surveys don't reveal characteristics about the kind of diving in which the respondents engage.

So What's a Diver to Do?

As a result of all the controversy, confusion and uncertainty, a workshop on asthma and diving was held in 1995 under the auspices of the Undersea and Hyperbaric Medical Society (UHMS). For the first time, medical experts did not suggest uniformly dismissing asthmatics from diving, but instead proposed a set of guidelines (see "Medical Recommendations for Diving With Asthma" on Page 130). The consensus of the group was that the risk of diving for asthmatics is probably acceptable if the diving candidate demonstrates normal pulmonary function at rest, and then again after strenuous exercise. It was also concluded that the "degree of competency in making a medical assessment of diving fitness is enhanced if the examining doctor has relevant knowledge or experience of the diving environment and its associated hazards."

So what does this all mean? Clearly, from the data currently available, we simply don't yet know whether asthmatics experience a greater risk from diving than do nonasthmatics. As in any activity that involves risk, prudence dictates that one be made aware of those risks, understand any limitation or uncertainty about the level of scientific understanding of those risks, and before participating have a thorough evaluation done by a knowledgeable physician to assess where you stand on the risk continuum. But in the final analysis, it's an individual decision whether or not to proceed. Certainly, many people with asthma have taken the plunge into diving, and many more will continue to do so. What's important is that asthmatic divers understand the special considerations their disease presents, which could have a detrimental physiologic consequence while diving. The decision of whether an asthmatic should pursue diving, like most important decisions in life, isn't black and white, but gray. Just be sure that, if you make the decision to dive, you do so fully informed. 🐬

CHAPTER 18

How Sweet It Is:
Diving With Diabetes

Having been a scuba

instructor since Nixon was in office, I'm happy to say that the good experiences have far outweighed the bad. In fact, I've had very few bad experiences in my career. For example, in all that time — with more than 5,000 dives under my belt — I've never once been involved with or even witnessed a serious diving accident. Actually, my worst experiences have come not from training divers, but from not training them. Occasionally, I'd encounter someone whom I simply could not accept into my course because of some pre-existing medical condition to which folks who knew far more than I about these matters, said, "no way." Luckily such conditions are few and far between; and whether some conditions even warrant disqualification as a diver is a source of contention.

One condition that has long fit into this category is diabetes. Should diabetics dive? And if so, what special considerations, procedures and guidelines should they follow? A lot has happened recently to help answer these questions.

Some Background

Before addressing diabetes in the context of diving, let's look at the disease itself. First, the correct term is diabetes mellitus, and it's a metabolic disorder affecting how our bodies metabolize carbohydrates. As you probably know, our cells use the sugar glucose for fuel, but to metabolize this fuel we need the hormone insulin. In diabetics, either the pancreas fails to secrete enough insulin or the body's cells resist entry of insulin. This allows dangerous levels of glucose to build up in the blood, temporarily starving the cells of energy. The primary characteristics of the disease are persistent high glucose blood sugar (hyperglycemia). Diabetes currently isn't curable, but it is manageable after proper diagnosis, treatment and lifestyle changes.

The term diabetes, coined by Aretaeus of Cappadocia, is from the Greek *diabaínein* meaning "passing through." The name is based on a major symptom of diabetes — excessive urine production. The more complete descriptor, diabetes mellitus, (mellitus is Latin for "honeyed" or "sweetened") was added in 1675 by Thomas Willis when he noted that the blood and urine of a diabetic had a sweet taste (yeah, tasting the urine was a common practice back then). In Western medicine, it was Matthew Dobson who, in 1776, confirmed that "mellitus" was, in fact, from an excess of sugar in the urine and blood. However, this wasn't a new observation, as it was already known to the ancient Greeks, Chinese, Egyptians and Indians. In fact, millennia before Europeans had a clue, physicians in India tested for diabetes by observing whether ants were attracted to a person's urine, and, as a result, called the ailment "sweet urine disease" (Madhumehalai).

Diabetes comes in three forms, termed types 1, 2 and 3. In Type 1 the pancreas is unable to produce insulin. It's also known as insulin-requiring diabetes mellitus (IRDM), and was referred to as juvenile onset diabetes. In Type 2 diabetes, the body is unable to use insulin properly. This is also known as noninsulin-requiring diabetes mellitus (NIRDM), and was called mature on-set diabetes. Type 3 or gestational diabetes develops in 3 percent to 5 percent of women during pregnancy, but usually resolves during recovery.

The three forms of diabetes are more accurately viewed as patterns of pancreatic failure rather than separate diseases. Type 1 is generally due to autoimmune destruction of the insulin-producing cells, while Type 2 and Type 3 are due to insulin resistance by tissues. Complicating matters further, Type 2 can progress to destruction of the insulin-producing cells of the pancreas — a characteristic of Type 1 — but is still considered Type 2, even though insulin administration might be required.

Since the therapeutic use of insulin began in the 1920s, diabetes has become a chronic but treatable condition. Its major health risks tend to be progressive damage to the eyes, kidneys, heart (doubling of the risk for cardiovascular disease) or peripheral nerves. Signs and symptoms of diabetes can include intense hunger, thirst and tiredness, weight loss, frequent urination, blurred vision, and even seizures and coma. Today, in the developed world, diabetes is the main cause for dialysis, as well as blindness in nonelderly adults.

The risk of having or developing diabetes increases with the number the predisposition factors present. These factors include age (over 45 years), obesity (particularly if carrying most excess weight at the waist); poor diet; family history; race (highest for Black, American Indian, Asian-American, Pacific Islander, Hispanic-American/Latino); a history of gestational diabetes; high blood pressure (> 140/90 mmHg); low high density lipoproteins (HDL) (< 35 mg/dL; 1.9 mmol/L); high triglycerides (> 250 mg/dL; 13.9 mmol/L) and limited regular exercise (< three times per week).

Diabetes is estimated to affect about 21 million people in the United States, with more than a million insulin dependent. But what's more alarming is that the condition is undiagnosed in one-third of the cases. Still, perhaps the most disturbing statistics is that as much as 14 percent of our population demonstrates what doctors call "impaired glucose homeostasis (balance)," also known as a prediabetic state. This group is likely to develop the disease within 10 years.

Clearly, millions of people live normal, productive lives with diabetes, so why all the fuss over scuba diving with the disease? The greatest potential risk for divers is having what's termed a "hypoglycemic episode" while underwater. Hypoglycemia (hypo=under) occurs when the glucose content of the blood falls dangerously low. This can happen for a variety of reasons, including too much insulin, too little food, or from stress (including exercise). What's more, even in well-controlled diabetics these episodes are extremely unpredictable. And making matters worse for divers, the early warning signals of an episode — tremor, sweating, chills, irritability, nervousness and hunger — can be easily overlooked or difficult to interpret while diving.

Yet the problem isn't just hypoglycemia; diabetics are at risk of high blood glucose (hyperglycemia), too. This occurs when insulin runs low enough that the body breaks down stored fat for energy. Like in hypoglycemia, this can cause breathing difficulty, alteration or loss of consciousness and shock.

Indeed, underwater isn't a place you'd want to be when suffering from these conditions, so it's easy to see why for many years most medical authorities simply wrote diabetics off as bad risks for diving. Fuel was added to the "no diving" fire in 1972 when a fatality was reported from Britain involving a diabetic diver (resulting in a ban on diving by diabetics in the United Kingdom).

A Changing View

When I began teaching scuba back in the dark ages, there were relatively few diabetic divers. One reason was that all diving candidates had to receive medical clearance from a doctor before being accepted into a course. So, almost everyone with any form of serious medical disorder was barred from diving, unless they wanted to dive badly enough to forge a physician's signature. Second, back then, the entire attitude toward diabetes was different. There were no famous diabetic athletes (at least, none who would confess to having the condition). It was just assumed, and rarely challenged, that a diagnosis of diabetes was an automatic disqualification from any so-called "high-risk" activity such as scuba diving.

By the 1980s the medical evaluation process for divers in the United States changed. No longer was a medical clearance by a physician required in all cases; only those who answered affirmatively to questions on a form had to secure such approval. Likewise, diabetic athletes were becoming very public about their disease, and questioning the medical rationale for the many prohibitions that diabetics faced in entering high-risk activities. It was becoming clear that, through good management of their condition, otherwise healthy individuals with diabetes were capable of elite athletic performance. In the diving community, this rising consciousness about the disease led many diabetics to "forget" about their condition when it came time to complete their medical history form, thus avoiding a physician's approval to pursue scuba training.

Over the next few years, a growing but unknown number of diabetics were actively diving. But the real surprise came when folks starting looking at causes of diving accidents; the analyses showed consistently that diabetes didn't seem to be a factor. Finally, some diving medical authorities were intrigued enough to abandon their steadfast and absolute "no way" position, and say "well, maybe."

Another crack in the dam was the aforementioned diving accident from the United Kingdom involving a diabetic. In the early 1990s, the case was re-examined and it was found that the disease in no way contributed to the accident. Around the same time, various organizations began anonymous surveys of diabetics who continued to dive despite the ban, and not one case was found in which someone suffered hypoglycemic attacks while diving. Based on these new insights, the British Sub Aqua Club (BSAC) began accepting diabetics as diving candidates in 1992, provided that they met certain medical criteria.

In 1993, the Divers Alert Network (DAN) distributed a survey to the recreational diving community through its *Alert Diver* magazine designed to gather data from active divers with diabetes. In total, 164 divers with diabetes responded, with 79 percent (129) reporting insulin-requiring diabetes mellitus (IRDM). Collectively, the group completed 27,000 dives, for an average of 165 dives per participant. There were reports of some symptoms of hypoglycemia but no unconsciousness. However, perhaps the most significant finding was that there was not one report of a major complication (an event requiring emergency intervention). The survey also verified what was obvious; most respondents stated that they never admitted to being diabetic to their dive instructors or dive leaders (and often not even to their buddies).

In 1996, DAN analyzed 550 diving fatalities reported from 1989 to 1994. It found that seven victims had diabetes mellitus, and that it might have contributed to their deaths. In terms of decompression sickness, they also reported that of the 2,400 cases, eight involved diabetics. They concluded that these incidence rates were consistent with those expected in the general population of divers.

What Research Says

Realizing that much of the research conducted on diabetes and diving had been based on surveys of past diving history, DAN embarked on a multiyear research project in 1997. The results of which were published in 2004. The study was conducted on a number of DAN-sponsored dive trips at many popular diving destinations. It included only certified, adult divers, both with IRDM and, for control purposes, those without. The IRDM divers provided detailed medical histories before the trip to confirm that they had no secondary complications of diabetes, and had not been hospitalized within the past 12 months for severe hypoglyce-

The HbA1c test (hemoglobin A1c test, glycosylated hemoglobin A1c test, glycohemoglobin A1c test, or A1c test) is a lab test, which reveals average blood glucose over two to three months. Specifically, it measures the number of glucose molecules attached to hemoglobin. The test takes advantage of the lifecycle of red blood cells. Although constantly replaced, individual cells live for about four months. So by measuring attached glucose in a current blood sample, average blood sugar levels over the previous two to three months can be determined. HbA1c test results are expressed as a percentage, with 4 percent to 6 percent considered normal. The HbA1c "big picture" complements the day-to-day "snapshots" obtained from the self-monitoring of blood glucose (mg/dl). The risk of secondary complications of diabetes is dramatically reduced by long-term efforts to keep HbA1c levels as close to the normal range as possible.

Source: Divers Alert Network

What Is HbA1c?

Selection and Surveillance

- Age more than 18 years (more than 16 years if in special training program).
- Delay diving after start/change in medication.
  - Three months with oral hypoglycemic agents (OHA).
  - One year after initiation of insulin therapy.
- No episodes of hypoglycemia or hyperglycemia requiring intervention from a third party for at least one year.
- No history of hypoglycemia unawareness.
- HbA1c less than 9 percent no more than one month prior to initial assessment and at each annual review.
  - Values more than 9 percent indicate the need for further evaluation and possible modification of therapy.
- No significant secondary complications from diabetes.
- Physician/diabetologist should carry out annual review and determine that diver has good understanding of disease and effect of exercise.
  - In consultation with an expert in diving medicine, as required.
- Evaluation for silent ischemia for candidates more than 40 years of age.
  - After initial evaluation, periodic surveillance for silent ischemia can be in accordance with accepted local/national guidelines for the evaluation of diabetics.
- Candidate documents intent to follow protocol for divers with diabetes and to cease diving and seek medical review for any adverse events during diving possibly related to diabetes.

Scope of Diving

- Diving should be planned to avoid:
  - Depths >100 fsw (30 msw).
  - Durations >60 minutes.
  - Compulsory decompression stops.
  - Overhead environments (e.g., cave, wreck penetration).
  - Situations that may exacerbate hypoglycemia (e.g., prolonged cold and arduous dives).
- Dive buddy/leader informed of diver's condition and steps to follow in case of problem.
- Dive buddy should not have diabetes.

Glucose Management On the Day of Diving

- General self-assessment of fitness to dive.
- Blood glucose (BG) ≥150 mg·dL-1 (8.3 mmol·L-1), stable or rising, before entering the water
  - Complete a minimum of three predive BG tests to evaluate trends.
    - 60 minutes, 30 minutes and immediately prior to diving.
  - Alterations in dosage of OHA or insulin on evening prior or day of diving may help.
- Delay dive if BG.
  - <150 mg·dL-1 (8.3 mmol·L-1).
  - >300 mg·dL-1 (16.7 mmol·L-1).
- Rescue medications.
  - Carry readily-accessible oral glucose during all dives.
  - Have parenteral glucagon available at the surface.
- If hypoglycemia noticed underwater, the diver should surface (with buddy), establish positive buoyancy, ingest glucose and leave the water.
- Check blood sugar frequently for 12-15 hours after diving.
- Ensure adequate hydration on days of diving.
- Log all dives (include BG test results and all information pertinent to diabetes management).

mia or ketoacidosis (a serious condition that can lead to diabetic coma). Furthermore, the IRDM divers had to document a good understanding of the dynamic relationship between plasma glucose and exercise, and had to have an HbA1c test of less than 9 percent within the two weeks preceding the trip. (See "What is HbA1c?" on Page 139.) In terms of their experience, IRDM divers had been diving for a mean of almost nine years and had diabetes for a mean of more than 15 years.

During the study, plasma glucose (PG) monitoring was conducted at intervals of 60, 30 and 10 minutes before every dive, and then immediately after the dive. Data loggers were worn by all participants to record time/depth profiles; and divers provided subjective ratings of physical effort and thermal comfort during each dive. The type and quantity of food eaten by the divers was recorded, as was any adverse or unusual event — whether it was related to diving or not. In total, the study included 83 divers (40 IRDM/43 controls) and involved 1,059 dives (555 IRDM/504 controls). The incidence of hypoglycemia (PG less than 70 mg/dL) was 7 percent of IRDM dives (37/555) and 1 percent of control dives (6/504).

In the end, no symptoms or complications related to hypoglycemia were reported (or observed) during any of the dives. Post-dive plasma glucose fell below 70 mg/dL^{-1} in 7 percent (37/555) of the IRDM group dives compared with 1 percent (6/504) of the controls. Moderate levels of hyperglycemia were also noted in 23 divers with IRDM on 84 occasions. The study concluded that, "While large plasma glucose swings from predive to post-dive were noted, our observations indicate that plasma glucose levels, in moderately controlled IRDM, can be managed to avoid hypoglycemia during routine recreational dives under ordinary environmental conditions and low-risk decompression profiles."

New Issues and Responses

By 2005, a new picture of diving with diabetes was emerging, in part based on a change in the legal climate. By then, the United Kingdom allowed medical clearance to diabetics for both recreational and occupational diving; and numerous recreational dive programs, specifically for persons with diabetes, had been around for more than a decade. It was clear that anti-discrimination laws in many countries, such as the Americans With

Disabilities Act, would have direct application to people with diabetes. And especially in light of the American Diabetes Association position to support claims of occupational discrimination against people with diabetes, including cases involving diving, a new review of the issues was overdue.

On June 19, 2005, a workshop jointly sponsored by DAN and the Undersea and Hyperbaric Medical Society (UHMS) was held in Las Vegas. The program brought together more than 50 diabetes experts and interested parties — mostly clinicians and researchers — from around the world. Their task was to come to a consensus agreement on appropriate guidelines for diving with diabetes. In the end, the workshop concluded that candidates for diving who use medication — either oral hypoglycemic agents (OHAs) or insulin — to treat diabetes but who are otherwise qualified to dive may undertake recreational scuba diving, provided certain criteria are met. The consensus guidelines consist of 19 points, under the categories of selection and surveillance, scope of diving, and glucose management on the day of diving. (A one-page summary of guidelines is provided on Page 140.) The full workshop proceedings, available from DAN, include a 136-page document that contains not only the guidelines, but all the papers that were presented, and condensed workshop discussions.

If you're interested in learning more about diving and diabetes, and you have about 45 minutes to spare, check out the Divers Alert Network's free online seminar, "Diabetes & Recreational Diving: History and New Guidelines." Log on to www.diversalertnetwork.org/training/onlineseminars and scroll down.

For More Information

Clearly, we've come a long way since I began my teaching career in our understanding of whether and how diving and diabetes can mix. The disease has gone from a secret rarely discussed to a topic in mainstream diving medicine. The number of diabetic divers has grown from a small handful to thousands all over the world. But make no mistake about it. Diving with diabetes requires that one understand their condition, have it well controlled, accept the limitations it imposes and follow the necessary special procedures. Equally important, diving with diabetes requires an understanding that it's not just the diabetic diver who could be at risk. Dive leaders and buddies, too, need to be informed and properly trained in how to deal with a diabetic incident. So, in the end, diving with diabetes is, in a sense, no different from diving under any other circumstance. Your own safety, as well as that of your buddy, depends on good judgment, thorough preparation and a good understanding of what you're getting yourself into. 🤿

CHAPTER 19

Diving Over the Counter:
How What's In Your Drug Store Can Hurt You

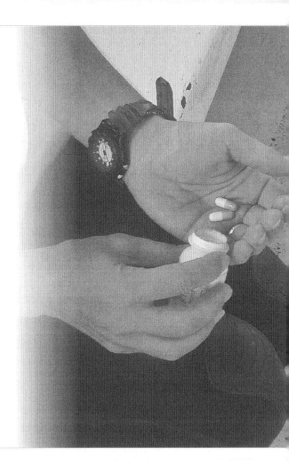

One can make a pretty convincing argument

that Western society is addicted to drugs. And I don't just mean the illicit kind. The simple act of watching TV — particularly the evening news, which skews toward an older demographic — will prove the point beyond question. I'll wager that a good portion of the commercials you'll see will try to sell you some type of drug, or at east entice you to beg your doctor for one. Whether it's acid reflux, high cholesterol, migraine headaches, incontinence, erectile dysfunction, depression, hemorrhoids or a combination thereof, the impression is that Americans clearly are in seriously bad health. It's a wonder that any of us can even get out of bed in the morning, let alone manage to live functioning lives.

Another trend of our drug-addicted society is that more and more of these pharmacological wonders are being made available without a prescription or, in the parlance of the drug industry, over-the-counter (OTC). And, of course, thousands of drugs that never required a prescription have long been available to anyone with money to pay for them. According to one source, more than 60 percent of all medications purchased by Americans are OTC, and this is growing by nearly 10 percent per year. While there are more than 65,000 prescription medications, that number pales in comparison with the more than 300,000 OTC drugs.

Perhaps the greatest potential danger of an OTC drug isn't what it can do to us but the attitude it may instill. Many misinformed folks think that, if a drug doesn't require a doctor's prescription, then it really can't do much of any harm. Of course, this belief is belied by the warning labels on every OTC medication in existence, but that assumes — quite naively — that people bother to read them.

While most of the time we tend to get away with this nonchalant attitude, the outcome can be dramatic when you combine OTC medications, no matter how seemingly innocuous, with diving. While it's impossible to address the thousands of drugs available over the counter, there are certain drug classes that warrant special attention due to their ubiquity and common use by divers.

No Prescription, No Problem

Hypochondriacs aside, folks take medications for a reason. While that might sound absurdly self-evident, it's an important point often overlooked by divers. A minor medical issue, such as mild hay fever, can seem like nothing but a small inconvenience to the average land-dweller, but for a diver it can be a serious concern. The same can be said for other common conditions such as a minor cough or cold, an upset stomach, heartburn or a headache. Certainly, these are conditions we just take in stride in everyday life, and think nothing of popping a pill to help relieve the symptoms. Yet, the consequences of self-medicating while diving can lead to serious and sometimes life-threatening outcomes.

Let's begin with one simple fact: No drug is completely safe because drugs are chemicals designed to alter body functions. Hopefully, this alteration will serve some therapeutic function, but there are no guarantees. What's more, virtually all drugs have side effects that can be highly variable among individuals and equally variable under differing environmental conditions. And especially relevant for divers is the fact that very few OTC medications have ever been studied in a hyperbaric environment.

Even a fool would agree that 90 feet (27 m) underwater is no place to deal with the unpredictable effects of a medication. So, as a diver, you should ask yourself two questions before taking any OTC medication: 1) Could the underlying reason for which I'm taking the drug compromise my safety or that of my buddy?; and 2) Am I fully aware of the side effects of the drug I'm about to take, and have I experienced those or similar effects when taking this drug previously? (This, of course, implies that you should never take any drug for the first time prior to diving.)

Good to the Last Drop

To complicate matters even further, there are circumstances when we aren't even aware that we're taking a drug. Take caffeine, for example. Given the enormous quantity that's consumed, and the central role it plays in many of our lives, it might seem strange to consider caffeine in a discussion of drugs. But make no mistake; it is a very powerful chemical compound that can have significant consequences — both positive and negative — on how your body functions underwater.

First, some chemistry. The term "caffeine" is often used to describe that substance itself along with a whole group of related compounds called methylxanthines. These occur naturally in coffee beans, tea leaves, chocolate, cocoa beans and cola nuts, as well as some other foods. Furthermore, methylxanthines are commonly added to carbonated beverages and many medications. As a result, it's almost impossible, even if we try, for us to avoid caffeine or even know how much we consume each day.

Physiologically, most of the caffeine that we consume is rapidly absorbed in the stomach, reaching a peak concentration in most individuals about an hour after it's ingested, although in some folks it can take up to three hours. Like tissue compartments in decompression models, the elimination of a drug is described in terms of halftimes; and the halftime for caffeine can range from three to seven hours. In other words, the maximum effect occurs about one hour after consumption, and every three to seven hours half of the remaining amount will be eliminated from the body. This means that you'll still retain 25 percent of the drug even six to 14 hours after drinking a caffeinated beverage. Note that the effect is highly variable, and some who consume moderate amounts of caffeine on a regular basis can become somewhat resistant to its effects.

Furthermore, quite a few drugs — including some antibiotics — can interfere with the caffeine elimination, which may serve to magnify its effects. On the other hand, smoking actually speeds up the elimination of caffeine by stimulating the liver, where it's metabolized. And women should be especially careful about caffeine intake, as it inhibits the absorption of calcium, and could become a factor in promoting osteoporosis.

Some of the effects of caffeine are well-known while others aren't so familiar. Its primary effect is stimulation of the central nervous system (CNS), which is the primary reason we consume it. However, caffeine also increases the effectiveness of painkilling medications, which is why it's often added to painkillers (analgesics) that are often described as "extra strength." Additionally, part of its CNS effect stimulates breathing, it's assumed, by enhancing the sensitivity of the medullary respiratory center (the breathing control center in the brain) to carbon dioxide. But its effects don't stop there.

Caffeine increases the heart rate, the force of cardiac contractions and thus the amount of blood output. In some especially sensitive individuals, it can even cause an irregular heartbeat (arrhythmia). Also, it reduces flow of blood to the brain, which is why it can be useful for treating migraine headaches, and increases blood pressure. For women, it inhibits uterine contractions, which explains why it comprises more than 10 percent of the popular drug Midol® used for treating menstrual cramps.

The Caffeinated Diver

While the effects of caffeine are generally well known, less familiar is the effect it can have on us while diving. In fact, one of caffeine's most powerful effects is completely inconsequential except to divers. This involves the interaction it may have on oxygen toxicity, which given the popularity of enriched-air nitrox in recreational diving, could be a significant issue.

As it turns out, the mechanism of interaction is complex because caffeine can have the effect of either increasing or decreasing susceptibility to oxygen toxicity. On one hand, it can stimulate the brain, making one more susceptible. Yet, it also reduces blood flow to the brain, thereby possibly reducing oxygen delivery. The problem is that it's impossible to predict which of these two opposite effects will predominate in any given situation. Of course, the only prudent conclusion to make, given the uncertain nature, is that caffeine could increase your susceptiblity to oxygen toxicity. So, the only wise action is to avoid caffeine before a dive in which you might be exposed to high partial pressures of oxygen, like diving with nitrox near its maximum operating depth.

Another downside of caffeine is that it increases the secretion of digestive acids from the parietal cells of the stomach. This, of course, can lead to heartburn and could increase the likelihood of vomiting, which when it occurs at depth, presents the risk of drowning. For many folks, caffeine is a diuretic, so it can contribute to dehydration, (or make the life of dry suit divers miserable).

Still, the effects of caffeine aren't all negative. For instance, while it won't increase your maximum strength, caffeine will allow you to work longer at a moderately heavy rate by increasing the force of muscle contractions and reducing muscle fatigue. In fact, this increased force of muscle contraction — the diaphragm being a major muscle — combined with the aforementioned breathing stimulus is why caffeine is often used to enhance athletic performance. In part, this is because caffeine increases the proportion of energy derived from the metabolism of fat, which conserves the primary energy store, glycogen.

In the final analysis, consumption of a moderate amount of caffeine will probably not have much or any effect on your diving under normal circumstances. And if you feel that you drink caffeine in excess, it's important that you not stop cold turkey, as it can make you quite ill. Gradually reduce your intake to a moderate level and, as a diver, be mindful of its potential effects. In other words, use common sense.

Dealing With a Stuffy Head

As someone who has suffered from sinus congestion my entire life, I've always had great interest in the use of decongestants while diving. Certainly, I've used, and continue to use, my own fair share of pills, capsules and sprays. In fact, I keep a bottle of Afrin® in my save-a-dive kit. The reason decongestants are of great interest to divers is, of course, because if you can't equalize, you can't dive; end of story.

Congestion can be caused by a variety of conditions, such as the common cold or other infections, as well as allergic reactions such as hay fever (allergic rhinitis). The mechanism involves swelling of the mucous membranes that line the nose and sinuses — due to dilated and engorged blood vessels — along with excess production of mucous (which is produced by these same membranes). The result is blockage of the openings to the eight facial sinuses and/or the two eustachian tubes connecting the throat to the middle ears.

Most drugs used to treat congestion are called sympathomimetic agents, and stimulate the sympathetic nervous system. The sympathetic nervous system (SNS) — responsible for the "fight or flight" response — along with the parasympathetic nervous system (PNS) are subparts of what's termed the autonomic nervous system (nerves that cannot be controlled by the mind). The two systems work in balance with each other and directly or indirectly affect almost every structure in the body. One author describes the sympathetic nervous system as having an active "pushing" function, while the parasympathetic has mainly a relaxing function. Generally, the SNS involves increases in sweating, heart rate, blood sugar, and temperature in response to stimuli. The PNS acts in the opposite direction and opposes SNS input. Activation of the SNS is by way of the hormones epinephrine (adrenaline) and norepinephrine (noradrenaline). So, drugs that are chemically similar to epinephrine or norepinephrine can also activate the SNS. Some of the drugs that can do this are ephedrine (currently banned in the United States), pseudoephedrine, phenylephrine, phenylpropanolamine and oxymetazoline. Another way to achieve the same result is with a drug that blocks the PNS response so the SNS activity is unopposed.

The net effect of these drugs is to cause blood vessels in the mucous membranes to shrink, thereby reducing any swelling. The major side effect of this class of drugs is their ability to increase heart rate and blood pressure. Another problem is that their effects are short-lived, lasting only about four to six hours. For divers this means that over the course of a day they may wear off, possibly while you're still at depth.

Pseudoephedrine, a key ingredient in Sudafed®, is a commonly used decongestant by divers. In fact, it's sometimes even abused. I've been on more than one dive boat where it was handed out like candy. However, it is one of the few decongestants that have been tested in divers. In one study, comparing it with a placebo in its ability to prevent middle ear squeeze, it was found that a 60-milligram dose administered 30 minutes before the dive was effective. This study was conducted to a depth of 40 feet (12 m), with objective data gathered only through otologic (ear) exam with side effects collected in a questionnaire.

To avoid systemic side effects like anxiety, trembling and rapid heart rate, some divers — me included — prefer to use topical nasal sprays. These have several advantages. First, as they're sprayed directly onto the mucous membranes, they start working very quickly. Second, the body absorbs only a small amount of the drug, thereby reducing the likelihood of side effects. And finally, many of these medications have an extended action, normally eight to 12 hours. However, nasal sprays do also pose a downside and that's, if they're used for more than three consecutive days, a rapid drug resistance (tachyphylaxis) occurs. The problem is that, rather than stopping the medication, people often use more to achieve the desired effect. There are also concerns over the potential for addiction to some nasal decongestants. As a result, many medical authorities recommend using simple saline mist sprays, though I've never found them very effective. And a problem with all nasal sprays is that, because of swelling, you may not be able to deliver the drug to some of the affected membranes.

No matter whether it's a spray or pill, if used excessively or too long, after stopping a decongestant the blood vessels will once again dilate, the mucous membranes will become engorged and mucous production will be increased. This is called a "rebound effect," and sometimes the return symptoms can be worse than the original. For a diver at depth, the inability to depressurize the sinus or middle ear can easily lead to an excruciatingly painful reverse squeeze on ascent. In extreme cases, a reverse squeeze can even cause rupture of the sinus into the space around the eye or the brain. The problem can be avoided by using the drugs only as directed, and for no longer than three consecutive days at a time. While it might be tempting to those, like myself, who suffer from chronic sinus problems, medical authorities warn that it's clearly a bad idea to get into the habit of taking a decongestant as a preventive measure when you're not congested.

Another potentially serious side effect of sympathomimetics is that they can interfere with the action of medications designed to lower blood pressure (antihypertensives). And they can do so in different ways. Some can reduce while still others elevate blood pressure. They also pose a serious risk from a rise in blood pressure for those taking, or who have taken within the past two weeks, a monoamine oxidase inhibitor. These are an older class of drugs used to treat depression.

...the relationships between drugs and diving:

■ Consider the condition/illness/disease for which the medication is being given. Go to the Scubadoc "Fitness to Dive" Web page (www.scuba-doc.com/fitdiv.html) to check if your condition could be dangerous underwater.

■ Determine if there are any effects of the drug that alter consciousness or decision-making ability.

■ Check in the linked Databases (www.scuba-doc.com/drugsdiv.html) for any side effects of the drug that could be dangerous underwater.

■ Consider complex relationships between drugs, the individual, other medications, diet and the conditions for which the drugs are taken.

Source: Scubadoc's Diving Medicine Online

As CNS stimulants, sympathomimetics can cause numerous side effects, such as nervousness, excitability, restlessness, dizziness, weakness and a forceful or rapid heartbeat. And despite the fact that these decongestants are CNS stimulants, they can actually cause drowsiness in some individuals. This condition can exacerbate the effects of nitrogen, making narcosis more severe or occur at shallower depths than usual. As a result, if you take a decongestant or any other medication, and it makes you drowsy, you should not dive, period. At least one highly respected diving medical expert suggests that, even if drowsiness does not occur, any diver taking a decongestant should still limit their diving to relatively shallow depths.

Unfortunately, the downside of taking decongestants doesn't end with concerns over nitrogen narcosis. As with CNS stimulants, sympathomimetics can reduce your tolerance to high oxygen partial pressure, thus increasing your risk of acute oxygen toxicity. As the primary symptom of this form of oxygen toxicity is seizure, drowning is a virtual certainty unless you're wearing a full-face mask. To emphasize the seriousness of this, some military diving programs limit divers to a depth of 60 feet (18 m) when taking any decongestant. From a recreational diving perspective, some medical authorities suggest that nitrox divers who take decongestants, like with the caffeine issue, also limit their depth so they are nowhere near the maximum operating depth of their enriched-air mixture.

Blowin' In the Wind

The immune system of about 10 percent to 20 percent of the U.S. population is overly sensitive to certain substances (allergens) like dust, pollen and molds that cause an "allergic reaction." These allergies are mediated largely, but not entirely, by specialized mast cells (mastocytes). These cells occur in several types of tissues but are especially abundant in those that come into direct contact with the environment such as the skin, respiratory tract and intestinal lining. Mast cells contain granules rich in a compound called histamine.

The function of histamine is to increase the supply of blood to an injury or to a site where a foreign substance has entered the body. In people with allergies, histamine is released even though it's not needed. In hypersensitive individuals this can lead to a dramatic fall in blood pressure and collapse, a condition known as anaphylactic shock. Others can be less sensitive but still experience bothersome signs and symptoms such as runny nose, congestion, sneezing, itchiness, tearing of the eyes and a cough with post-nasal drip.

Once released, histamine causes blood vessels to expand (vasodilation), and increases vessel permeability. This leads to localized swelling (edema), redness (erythema) and the attraction of other inflammatory cells to the site of release. Other common signs of histamine release are inflammation of the nasal membrane (allergic rhinitis) and inflammation of the membrane covering the eyeball and inside of the eyelid (allergic conjunctivitis). It also irritates nerve endings, leading to itching or pain (the mechanism seen when we're bitten by a mosquito). In addition, histamine release causes constriction of bronchial smooth muscle in the lungs as well as an increase in gastric secretions. Antihistamines are a class of drugs that weaken the allergic response by blocking the action of histamine.

There are actually two distinct forms of histamine receptors. Type I receptors occur in the skin, blood vessels, nasal passages and airways, while Type II receptors are found in the stomach, salivary and tear glands. Drugs that block Type II receptors are used in the treatment of stomach ulcers, and aren't relevant to our story here. It's the Type I histamine blockers that are used to treat allergy symptoms, and that have become one of the most common of all medications.

Type I antihistamines are generally divided into either first-generation or second-generation categories. The first-generation are relatively powerful sedatives which, when combined with the effects of nitrogen at depth, make them a bad choice for divers. They also produce other side effects, such as dry mouth (which can be made worse by breathing the extremely dry air from a scuba tank), blurred vision, urinary retention and increased heart rate. Drugs in this first-generation class, such as Benadryl (diphenhydramine), should not be taken while diving.

The second-generation class of antihistamines, introduced in the late 1980s, are less sedating, mainly because they do not enter the brain (or only very limited concentrations enter the brain). In addition, the second-generation antihistamines tend not to have the side effects of the first-generation drugs and, therefore, are more appropriate for diving or in any situation where you want to avoid drowsiness.

Three of the most popular second-generation antihistamines are cetirizine (Zyrtec), fexofenadine (Allegra) and loratidine (Claritin), but only the latter is available OTC. However, a relatively new drug, cromolyn sodium, has come on the market as a nonprescription nasal spray. Technically, this is not an antihistamine, but rather a mast cell stabilizer. It does not have the side effects associated with antihistamines, but must be taken prior to exposure to an allergen.

Mal De Mer

Someone once remarked about seasickness that, "At first I was so ill I was afraid I'd die, and then it got so bad I was afraid I would not." Given that the majority of scuba diving takes place from boats, many divers can relate to this sentiment. In fact, some divers are so plagued by the mal de mer that they'd never consider leaving the dock without taking some form of preventive. Some of these measures do not involve drugs (see "Nondrug Therapy for Seasickness" on this page), but in the vast majority of cases drugs are the choice.

While sea/motion sickness has plagued humans from time immemorial, it's interesting to note that science still doesn't fully understand its mechanism. Humans instinctively seek to remain upright by keeping their center of gravity over their feet, and accomplish this, in part, by visual reference to surrounding objects. However, when on a boat or other forms of transport, visual confusion results when nearby objects move with the motion of the craft. It's believed that seasickness has such a remarkable effect because not one but two senses — sight and touch — are disturbed by that motion. It has also been hypothesized that the severity of seasickness is influenced even by the irregular pressure of the bowels against the diaphragm as they shift with the rising and falling of the ship.

Most theories of motion sickness are based on the idea of conflicting sensory input. One current theory maintains that our brain senses motion through three different pathways of the nervous system. Two are obvious, but one is less so. The first pathway is by sensing motion, acceleration and gravity from the inner ear (labyrinth). The second sense is vision through the eyes. The third less well-known sense is from sensors called proprioceptors housed within the deeper tissues of the body surface. During intentional movement, like walking, our brain coordinates the input from all three pathways. But when we experience unintentional movement, like when riding on a boat, the brain is not coordinating the input; and this lack of coordination, and conflict among the inputs, is what causes seasickness.

Adding strength to the conflict hypothesis is the fact that without the motion-sensing organs of the inner ear, seasickness does not occur. Also, since blind people can develop motion sickness, visual input seems to be less important than motion sensing. Furthermore, research indicates that the complexity of motion plays a role. For example, seasickness is more likely to occur with movement that is slow and involves two different directions at the same time, like up and sideways. Little wonder boats are prime locations for the malady.

Nondrug Therapy for Seasickness

For those who are drug-averse, there are nondrug therapies for seasickness that have met with varying success. Among these are remedies that work according to acupressure principles via stimulation of what's termed the Neiguan point. This point is located three fingerbreadths from the wrist joint on the inner arm, between the two central flexor tendons. To stimulate the point, specially made elastic bands, such as Sea-Band® and similar products, are worn around the wrist. A plastic dome is attached to the bands, pressing on the acupressure point. Some users have suggested that these bands can stop nausea, even after it has started.

There's also another natural remedy reported for seasickness: ginger. Ground ginger root capsules, available from any health food store, have been shown to help prevent motion sickness, and in some cases even better than OTC drugs. And unlike Dramamine, it has no side effects. Medical professionals who subscribe to the ginger remedy advise taking two or three capsules an hour or so before leaving the dock, and one or two every three or four hours thereafter. An alternative is drinking ginger tea (either hot or iced).

Source: Divers Alert Network and Alternative Medicine and Health.com

Biochemically, the conflicting input within the brain appears to involve levels of the neurotransmitters. These are substances that enable transmission of signals along nerve cells and include, among many others, histamine, acetylcholine and norepinephrine. Therefore, many of the drugs that are used to treat seasickness act by influencing or normalizing the levels of these compounds within the brain.

Exactly why nausea and vomiting are associated with seasickness has long been a mystery to science. However, some evolutionary biologists have offered an intriguing theory. They've proposed that the mechanism is a survival response. The theory is that dizziness caused when early humans were sickened by consuming contaminated food was a trigger to evacuate the food from the stomach.

Seasickness is commonly treated with antihistamines, which appear to both prevent and treat the associated signs and symptoms of nausea, vomiting and dizziness. But as anyone who has suffered from the disorder knows, once seasickness occurs, medications are often ineffective in treating it. So, the key is doing what you can to minimize the effects of motion. Standard advice in this regard includes staying above deck near the center of the vessel, away from engine exhaust, keeping a visual reference on the horizon and taking seasickness medication long before leaving the dock.

Meclizine is an antihistamine with anti-nausea (antiemetic) and anti-muscle spasm (antispasmodic) properties, and therefore often used to treat seasickness. OTC forms of meclizine are the commonly used drugs Dramamine and Bonine. Meclizine prevents nausea and vomiting by reducing the activity of the center in the brain that controls nausea (it blocks the action of the neurotransmitter acetylcholine). It also prevents motion sickness by reducing excitability of neurons in the motion and balance center (vestibular region) of the brain. Meclizine's effectiveness is based on the drug's ability to cross the blood-brain barrier, but that's also its downside. Because of this, meclizine can be highly sedative, something that makes it ill advised for use by divers.

While it's not available in an OTC form, a better alternative medication for divers may be scopolamine in the form of a transdermal patch (Transderm-Scop). The patch impregnated with the drug is worn behind the ear, gradually releasing scopolamine onto the skin where it's then absorbed. It's not yet completely clear how scopolamine prevents nausea and vomiting, but it's believed that, like Meclizine, it suppresses the neurotransmitter acetylcholine, blocking nerve signals between the vestibular system and the part of the brain that controls vomiting. The alternative theory is that it acts directly on the vomiting center. Importantly, the patch must be applied at least four hours prior to exposure to motion. Its side effects can include drowsiness and mental confusion, although these tend to be minor.

The Take-Home Message

It should be crystal-clear that if you're considering combining any OTC medication with diving you must first have all the facts available. Also, recognize that individuals react differently to medication. In addition, you must always first try out any new medication before diving to identify any side effects (especially if the drug has known side effects like drowsiness). And make sure that you're in an environment where any undesirable or unexpected side effects won't be a problem. Finally, if you're uncertain about a particular drug, don't hesitate to call the Divers Alert Network (DAN) on their nonemergency information line at 800-446-2671 or 919-684-2948, Monday through Friday, 8:30 a.m. to 5 p.m. (Eastern Standard Time).

In the end, almost all OTC medications have possible side effects that could be a problem for divers. Therefore, you should always know what, if any, side effects happen to you before taking any drug prior to diving. And if you do experience certain side effects, it's probably a good idea to avoid combining that medication and diving. Meanwhile, use caution the next time you pop a pill before diving. ⌃

CHAPTER 20

The Next Generation:
What You Need to Know About Kid Divers

I've always had difficulty thinking of scuba diving as a sport because of its fundamentally noncompetitive nature. In diving, there's no such thing as "par," and the only time the topic of an "average" ever comes up is when talking about how long a tank of air might last. But the lack of any competitive nature or spectator appeal of diving also presents an advantage; that being almost anyone in reasonable health can participate. Age, too, is no significant obstacle. As there are numerous octogenarian divers still active, the upper end of the age limit is anyone's guess. Yet, it's the lower limit that's been the subject of more than a little interest and controversy in recent years.

Just how old one should be to become a scuba diver has been a subject of fierce debate for almost as long as recreational diving has been around. Scuba's own pappy, Jacques Cousteau, had both of his sons on scuba by the time they were barely out of diapers; and for many years the scuba training organizations had no lower age limit for certification. In fact, it wasn't until the early 1980s that an arbitrary minimum age of 12 was set for the restricted credential called "Junior Diver": but that all changed in 2000 when several of the training agencies reduced the minimum age of certification to a mere decade of life. Today, PADI (Professional Association of Diving Instructors) alone certifies more than tens of thousands of youngsters per year between the ages of 10 and 14.

While the subject of training children under the age of 15 remains controversial, this discussion accepts the reality that a growing number of young people — some of whom haven't even reached puberty — are active scuba divers. Of course, any diver below the age of majority — 18 in most but not all cases — requires parental permission; and making the decision of whether to allow their child to become a scuba diver is not an easy matter for a parent. It's an especially tough decision if the parent himself or herself isn't a qualified diver, thus lacking any perspective or appreciation for the challenges involved. So what's a parent to do?

On one end of the continuum there are some parents, diving educators and child health care professionals who take an uncompromising position that children have no place in diving. Some instructors even refuse to train anyone who's not an adult. The other extreme are those who see virtually no difference between children and adults when it comes to risk. "Yes," they say, "there are some 10-year-olds who should never become divers, but there are also plenty of 40-year-olds who have no business, either." As with most issues in life, the truth seems to lie somewhere between the extremes. One point is for certain: Children are certainly not miniature adults, neither from a physiological nor psychological perspective. Their growth and development do warrant special considerations that no prudent parent, diving instructor or potential diving buddy should ignore.

The Kid Body

What distinguishes kids from adults psychologically is pretty obvious. Less obvious, aside from size, is what makes them different in their physiology, especially as it relates to the challenges of being at depth. So let's start by looking at some of the issues that concern medical experts when the subject of child divers arises.

A few years ago, pursuant to a request from the Recreational Scuba Training Council, the Divers Alert Network (DAN) conducted a search of medical literature going back to 1966 and found no studies dealing with the issue of how the physiological differences between adults and otherwise healthy children would alter the child's capability and risks associated with diving. Therefore, they concluded, "any recommendations made [about the minimum age for certification] would be based on theoretical considerations taking into account what is known about normal growth and development." Using this approach, DAN prepared a document that addresses salient issues such as decompression risk, pulmonary development, asthma, oxygen toxicity and equalization problems. The issues they raised provide a useful perspective on concerns that medical experts — as well as parents — should consider in determining the risk of scuba diving to children. Accepting its speculative nature, let's look at each topic, and what we might conclude from the medical evidence.

One of the first concerns ever raised by medical experts when the child diver issue was first raised many years ago was the potential susceptibility of growing bones to injury from decompression sickness or silent bubbles. To understand this requires some background information. Long bones (arms and legs) mature from growth regions known as epiphyseal plates. The last of these growth plates generally do not cease activity until the late teens or early 20s. The epiphyseal plates consist mostly of cartilage, and having no blood supply, they depend on diffusion from adjacent tissues that do have a blood supply for oxygen and nutrition. Diving medical experts have long had a theoretical concern that nitrogen bubbles might damage these critical tissues. Damage to growth plates is a very serious matter because, if injured, abnormal bone growth will occur. The result could be the affected leg or arm not growing to a normal length, a condition seen normally as a result of fractures or injuries from sports that require heavy weight-bearing activity, like skiing, rollerblading, ice hockey or football.

We know from studies of adult bends victims that joints are affected in musculoskeletal decompression sickness, and furthermore that osteonecrosis (bone death) occurs in commercial divers and caisson workers who engage in very prolonged (several hours to days) exposures to depth. Still, it's impossible to draw any definitive conclusions because scientists still do not know the exact anatomical site of joint pain, and there's no published evidence suggesting that the growth plates are more susceptible to decompression sickness in children compared with other tissues in adults. Furthermore, like all recreational (no-decompression) divers, kids are unlikely to be exposed to the conditions associated with osteonecrosis in adults. (However, some recreational divers do occasionally develop the condition.) The take-home message from this should be abundantly clear: However unlikely, even a theoretical risk to growing bones requires that special measures be taken to minimize the risk for decompression sickness in children.

Other questions regarding decompression illness in children have been raised as to whether they have a higher propensity to develop silent bubbles, whether they're innately more susceptible to DCI (decompression illness), and whether the disorder in kids is likely to be more severe than in adults. However, to date no studies have been done comparing post-dive silent bubbling incidence in children with adults; and there are no published data that can provide a basis to draw any conclusions about either the susceptibility or severity of DCI in children.

One area in which there's both concern and at least some data is the increased incidence of patent foramen ovale (PFO) in children. While we addressed PFO in Chapter 11, let's review. The foramen ovale is an opening in the upper chambers of the heart. In a fetus, the lungs are inoperative, so this opening facilitates transfer of oxygenated blood via the umbilical cord. At birth this opening is supposed to close, shunting blood to the now-functioning lungs. Usually this opening seals by the third month of life, but in many cases remains partially open; and when it doesn't close completely, it's termed "patent." An incomplete closure means that blood can flow from the right to the left side of the heart without passing through the lungs. When divers equalize their ears using the common "pinch and blow" procedure (Valsalva maneuver), there's an increase in right chamber pressure that can move blood through the opening, bypassing the lungs. Having bypassed the filtering action of the lungs, nitrogen bubbles in the venous blood can pass directly into the arteries. This mechanism has long been suspected in some cases of decompression illness.

It's known that the rate of closure of a PFO is highly variable, and in some children it will not have completely closed until around age 10 (in some individuals it never closes completely). Some have suggested that there might be an incomplete closure in as many as 50 percent of children. But while the true percentage is unknown, medical authorities believe the percentage of children with PFO could be higher than the known rate of 25 percent in the general population. One study found, by looking for PFO on autopsy in 703 cadavers down to age 10, an increased incidence was observed in the 10-to-20-year age group compared with those older.

In the light of such uncertainty over decompression illness, all diver training organizations impose significant depth restrictions on junior divers as a way to reduce decompression stress. Divers below 12-15 years of age are limited to no deeper than 60 feet (18 m), while those programs that allow divers 10-11 years of age typically allow no diving deeper than 40 feet (12 m). But like all diving practices, these are voluntary standards, so it's incumbent on parents and other adult supervisors to ensure unyielding adherence to these limits.

While concern over DCI tends to get most of the focus, there are other medical issues of note unrelated to bends. One important issue involves lung development, and whether differences in lung tissue or the chest wall might make children more susceptible to pulmonary barotrauma. Such concerns are based on the fact that, up to the age of about 8, pulmonary alveoli are still multiplying, pulmonary elasticity is decreased, and chest wall compliance increased. Although there have been no published data addressing this specifically, this puts children 8 and younger at a theoretically increased risk of pulmonary barotraumas. This is, however, the rationale for why no North American-based diver training organization allows any form of compressed air experience — even in a swimming pool — with children younger than age 8, and another rationale for why age 10 is the absolute minimum set for open-water diving.

In almost any discussion of medical conditions that affect children, the subject of asthma will arise. The reason is that this serious lung disorder has reached almost epidemic proportions in children. And as it is a lung

aliment, asthma is also a major concern — and long a subject of controversy — within the diving community. One question asked is whether children are more likely to have an asthmatic episode while diving than adults. Medical authorities agree that for all asthmatics, because of the possibility of saltwater aspiration, diving imposes an added risk that just isn't a concern on dry land. Some have expressed concern that a child's reaction to an asthmatic attack underwater might induce panic sooner or more intensely than in an adult, putting them at increased risk of injury. The problem is that there's simply no data to support or refute such an assertion. The only advice to parents of asthmatics is to stay informed about the disease, and the implications it has on diving.

Another concern for younger divers is equalization, and whether children have an increased propensity for ear barotrauma. The rationale for such concern is based on the structure and development of the eustachian tube. Up until the age of around 8, the eustachian tube is narrower, more horizontal and more tortuous than later in life. This is why ear infections are more common in children than adults. Perhaps not surprisingly, one unpublished study from a European dive club of 234 children ranging in age from 6 to 12 found ear barotrauma and infections to be the most common medical problem reported. By age 12, the eustachian tubes develop into their more adultlike form, and equalization problems become less likely. The take-home message here is that younger divers need to be able to understand the importance of equalization, and be trained to recognize, and not be hesitant to tell someone, if they are experiencing problems.

A lesser-known concern in younger divers involves oxygen toxicity, and whether kids might be more susceptible to it than adults. Some have raised the issue of if, and how, elevated oxygen partial pressure might affect the development of bone and connective tissue. Here again, no one knows. DAN has stated that clinical experience at Duke Medical Center shows no difference in susceptibility of children down to age 8 to either pulmonary or CNS oxygen toxicity (the variety seen in most diving incidents). In the literature search conducted by DAN described earlier, only one study was found that addressed this issue, and it stated only that studies in animals showed that the effect of age on susceptibility to pulmonary oxygen toxicity was species-specific. In some, younger animals were less susceptible to oxygen toxicity than adults, but in other species there was no difference. As with most other issues, when it comes to how kids are affected, the jury is still out.

While issues involving DCI, lung development and oxygen toxicity are still speculative, there is one area in which there are clear and important differences between children and adults: heat loss. Kids have a higher surface area-to-volume ratio and smaller body mass. This means that under similar conditions with similar thermal protection a child will cool faster. So, parents, educators and anyone who dives with kids must understand this, and pay particular attention to ensure that children do not become hypothermic while diving. Pediatrician Dr. Maida Taylor provides some excellent and rarely considered insight into this

One of the concerns often expressed by both dive professionals and those in the mental health professions is that parents might push their children into diving even if they aren't especially interested or capable. And, as a child is far less likely to object to or question an adult, they might too easily agree solely to please a parent. This imposes a tremendous responsibility on parents in evaluating whether diving is appropriate for their child. It's imperative that the motivation and desire to dive be authentically that of the child and not of the parent. There's simply too much at stake for a parent to make the decision on the basis of their own wishes instead of their kid's. Under no circumstances should an unwilling, or even a minimally motivated, child be coerced into scuba.

The other concern is the capability and readiness of kids who are honestly enthusiastic about becoming divers. Here, some important and sometimes difficult decisions are necessary. Regardless of the level of supervision, all divers, be they children or adults, can be placed in dangerous situations. Therefore, parents must recognize that before enrolling their children in scuba classes, they should first look for evidence that their child has the requisite psychological and emotional maturity. Ask yourself questions like the following: What evidence do I have that my youngster will understand concepts such as pressure/volume relationships or decompression illness? From the emotional perspective, ask: How might my child react in a stressful situation? Does my child sometimes engage in foolish risk-taking behavior that could result in serious injury if he or she were diving? While these may be difficult questions to assess, and the true answers may be difficult to accept, such an unabashed evaluation is absolutely essential, and it's only a parent who can truly make such an assessment.

Furthermore, parents should accept their role in supervising their children once they become certified. In the final analysis, should the child not understand or forget some important concept, or be unable to perform a skill, an attentive adult will be there to respond immediately. This means that when an adult is diving with a child, the adult's enjoyment must be secondary to the child's safety. I also believe strongly that parents should never even consider scuba as an option for their younger children until they themselves are highly competent and experienced divers. As a diving educator, I simply do not believe that the supervision of a young child is a role that should be relegated totally to another diver or even to a dive professional. In my opinion, the only appropriate buddy for a very young diver is his or her parent.

problem of heat loss, specifically among female divers. She cites some evidence showing that girls incur a higher oxygen expenditure when exercising than women, meaning that girls generate more metabolic heat and burn more energy than adult women. So, girls get colder more quickly than women do under similar environmental conditions. In studies of open-water swims in water 20.3 degrees Celsius (68.5 degrees Fahrenheit), girls age 8 showed a 2.5 to 3 C decline in core temperature, while girls ages 16-19 showed little thermal stress. "These characteristics, in combination with higher rates of peripheral blood flow in children," Taylor says, "put preadolescent and early adolescents at an increased risk of cold stress." Furthermore, she says that understanding the full implications of heat loss in child divers is important because, as adults don't lose heat as fast, they may not understand or even perceive that a serious level of cold stress is happening right before their eyes. "A bad wet suit," she says, "is almost worse than no wet suit for the young diver." According to Taylor, the double whammy of increased heat loss and poorly fitting gear can easily lead to accidents. So, in smaller children, postponing diving until they're a bit older (bigger) is often the better option, rather than providing a miserable or even potentially dangerous experience.

Taylor's emphasis on size as opposed to age highlights a long-standing concern raised several years ago when the idea of reducing the minimum age for certification to 10 was first discussed: Does a child have the strength and endurance to cope with the challenges diving might present? Obviously, children have less strength and endurance than adults; and there certainly have been no studies done to determine whether kids have sufficient capabilities to deal with emergencies (or even deal with other demanding but nonemergency situations). Some dive-savvy pediatricians recommend that, given the challenges of the environment and cumbersome equipment, any child being considered for certification should have a body mass of at least around 100 pounds (45 kg) and be at least 5 feet (152 cm) in height. For girls, some pediatricians have recommended that diving be postponed until six to 12 months after their first menstrual cycle, when most physical growth is completed. Clearly, this would exclude a large number of kids who are active divers today, which points up the need for great care in selecting gear that's small

enough to fit properly. This is no time for hand-me-downs, or the "good enough" attitude. If anything, outfitting a child requires even more careful consideration than for adults. So, equipping your kid is certainly no place to scrimp.

In the final analysis, most diving professions advise that, when diving with any child, you should assume that you're essentially diving buddyless. Because of this, some even advise that buddy teams involving children should be threesomes, with two adults, so that there's adequate provision for emergency situations.

The Kid Mind

While it's vital to consider medical and physiological factors in determining the risk of diving to youngsters, most experts in the field believe that psychological and behavioral issues are even more important. Just as kids aren't simply scaled-down versions of adults physically, so too do they differ in fundamental ways psychologically. At issue is how the cognitive and emotional capabilities of children develop. Most cognitive development theory today draws on work done by the well-known Swiss biologist-turned-psychologist Jean Piaget. He proposed that children pass through four developmental stages (only three of which will be addressed here) as they mature into adulthood. These stages conform, generally, with age. (See "Piaget's Developmental Stages" on Page 160.) Understanding these developmental stages is important because a child's development stage will determine his or her ability to acquire, manipulate and comprehend information.

Piaget's first stage is termed the Preoperational, and begins at about age 2, extending to about age 6 or 7. (The exact age at which individuals enter each stage is somewhat variable.) This is when children develop symbolic thinking, meaning that they can represent objects and events in their minds without the physical object or event being present. In the later phase of the Preoperational stage, a kid does acquire an intuitive but rudimentary grasp of some logical concepts, but only in a very limited sense. For example, a kid will tend to focus attention on only one aspect of an object or task and ignore the rest. At this stage they're incapable of comprehending underlying principles. In terms of behavior, they must rely on rules imposed by authority.

Stage	Characterized by:
Preoperational **(2 through 6-7 years)**	Recognizes self as agent of action and begins to act intentionally; e.g., pulls a string to set mobile in motion or shakes a rattle to make a noise. Achieves object permanence; realizes that things continue to exist even when no longer present to the senses. Learns to use language and to represent objects by images and words. Thinking is still egocentric; has difficulty taking the viewpoint of others. Classifies objects by a single feature; e.g., groups together all the red blocks regardless of shape or all the square blocks regardless of color.
Concrete operational **(6-7 through 11-12 years)**	Can think logically about objects and events. Achieves conservation of number (age 6), mass (age 7), and weight (age 9). Classifies objects according to several features and can order them in series along a single dimension such as size.
Formal operational **(11-12 years and up)**	Can think logically about abstract propositions and test hypotheses systematically. Becomes concerned with the hypothetical, the future, and ideological problems.

Source: www.learningandteaching.info

Most children pass from the Preoperational stage to the Concrete Operational stage by the age of 8. When it comes to diving, perhaps the greatest concern is that a late-developing child, who's incapable of grasping the concept of pressure/volume relationships, could forget to continue to exhale while making an emergency ascent. Emotionally, such a child will also not tend to place someone else's safety on par with their own.

The Concrete Operational stage generally covers the ages of about 6 to 7 through 11 or 12, and is when logical thought processes develop. But what's important to understand is that, while adultlike logic appears, it's limited to reasoning about concrete reality. It's vital that parents and diving educators understand the implications of a child in this stage of development because it imposes important limits on their understanding. For example, a kid at this stage may be able to understand basic pressure/volume relationships, and solve simple problems related to the concept. However, he or she could not make any hypothesis about how such principles extend to a wider application, such as understanding the concept of a reverse sinus squeeze or deduce why it's important to avoid diving with a cold. Of even greater concern is that children at this developmental stage can generate multiple solutions to a situation, a necessary skill when faced with an emergency situation.

Around the age of 11-12 children enter the final stage of development called Formal Operational. Gradually, thinking becomes less tied to concrete reality and becomes more abstract. Children acquire the ability to generate abstract ideas on their own, can form multiple hypotheses, and can assess the possible outcomes of their actions. In essence, this is when a child is able to think about what might be, rather than just what is. This, of course, is the ideal stage of development for children to engage in open-water scuba diving.

One important aspect of understanding the psychological development of kids is how this relates to behavior. Certainly, children are notorious for being exuberant and impulsive. They also believe that they're invincible. These are normal childhood traits that are going to be part of a kid's psyche until their late teens. In fact, we now know that brain development continues, especially in males, beyond even the teenage years. As unrestricted diver credentials are awarded to those 15 and above, this can have important implications for the appreciation and avoidance of risk, as well as the ability to act as a responsible dive buddy.

Those who study children also recognize that emotional development is very closely tied to cognitive development. As a result, children often do not understand their limitations, or the realities of a situation. They're also used to others, such as parents or teachers, looking out for their welfare, and can become overly reliant on an adult dive buddy. Under conditions of stress, this can be problematic because a child may panic or become helpless, waiting for someone else to solve a problem for them.

It's also important to recognize that there's a link between emotional development and problem solving. As one child psychologist has put it, "We often make mistakes not because we don't think of the right answer, but because we don't act on it." In other words, our emotions can overrule our thinking in many situations; and this is a very common problem with children. There's also the issue of whether a child will even be willing to tell an adult buddy that he or she is cold, or is low on air or having some other problem.

While there's a theoretical debate over just when a child is ready for diving, the reality is that we now have several decades of experience, and hundreds of thousands of dives performed by junior divers indicating overwhelmingly positive results. But as I began diving myself at the young age of 13 — and have trained several 10-year-olds — I'll admit that I'm probably a bit biased in my view. Clearly, diving is certainly not without risk, but it does seem unjustified to deny children access to diving, and yet allow them to participate in activities that are far more likely to result in serious injury. It can be a tough decision, but no one ever said that parenthood was easy.

CHAPTER 21

As Young as You Feel:
Diving and the Effects of Aging

It was Mark Twain who best summed up what it means to get old. "Age is an issue of mind over matter," he said. "If you don't mind, it doesn't matter." That also sums up how aging has — or hasn't — affected my own lifelong passion for diving. I have to admit that, now that I'm in my sixth decade on Earth, I'm becoming increasingly interested in how diving might affect my aging body and vice versa. Plus, with the demographics of divers continuing to move up the age scale as well, there's probably no more relevant topic to us boomers. But is the belief that "age only matters if you let it" a reality when it comes to diving, or is it simply whistling past the graveyard?

I'm certainly not foolish enough to believe that I have the same physical capabilities that I did even 20 years ago. But I've convinced myself that it all balances out in the end because what I've lost in physical prowess I've made up for through wisdom and experience. Of course, we can play this philosophical game until the cows come home. It still doesn't get us any closer to understanding the physiological consequences of aging, and how the aging process is relevant to those of us who insist on going places where evolution tells us we have no place being. In short, what does it mean for a diver to get older?

An Inevitable Process

Like the saying goes, getting old is a, well, you know. Anyway, Ponce de Leon never accomplished his mission, so there's nothing that we can really do about it but try to delay the inevitable. The facts are pretty clear. With age comes reduced physical fitness, injuries become more common, healing takes longer and it's less effective. Aging also brings with it other physiological changes, such as deteriorating vision and increased susceptibility to temperature extremes. However, an important distinction must be made between the number of candles on our birthday cake and our body's actual physiological age, as it's the latter that really defines our fitness, health and performance.

Take, for example, what happens at a cellular level.

Most cells of the body are replaced continually throughout our lives; some due to damage from injury and others because they simply wear out. Many physiologists believe that aging is genetically programmed into the cells of every organism, and it's this rate at which individual cells age that defines the average life span of a species. Cells taken from humans and other mammals, grown in the laboratory, have been found to go into a senescent phase (unable to divide) and die before reaching 50 cell divisions. Therefore, as we get older, cell replacement becomes less effective, and we are less able to heal damage. Furthermore, tissue blood flow is reduced with age, and we accumulate more scar tissue.

What about fitness and performance? These can be measured in many different ways such as cardiovascular endurance, anaerobic capacity, strength, power (a measure of force and speed), muscular endurance and flexibility. It's also important to note that these different aspects of performance peak at different ages. For instance, kids demonstrate the greatest flexibility, while teens excel in the reflex, balance and coordination arenas. But strength and power don't reach their peak until the middle-to-late 30s. Still, like all rules, there are exceptions. Let's not forget that elite athletic performance is seen in men and women well beyond their supposed peak years. Take, for example, Dara Torres, who in 2008, at the age of 41, made the U.S. Olympic Swim Team for the fifth time. In 2012, Torres missed out on a sixth Olympic bid by a mere 0.09 seconds.

Disease, too, is a companion of aging, though some are more common and age-related than others. Hypertension, coronary artery disease, atherosclerosis, osteoporosis, pulmonary disorders, diabetes, and a whole host of cancers can all have an effect on diving, ranging from a minor inconvenience to complete prohibition. The problem is that many divers — especially males — don't even know they have the disorders, or the precursors for them. This makes regular medical checkups — something you might have never considered in your 20s to even 30s — an absolute must as we age. It also requires that we become knowledgeable about how any disorder we might have can affect us as divers, and make the necessary adjustments. Moreover, if we're fortunate enough to avoid any serious medical conditions, we need to take steps to stay healthy by eating right, getting sufficient sleep and exercising enough to maintain a good state of health.

At least some of the reasons that injury accompanies aging is psychological in origin. For example, people often try to live up to past performance levels in a body that can no longer live up to former glory. It's what some have called the "Saturday Morning Football Hero Syndrome," which can exact a painful price on Sunday morning. Athletes like Dara Torres aside, the inescapable fact is that, as we age, our tissues simply aren't as strong, our flexibility and muscles are reduced and — no matter how much we might insist that our clothes keep shrinking — we typically get thicker around the middle.

Finally, there's the issue that most of us deny, probably because it's often the first sign of aging: deteriorating vision. Though many middle-agers insist that all they need is longer arms, the reality is that almost everyone begins to lose close vision by the time we're in our 40s. This is the result of a progressive decline in the flexibility of the eye's lens resulting in the inability to focus on nearby objects. While this is individually variable, after age 40 the nearest point at which our eyes can focus tends to move out about one centimeter (0.0393 inch) per year.

The Big One: Heart Disease

It should be anything but shocking to learn that, given the aging diver population, heart disease has become a far more significant factor in diving than in the past. According to diving accident statistics from the Divers Alert Network (DAN), the mean age of diving fatalities is gradually increasing, and is now about 42 years. This is happening for two reasons: 1) more experienced divers are getting older, and 2) older folks are getting involved in diving. (The second factor is hardly surprising given that they're more likely to have the discretionary income to afford diving than younger folks.)

Today nearly 10 percent of diving fatalities are caused directly by heart disease; and heart disease is the direct cause of death for more than a quarter of the fatalities involving divers over the age of 35. In addition, 25 percent — one in four — of divers involved in diving fatalities were also reported to be taking heart medications. It's a shame that divers don't take exercise and diet as seriously as they do safety stops because for older divers they could be even more important in keeping us from becoming an accident statistic.

Yet the real risk of heart disease, and its consequence on the image of diving, doesn't end there. Many believe that a more thorough reporting and analysis of diving accidents would show that it's an even bigger factor than indicated by current statistics. The reason is that when a diver dies in the water, the cause of death is often reported as drowning. As autopsies aren't always done, whether the underlying mechanism was actually a heart attack is never firmly established. This scenario also tends to confuse the actual risk, and thus perceived danger, of scuba diving, as such an event is recorded as "another diving accident." Yet, a heart attack victim who succumbs on a golf course would never be classified as "golfing accident."

Finally, Some Good News

While it may sound like diving and aging don't mix very well, that's not the intended message. In fact, a recent study has actually surprised researchers in that, for some aspects of diving, good-old Sam Clemens was right on target: Age doesn't seem to really matter. In fact, in a news article highlighting a report published in the February 2003 issue of the *Journal of Applied Physiology*, researchers at the Duke University Medical Center concluded that "as long as older divers remain healthy, the gradual decline in pulmonary function that is a normal part of the aging process is not large enough to keep them out of the water."

The Duke study involved 20 volunteers, with 10 ranging in age from 19 to 39, and another 10 ranging in age from 58 to 74. All divers had healthy lungs and hearts. Researchers simulated dives at a depth of 60 feet (18 m) — both at rest and while performing exercise — while scientists took complex measurements of the levels of gases in the bloodstream of both younger and older participants. The objective was to determine the effect of aging on the ability to balance oxygen and carbon dioxide levels while making a typical recreational dive. "One of the key questions was whether older divers retain carbon dioxide at higher levels while diving," said lead author Dr. Heather Frederick. "We found that even at a depth of 60 feet with moderate exercise, healthy older people experience increased levels of retained carbon dioxide that were statistically significant from those at the surface, but clinically insignificant compared to younger subjects."

The study was especially significant because carbon dioxide retention is a major diving safety issue. In addition to lung disease, it can occur due to heavy exertion and with high regulator breathing resistance. The outcome of carbon dioxide retention can be mental confusion, seizures and, in extreme cases, loss of consciousness while diving. "Because this is the largest such study of its kind, and the fact that with the hyperbaric chamber we were able to have rigorous control over multiple physiological variables, the results of this study should help older divers feel confident about diving," Frederick said.

Frederick's enthusiasm was shared by Richard Moon, M.D., senior member of the team and clinical director of the Duke Center for Hyperbaric Medicine and Environmental Physiology. "The results of this study should provide reassurances that from the point of view of the lungs, diving is safe for older divers," he said. "Even while exercising, the older group performed very similarly in all measures to the young people. It was a real shock to me that they did just as well as the younger participants."

Score one for our side.

Older Divers and the Bends

Invariably, when discussions turn to diving risks, the subject of decompression illness arises; and common wisdom is that older divers are definitely at a higher risk of DCI than younger divers. But why and to what degree? Statistics seems to bear this out, but the jury isn't in yet as to whether this is because older divers truly do have a greater risk, or that statistics are skewed because there are simply more older divers. Regardless, there is some sound theoretical underpinning for a positive correlation of DCI with age.

One idea is that, no matter what we do to help mitigate the problem, old bodies just can't deal with the stress of decompression as well as younger bodies. But what exactly are the mechanisms we're talking about that might cause this to happen?

One popular theory is that older divers literally produce more intravascular silent bubbles than younger divers; and it's these bubbles that are the precursors of decompression illness. There are several possible explanations for why bubbles may be more prone to form the older we get, but you need to know something about how they form. First, contrary to what you might think, bubbles cannot form from nothing (what science calls *denovo*). They need a seed from which to grow. These seeds are called micronuclei, and there are lots of reasons older divers could be expected to produce more of them than their younger counterparts. Canadian diving medical expert, Dr. David Sawatzky, explains it this way: Bubbles form inside the veins, and it's well-known that the thin flat cells that line the veins have a space about 90 angstroms between them. (An angstrom is equal to 0.1 nanometer or 1×10^{-10} meters.) It's within these spaces where bubble nuclei could lodge, allowing nitrogen to diffuse from the surrounding tissues, and form bubbles that could bud off into the circulation. As it relates to aging, cells that line the veins are much smoother in a younger person compared with someone who's older. (This has to do with that cell-dividing issue explained previously.) In older folks, the surface of the veins and arteries becomes rough, and these areas provide a greater potential for the creation of micronuclei.

It's also well established that our bodies have a proclivity to produce microbubbles in other ways. They're formed from various biochemical reactions as well as by the suction effect of joint motion. At any time, even without diving, our bodies contain millions of these very stable microscopic bubbles. Just like the interior of blood vessels, joint surfaces become rougher as we get older (that's why osteoarthritis is a common disease of aging). As a result, the rougher joints generate more microbubbles than the smoother joints of younger people.

There's yet another reason for an increased risk of bends in older divers. As we know, it's assumed that the root cause of all the problems related to decompression sickness is the formation of bubbles. However, not just any bubbles, but bubbles comprised of nitrogen. To refresh your memory, while the air we breathe is made up of both nitrogen and oxygen, the oxygen portion is used up in the metabolic process, while the nitrogen portion is physiologically nonreactive. So, whatever nitrogen goes into our tissues will eventually have to come out again. On ascent, when the pressure is reduced, excess nitrogen can be eliminated in either of two ways. Ideally, it exits while still in solution — the way it entered. But it can also coalesce into bubbles. In the end, it all comes down to how much nitrogen we absorb while at depth; and that's where the age thing rears its ugly head once again. A good way of understanding this idea has been, again, proposed by dive medico David Sawatzky.

Nitrogen gets into our body via respiration, and the amount absorbed by any tissues during a dive is primarily a function of the amount of blood delivered to our tissues. So, the total amount of nitrogen absorbed becomes a function of the amount of blood pumped by the heart during the dive. Generally, regardless of how fast our heart beats, the amount of blood pumped by the heart in any one beat (what's termed the *stroke volume*) is pretty constant. This means that the primary determinant of how much nitrogen we absorb is our heart rate. Therefore, anything that causes an increased heart rate while diving will result in more nitrogen being delivered to the tissues during the dive. Translation: More nitrogen equals more intravascular bubbles and, therefore, a higher risk of bends.

Now the operative question becomes, just what might make a heart rate speed up? One answer is, of course, age. But why should the heart of an older diver beat faster than the heart of a younger diver? That answer is fitness. As a result of decreased fitness with aging, more work is required of the older diver compared with that of a younger counterpart. This is what accounts for the faster heart rate, and with more beats, more blood and more nitrogen.

Sawatzky also theorizes that there's still another reason why older divers might be at increased risk of DCI, and it involves something else we addressed previously. As we age our circulation becomes less efficient, particularly our microcirculation. This happens often because of accumulated damage from injury. To illustrate the point, Sawatzky uses the example of frostbite. From research we know that those who've had the condition become more susceptible to cold for years after the event resolves. It turns out that, due to microcirculation damage, it actually takes nearly five years for a victim to recover, even those who show no lasting damage from frostbite. In diving, it's also been established that a previous injury can have an effect on bends. For example, after an injury, should you get decompression sickness over the next several years, the pain is often centered in the injured area. The theory is that the site of the injury may be less efficient at getting rid of the inert gas than uninjured tissues. This double whammy of accumulation of injuries, combined with compromised microcirculation, could be a significant factor in explaining the increased DCI risk with age.

It's easy to become discouraged anytime the discussion turns to any aspect of aging and health. But it's important to keep the proper perspective. What we've been addressing here is physiological age, not chronological age. Nothing can stop the aging process, but we can dramatically reduce the rate of decline by the way we live. As Olympian Dara Torres shows us, to a great extent it's not the number of miles on the odometer but how we've taken care of the engine and associated parts. Just as sensible driving and proper maintenance can keep classic cars on the road long after their assumed life span, so can a similar approach to aging and fitness create a human machine that keeps on running long into the future — even when we take that machine underwater. ॐ

CHAPTER 22

OxTox:
Understanding the Perils of Oxygen

"Nothing in excess" once read the inscription on the Temple at Delphi. It was the ancient Greeks' way of telling us that it is, in fact, possible to have too much of a good thing. And that applies even when what's in question is essential to life. Sugar is a good example. Sugar is, of course, a food but too much sugar can be quite harmful. Refined sugar provides so-called "empty calories" and — when it makes up a large part of your diet — can leave little room for the nutrients you need to stay healthy.

Then, there's the obesity problem.

One nutritionist summed it up: "Where there's sugar, there's fat." And being fat is a major risk factor in the development of diabetes. There's even increasing evidence that too much sugar has detrimental effects on the immune system, lowering resistance to disease, and may contribute to a host of problems, from dementia to wrinkles.

If the idea that the food we eat can be harmful comes as a surprise, then here's another tidbit that may startle you: Under the right circumstance, the very air we breathe can actually kill us. Well, not the air so much as the oxygen component within it. If you're a seasoned diver, particularly if you hold a nitrox certification, you may already know that. But if you're new to diving, the fact that the gas we depend on to sustain life can, under the right conditions, become deadly poisonous may come as a real shocker.

The condition I'm referring to is called oxygen toxicity — oxtox, for short — and is a subject that's all but ignored in many Open Water training courses. Even in some basic nitrox classes, the subject isn't dealt with on the level of detail that may be warranted. So, if you're still new to diving, or it's been a while since your nitrox class, it's not a bad idea to review the downside of our good friend oxygen.

We sometimes forget that supplemental oxygen is considered a drug, and like any drug it can be toxic at high doses. Being a gas, the "dose" of oxygen one receives is based on both the length of time it's breathed and the pressure at which it's delivered. There are actually several types of oxtox, but the two that are relevant to diving are the chronic form that affects the lungs and the acute form that affects the brain (central nervous system). The two disorders are also sometimes referred to by the names of the people who first described the problem. In the first case it was James Lorraine Smith, and in the second the imminent French physiologist (who also made significant contributions to our understanding of decompression illness), Paul Bert. Thus, pulmonary oxtox is also known as the Lorraine Smith effect and the CNS (central nervous system) form, the Paul Bert effect. The chronic form of the disorder, sometimes referred to as low-pressure oxtox, requires breathing oxygen for hours. So, except when recompression therapy is involved, it's not something a recreational diver breathing air need worry about (though it can be a concern when using nitrox). The acute form, sometimes referred to as high-pressure or CNS oxtox, is a very different story. While chronic oxtox isn't likely to be more serious than a bad case of the flu for a healthy individual, the end game of acute oxtox is a grand mal-like seizure which, when it occurs underwater to a diver, normally means drowning.

The Physics of Oxtox

When we talk about the oxtox problem arising from "too much oxygen" we don't mean the percentage of oxygen you breathe. At the right depth, any gas mixture containing any percentage of oxygen can become toxic. The critical factor in the acute form of oxtox is the molecular concentration, not the percentage, and that's defined by what's known as the oxygen partial pressure (pO_2). Unfortunately, it's probably because of the need to delve into this confusing realm of physics that instructors avoid discussing oxtox in entry-level scuba courses. So, as you may have no idea what I'm talking about — or you haven't read Chapter 4 — here's a brief, simplified version of the physics involved.

When gases occur in mixtures, they still retain their own identity. This phenomenon was first described back in the early 19th century by the famous English scientist John Dalton (the first person to propose that matter was composed of atoms). He found that even though a gas mixture was made up of several different constituents, each gas continues to demonstrate its own behavior, as though the other gases didn't exist. For example, if a gas mixture is made up of 80 percent nitrogen and 20 percent oxygen — like air — then 80 percent of the pressure is exerted by the nitrogen and 20 percent by the oxygen. These individual pressures are what he termed "partial pressures," and the phenomenon that each partial pressure is proportional to the number of molecules of that gas within the mixture is described as Dalton's law.

To understand oxtox you have to have a grasp of Dalton's law. Let's review. For ease of arithmetic, we'll assume that the gas mixture a diver breathes is 20 percent oxygen and 80 percent nitrogen, and we'll further assume the surface pressure is 15 psi. According to Dalton's law, oxygen exerts 20 percent of the total pressure of the gas, while nitrogen exerts 80 percent. Another way of stating this is that of the 15-psi total pressure, the partial pressure of the oxygen exerts 3 psi (20 percent) while nitrogen partial pressure exerts the other 12 psi (80 percent).

Now, if we double the total pressure to 30 psi — as we do when we dive to 33 feet (10 m) — each gas component continues to exert its partial pressure in proportion to the 80/20 mixture. So, of the total 30 psi, nitrogen exerts 80 percent or 24 psi, and oxygen exerts 20 percent or 6 psi. Note that the partial pressure has doubled while the percentage of gases has remained unchanged. Here's why that's important: As the pressure increases with depth, the pressure inside our lungs must increase as well to maintain a full lung volume. Accordingly, a diver must inhale more gas molecules from the tank. So, the gas density is twice that of the surface (15 psi), so twice the number of gas molecules reach the lungs.

Let's illuminate the concept a bit more with an example by assuming a lung volume at the surface contains 100 molecules of air. (An absurdly low number, of course, but easy to understand.) At the surface, if we continue breathing an 80/20 nitrogen-oxygen mixture, then of the total 100 molecules, 80 will be nitrogen and 20 oxygen. Now what happens if the diver descends to 132 feet (40 m) or 5 ATA (atmospheres absolute)? At that depth the ambient pressure is five times what it was at the surface. So, to maintain a normal lung volume, the diver must inhale not 100 but 500 molecules with each breath, or five times the number he breathed at the surface. As this is still an 80/20 gas mixture, nitrogen accounts for 400 molecules or 4 ATA, while the oxygen component is responsible for 100 molecules or 1 ATA. Now for the real take-home message: Notice that breathing this air mixture at 132 feet is physiologically equivalent to breathing pure oxygen at the surface — 100 molecules at 1 atmosphere. Yet, the gas mixture within the tanks has in no way changed. What's important is the gas concentration — the number of molecules that actually reach the lungs.

Still, even at 132 feet (40 m) — the limit of recreational scuba diving — oxtox really isn't a concern. As it turns out, acute oxtox doesn't become a factor until the pO_2 reaches around 1.6 ATA, which doesn't happen when breathing air until a depth of 218 feet (66 m). So, as recreational divers, why should we care about oxtox? The reason can be summed up in one word: nitrox. When breathing gas mixtures enriched with oxygen, because of those pesky partial pressures, the rules change completely. For example, a diver breathing a 40 percent nitrox mixture will reach the 1.6 ATA point at just 99 feet (30 m). This is why it's so critically important for nitrox divers to know for certain the oxygen content of their breathing mixture, and adhere to its "Maximum Operating Depth" (something you'll learn about when you take a nitrox class). Another concern is that some divers now use pure oxygen to facilitate nitrogen elimination during decompression. In this case, the pO_2 of 1.6 ATA occurs in a mere 20 feet (6 m). Of course, in the technical diving realm, where gas mixtures other than air are used routinely, oxtox is a critical concern that must be taken into account on every dive.

The Mechanism

Exactly why the acute form of oxtox occurs isn't fully understood, but we do know how life-giving oxygen can damage cells and have other harmful biochemical effects. It all starts in structures within every cell of our body called mitochondria. If you remember your high school biology, mitochondria serve as the cell's "power house." They take oxygen — O_2 — from our blood and disassemble it into its two component atoms. In the process, by attaching some hydrogen nuclei, some water is formed. The problem is that during the process other molecules called oxygen radicals are also formed, and these are the culprits. Radicals are molecules that contain one or more unpaired electrons, making them highly reactive. Generated from collisions between oxygen molecules during the metabolic processes, oxygen radicals are formed continuously in all cells. (This is why there's such great interest in the role of antioxidants as in our diet.) One physiologist has described these radicals as acting like "coals in a furnace," meaning as long as they're contained within the mitochondria, we get lots of safe chemical energy. But if they get out, they can do some real damage. Of course, some do escape, but we have evolved ways of neutralizing most of these radicals. The problem stems from, when the number of radicals is too high, the cell's defenses are overwhelmed and damage occurs.

There are literally hundreds of ways that oxygen radicals can be harmful, but generally there are three fundamental mechanisms involved. First, oxygen radicals can cause inactivation of enzymes — molecules that act as catalysts for chemical reactions — so certain bio-

chemical processes cannot take place. Second, radicals can literally change the shape of some proteins, and the shape of a protein is as important to its proper function as its chemical composition. Lastly, radicals can cause degradation of lipids (fat-based molecules) by stealing electrons in a process called peroxidation. This is bad news because the very membranes of our cells are made up of lipid-based compounds.

While these effects can occur in all cells of the body, at partial pressures below about 1.6 ATA, the damages tend to happen most rapidly in the lungs (chronic oxtox). However, above 1.6 ATA, the toxic effects occur most rapidly in the brain. The exact cause is still uncertain, but one popular theory is that the high pO_2 halts or slows the production of a neurotransmitter called Gamma-aminobutyric acid or GABA. This inhibits muscle contraction, so without it, the neurons fire uncontrollably, causing convulsions.

Typically, the seizure starts with an immediate loss of consciousness and a period of about 30 seconds when the muscles are relaxed. Then, all of the muscles of the body contract violently for about one minute. This is followed by rapid breathing and, when consciousness returns, a state of extreme confusion. In hyperbaric chambers, people who succumb to acute oxtox — provided they don't hurt themselves by thrashing about during the seizure event — recover fully once the pO_2 is reduced. However, it's a whole different matter when this happens to divers; anyone experiencing a seizure underwater, and not wearing the proper equipment, is virtually certain to drown. The reason is that their second stages most likely will not remain in place. This is why, when the risk of acute oxtox is high, full-face masks are used, rather than a standard second stage. That's also one reason why full-face systems are used more commonly in technical and commercial diving. Another concern is that if a diver in seizure is brought to the surface, and the glottis is closed, a lung expansion injury is likely.

There are factors that are known to increase the risk of acute oxtox. The first is just being underwater. Although we don't know why, it's clear that divers have a much higher risk than those breathing high-pressure oxygen in recompression chambers. In a chamber, some individuals can tolerate a pO_2 as high as 3 ATA, nearly twice the assumed 1.6 ATA limit.

An even more important factor is the workload one encounters while diving; the higher the workload, the greater the risk of acute oxtox. The reason is the increased carbon dioxide level associated with exercise, along with increased blood flow to the brain. It's also believed that some drugs and hormones like adrenaline, atropine, amphetamine and other stimulants could increase oxtox susceptibility. Even aspirin is suspected.

The Squishy Limits

As explained in Chapter 12, at what partial pressure oxygen becomes problematic isn't definitive. This is illustrated in the wide oxygen tolerance between those in chambers versus divers. Yet even among divers there's huge variation among individuals, and an equal variation within individuals from day to day. This can be insidious because a diver can make numerous dives exposed to a high pO2 with no difficulties one day, and then, for no apparent reason, succumb to oxtox at a lower pO2 on another.

Like any "limit," whatever we consider the maximum tolerance for oxygen exposure is just a commonly agreed-upon guideline because, when it comes to human physiology, few things are rock-solid. The reality is that there are lots of complicating factors that make it a virtual impossibility to predict with certainty at what point someone will experience symptoms of oxtox. So, to be on the safe side, most diving organizations use a lower limit than 1.6 ATA. In recreational diving it's typically 1.4 ATA, while the U.S. Navy uses 1.3 ATA for its closed-circuit rebreathers.

In the final analysis, there simply is no magic, absolute limit beyond which everyone will experience a problem and above which no one will. Human bodies just don't act that way. Our understanding of acute oxtox, and the quirks of individual variance, make predicting any hard-and-fast limit very problematic. All we can do is follow the established safe practices and guidelines using a healthy dose of common sense. Just remember what the ancient Greeks told us: Nothing in excess. ♋

To remember the symptoms of acute oxtox, nitrox and technical divers are taught the acronym VENTID. This stands for Vision (blurriness), Ears (ringing sound), Nausea, Twitching, Irritability and Dizziness. These are some of the *possible* warning signs of the onset of convulsions, and occur commonly in a recompression chamber environment. Unfortunately, in actual diving situations most convulsions are not preceded by any warning symptoms at all. Even an EEG is completely normal until the convulsions start. Further, many of these warning signs, such as tunnel vision and dizziness, can be symptomatic of nitrogen narcosis, and some signs may even be masked by narcosis.

CHAPTER 23

Immersion Pulmonary Edema:
The Diving Disorder You Never Heard Of

A diver surfaces complaining of shortness of breath and coughing profusely.

Back on board you note that he's coughing up pink sputum. To anyone even remotely aware of diving disorders, the reason seems simple: a lung expansion injury such as an air embolism. Maybe, but maybe not. It's not necessarily as straightforward as you might think.

A small but growing number of divers have reported the symptoms described, and they've had nothing to do with breath-holding nor expanding lung volume. In fact, these symptoms often occur while the diver is at depth, and sometimes after just a few minutes underwater. This somewhat rare and mysterious disorder, which is still not completely understood even by medical experts, is termed immersion pulmonary edema or IPE.

Never heard of it? Join the club; not many outside the diving medical community have. In fact, the syndrome wasn't even widely noted until a paper was presented at a conference in 1990. It described several cases of IPE, all in cold water and involving patients over the age of 50. Given the circumstances and age, it was thought that these were heart-related problems occurring to new or first-time divers in a stressful environment. However, this theory was blown out of the water when several new cases were reported. These victims were much younger, in warm water and had no history of any disease. The common features were that, on admission to a hospital, they were found to have fluid scattered throughout the air spaces of the lungs and inadequate oxygen in the blood. So what happened?

Some Background

Before we get to the diving part of the story, let's first start with some basics. Pulmonary edema is a condition in which fluid accumulates in the lungs, usually because the heart's left ventricle doesn't pump adequately. Edema refers to the buildup of fluid in the spaces outside the blood vessels. It's actually a common complication of heart disorders, and most cases of the condition are associated with heart failure. Pulmonary edema can be a chronic or acute condition, and quickly becomes life-threatening. This happens when a large volume of fluid suddenly shifts from the pulmonary blood vessels into the lung.

In forms of pulmonary edema related to heart disease, the left ventricle — the heart's main chamber — is weakened and does not function properly. Failing to completely eject its contents, blood begins to back up and cardiac output drops. To compensate, the body responds by increasing blood pressure and fluid volume that, in turn, increases the force against which the ventricle must expel blood. Like a snowball rolling down hill, the blood continues to back up, forming a pool in the pulmonary blood vessels. The increased volume causes fluid to leak into the spaces between the tissues and accumulate. As a result, it becomes more difficult for the lungs to expand, and effective gas exchange is compromised. The condition also can be brought on by severe ischemia (insufficient supply) and a heart valve disease called mitral stenosis. Nonheart-related pulmonary edema can be caused by pneumonia and other lung diseases, excess intravenous fluids, some types of kidney disease, severe burns, liver disease, nutritional problems, trauma, inhalation of some toxic chemicals and Hodgkin's disease.

Early symptoms of pulmonary edema include dyspnoea (shortness of breath); sudden respiratory distress after sleep; and coughing. In some cases these symptoms will worsen to labored and rapid breathing; coughing of frothy, bloody sputum; a fast pulse with possible serious disturbances in heart rhythm; cold, clammy, sweaty, and bluish skin; and a drop in blood pressure.

The Immersion Factor

While it's clear why pulmonary edema occurs in some cases, the immersion form is much less well understood. It seems to occur more frequently in cold water, though as mentioned in the introduction, it does happen even in warm-water environments. It's also known that, during immersion in water, about 750 milliliters of blood is redistributed from the extremities to the core, mainly the heart and blood vessels in the lungs; and cooler water temperatures may accentuate this shift of blood due to vasoconstriction. Normally, the body compensates for this, but sometimes the resulting increased pressure within the blood vessels in the lungs causes blood plasma to diffuse across the pulmonary capillaries and enter the gas spaces of the lungs. Cold water may predispose one to the condition because this can cause small arteries to constrict, increasing the resistance to the flow of blood. The condition is further exacerbated by hypertension (high blood pressure), although IPE has been reported in young, healthy individuals, including military divers.

Additional predisposition factors for IPE are heavy exercise and negative-pressure breathing. (Negative-pressure breathing happens when your second stage is in water that's slightly shallower — and thus in less pressure — than your lungs, as is common in a normal head-up swimming position.) Neither factor can be avoided

when diving. Exertion is an inevitable consequence of almost all diving activities, as well as some level of negative-pressure breathing. However, a poorly adjusted regulator, with a high breathing resistance, can greatly increase the effect of negative-pressure breathing. Some have speculated that a tight-fitting wet suit might be another predisposing factor; and even the possibility of predive fluid overload (drinking too much fluid) has been mentioned.

Divers who have experienced the problem normally have the sensation of not getting enough air while at depth, and often report this after only a few minutes in the water. Sometimes IPE is mistakenly assumed to be cardio-respiratory decompression sickness, commonly called the "chokes." However, this is easily ruled out, as symptoms typically start before ascent, and it often occurs at a depth/time combination where DCS is unlikely. Chest pain is usually absent (unless the condition is due to a heart attack), and the diver may exhibit confusion or loss of consciousness. Highlighting the uncertain nature of IPE, some medical authorities also report that divers may dive for many years before first experiencing symptoms; thereafter, they may experience recurring episodes interspersed with periods of normal diving.

IPE can be easily confused with another condition known as saltwater aspiration syndrome, and it is possible to have both at the same time. In fact, it's quite possible, if not likely, that a diver experiencing symptoms of IPE, such as shortness of breath, would remove his or her regulator to gain more air and accidentally breathe in water.

Yet scuba divers are not the only victims of IPE. It has also been reported in breath-hold divers and endurance swimmers. One recent study reviewed 60 cases and examined the following variables: age, medical history, activity, water depth, type (salt or fresh) and temperature, clinical presentation, management, and outcome. The data showed that the most affected individuals were healthy. But the researchers admit that with more complete study it may turn out that older individuals are at higher risk. Reflecting the relatively small number of cases, the Divers Alert Network (DAN) received only 12 IPE incidents in 2005 and 16 in 2006, though it's likely that more cases occurred but went unreported. The military reports slightly more cases, indicating that IPE clearly is a disorder from which healthy individuals are not immune. For example, according to one study, each year the Naval Medical Center in San Diego sees more than 20 cases of IPE associated with surface swimming. These are found mostly in Special Forces combat swimmers during intense training, and many victims are under age 30.

Dealing With IPE

IPE is a medical emergency. Although fatalities have been reported, most cases resolve on their own during observation in a hospital setting. On closer examination some instances reveal underlying medical conditions such as hypertension or some form of heart disease.

There's also a great deal of uncertainty about chances for a reoccurence of IPE. The answer is that nobody really knows for sure. As a result, some physicians consider any history of IPE a contraindication for diving and will not approve candidates with this condition. Moreover, they recommend that divers who experience IPE discontinue diving. Others are less restrictive and instead recommend taking an antihypertensive (high blood pressure) medication before diving. However, regardless of these guidelines, most medical authorities, including DAN, recommend the diver always consult a doctor who is knowledgeable about IPE.

While diving, even what might appear as a mild case of IPE can have a severe outcome. For example, shortness of breath might provoke a panicked ascent and possible lung expansion injury. On the surface — in a choppy sea especially — any attempt to remove a regulator to get more air can easily lead to the aforementioned saltwater aspiration syndrome.

Of course, the first response to IPE is getting the victim out of the water immediately. They then should be maintained in a comfortable head-up position and, like other diving disorders, put on oxygen (as close to 100 percent concentration as possible) while in transit to a hospital.

Preventing IPE

While it's important to know what to do if IPE occurs, it's certainly better to try and avoid it in the first place. The problem is, given how little we know about what causes IPE, there's little advice on how to prevent it. Yet, there are some considerations that make sense. First, a malfunctioning regulator, particularly one that "breathes hard," increases significantly what's believed to be one major predisposing factor, negative-pressure

breathing. So, make sure that your regulator is always in good working order, and make regular annual service a habit. If you do notice some breathing difficulty, have it checked out as soon as possible; and if it seems excessive, don't dive with that regulator.

There's also evidence that hypertension may be a predisposing factor in IPE. This means that it's important for you to know whether you have the disorder, and have it treated if you do. The problem here is that perhaps as many as a third of all people with hypertension have no idea they have it. So, get checked out.

Another concern raised is how excess fluid intake might contribute to IPE. There have been documented instances involving military personnel in training in which IPE has occurred after consuming large quantities of water in preparation for long-distance swims. Of course, this must be balanced with the need to maintain proper hydration to minimize decompression risk.

Although most victims of IPE have been found to have no underlying heart or lung disease, it should go without saying that anyone with heart or lung problems still needs to discuss their condition with a physician knowledgeable in diving medicine. Furthermore, if you have a heart condition, avoid diving unless your condition is stable and well controlled with medication.

Finally, if any time during your dive you experience shortness of breath or a productive cough, terminate the dive immediately. If your symptoms persist on the surface, breathe pure oxygen if it's available. Afterward, discuss these symptoms with your doctor before your next dive. And never hesitate to call DAN if you have any questions or concerns. Like most diving disorders, the risk is too great to consider any symptom insignificant.

In the end, it's important to remember that IPE doesn't discriminate; it happens to both young and old, and to those with and without underlying medical conditions. And while cold water appears to be a predisposing factor, it happens in warm water as well. Like decompression sickness, there's more we don't know than we do about IPE. As in all other aspects of diving, the nature of IPE highlights the need for caution, conservatism and prudent decision making.

In addition to immersion pulmonary edema, another disorder you may never have heard of is saltwater aspiration syndrome. In fact, it has been confused with, and sometimes accompanies, IPE. Its symptom also can be confused with decompression sickness. It has even been mistaken for bronchitis or pneumonia.

Saltwater aspiration syndrome often presents with flulike symptoms such as whole-body ache, fatigue, low-grade fever, nausea, headache and shivering. Even some shortness of breath and a productive cough have been known, which is why it's sometimes confused with IPE.

Saltwater aspiration syndrome was first reported by Australian diving medical expert Dr. Carl Edmonds and is described as a short-term respiratory distress in divers occurring when even small amounts of saltwater mist is inhaled into the lungs.

Most divers are not so severely affected that they seek medical care. Others become ill quickly with the symptoms mentioned previously as well as severe cough with bronchospasm. Hospitalized patients are usually treated similarly to victims of near drowning.

Preventing saltwater aspiration syndrome involves keeping as much water out of your regulator as possible. Unfortunately, as any diver can attest, it's virtually impossible to keep our inhalation completely dry. Regulators are especially prone to "wet breathing" anytime you're in an unusual position such as upside down or swimming on your back. And, of course, anytime you have to remove and replace your regulator while underwater.

As with IPE, keeping your reg as dry as possible is another excellent rationale for maintaining regular service. A simple bad nonreturn valve can make a regulator breathe as though you're sucking air though a straw from the bottom of a near-empty glass of soda.

Another good rule is keeping your regulator in your mouth as much as possible, and keeping it firmly sealed. (Due to loss of sensation, the latter can be difficult in extremely cold water.) If you do have to clear your regulator, take your first breath cautiously. And, like your instructor told you, always exhale before you inhale. Of course, if you use the purge button, remember to lift your tongue to block any water from being blown back into your throat.

More information on saltwater aspiration syndrome can be found at Scubadoc's Diving Medicine Online at www.scuba-doc.com/saltwasp.html.

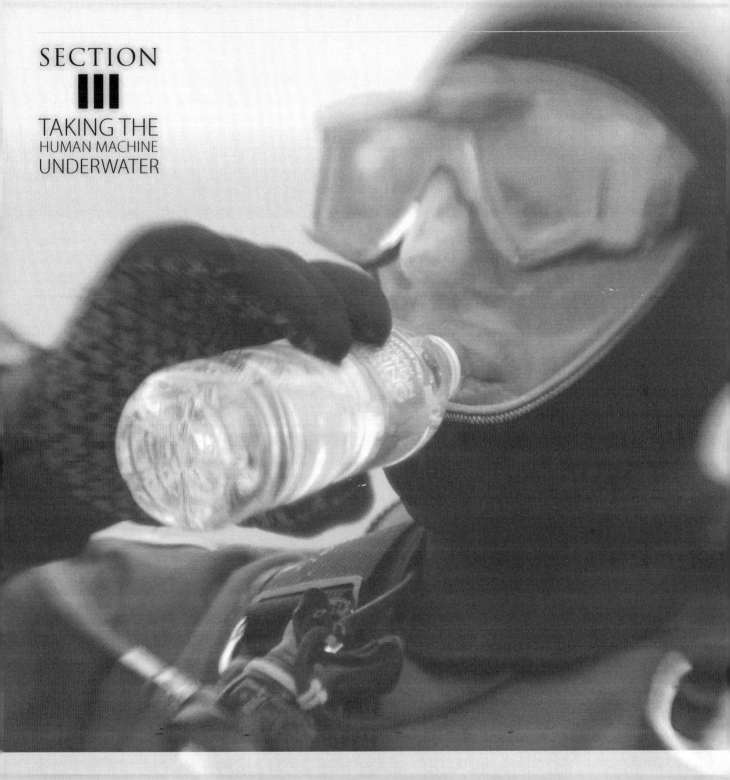

CHAPTER 24

Water, Water Everywhere:
The Facts About Hydration and Diving

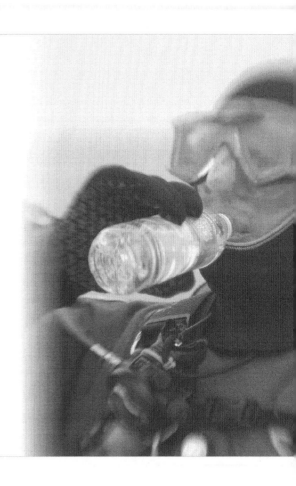

Earth is often described as the "Blue Planet"

because almost three-quarters of its surface is covered by a volume of 332 million cubic miles of water; 97 percent of it seawater. Life almost certainly began in the sea, a point we're reminded of by the fact that a saline solution is contained in every cell of every living creature. As humans, most of our bodies are composed of water. And the idea that water and life are almost synonymous is exactly why planetary scientists prioritize their search for extraterrestrial life on places where liquid water might exist. In the grand scheme of things, water is even more important than food. While we can go about three weeks before we starve to death, with no water we can last less than a week.

Of course, understanding the importance that water holds for good health and performance is anything but new. Today, drinking water has become almost an obsession. For decades we've been admonished to drink eight glasses a day (a recommendation with no scientific basis, by the way); and each year — excluding what we slurp from the tap — Americans alone spend $11.7 billion buying 8.82 billion gallons (33.5 billion liters) of bottled water. In some places, water bottles and accessories are so ubiquitous that they've become fashion statements, like cellphones. Canteens have even been replaced by hydration packs on the battlefield.

However, what I find odd is how soon we seem to forget our obsession with hydration when it comes to diving, which is curious considering that it's the very medium where diving takes place. Hydration and diving also present a challenge because the circumstances and environment we place ourselves in as divers conspire to dehydrate our bodies almost as much as if we were taking a hike on a desert trail at noon. Make no mistake; having all the training in the world, using the best equipment on the market and following every safety rule in the book can be rendered

useless simply by not maintaining enough water in our body before, during and after we dive.

A Primer On Water and Fluid Balance

While we often hear that "75 percent of our bodies are water," it's a bit more complicated than that. The reality is that water can constitute as little as 40 percent to as much as 75 percent of the human body, depending on the composition of the body in question. It all comes down to fat content. Most tissues, such as our organs and muscles are, as most assume, 70-80 percent water. Fat, however, is a mere 10 percent. As a result, the fatter you are the less water will comprise your overall body mass. Probably a more accurate estimate is that young males are more like 60 percent water, and young females (as they have a higher percentage of body fat) about 50 percent. But this is looking at water in the body as a whole. Where exactly does all that water reside?

There are three reservoirs of water in our body. The first and most obvious is our blood, which in an average-size person of about 150 pounds (68 kilograms) is about

Some new studies have been published recently that are starting to shed light on the relationship of water balance and decompression illness. The articles aren't for the scientifically squeamish, but if you're up to reading medical journals, here are two that are especially relevant.

"Dehydration Effects on the Risk of Severe Decompression Sickness in a Swine Model," by Andreas Fahlman & David M. Dromsky.

Aviation, Space, and Environmental Medicine 2006, vol. 77, no. 2, pp. 102-106.

Results and Conclusion: Dehydration significantly increased the overall risk of severe DCS (decompression sickness) and death. Specifically, it increased the risk of cardiopulmonary DCS, and showed a trend toward increased CNS (central nervous system) DCS. In addition, dehydrated subjects manifested cardiopulmonary DCS sooner and showed a trend toward more rapid death ($p < 0.1$). Hydration status at the time of decompression significantly influences the incidence and time to onset of DCS in this model.

"Preventive Effect Of Pre-Dive Hydration On Bubble Formation In Divers," by E. Gempp, J.E. Blatteau, J.M. Pontier, C. Balestra, P. Louge.

British Journal of Sports Medicine, March 4, 2008.

Results and conclusion: Predive oral hydration decreases circulatory bubbles, thus offering a relatively easy means of reducing DCS risk. The prehydration condition allowed subjects to attenuate dehydration and prevent hypovolemia induced by the diving session. Hydration and diving did not change plasma surface tension in this study.

10.5 pints (5 liters). While this may seem like a lot, it only accounts for about 5 percent of the water inside of us. The largest fluid store is the water inside our cells. What's more, though the role of blood is obvious, the water balance within our cells is no less critical. Our cells simply cannot function without maintaining the proper chemical concentrations, and this can occur only when they contain the right proportion of water. Furthermore, as we'll see later, this proportion involves a very narrow range of water content. The last reservoir is the water in the space between and outside the cells. In all, a little over 60 percent of our water store is intracellular, while the remainder is extracellular water stored in our blood, lymph, saliva, liquid portions of the eye, organs such as the intestines and kidneys, and in tissues between cells.

We refer to fluid balance when we talk about proper hydration because the amount of water in our body is the product of what we take in compared with what we get rid of daily. As you probably realize, water intake varies greatly among individuals and according to circumstance, but a normal, sedentary adult requires about 2.6 quarts (2.5 liters) per day. Additionally, we get water from sources other than by drinking it. Depending on our diet, we can take in quite a lot from the food we eat. In many individuals as much as half their daily water requirement is met by eating, not drinking. (Discounting this food-related intake is why some nutritionists believe that the "eight glasses of water" recommendation is probably too much.) The other fact also ignored, or unknown, to many is that our bodies make water when we digest food, about 300-400 milligrams per day. How? Digesting food is no different from slowly burning fuel. The byproduct of burning that fuel (respiration) is, in addition to energy, carbon dioxide, some waste products and — ta-da — water.

However, fluid balance from metabolizing food is a two-edged sword. While carbohydrates and fats are largely broken down to water and carbon dioxide, not so with all food. Protein metabolism produces a large amount of nitrogen waste. As this can be poisonous in its initial form, this nitrogen is converted to urea, and most is washed out through the kidneys. Flushing the kidneys, of course, requires water to make urine, thus contributing to dehydration. (This is why you tend to urinate so much on a high-protein diet.)

In the balancing act of the body's water cycle we also have to consider the amount lost. Amazingly, each day we lose about 800-1,000 milliliters (27-34 ounces) by evaporation through our skin and lungs, another 1,000-2,000 milliliters (a quart to a half-gallon) in the urine we put out, and even 100-200 milliliters (3.4-6.8 ounces) in our feces (and far more than that if we're having a bout of diarrhea). The wild card in the formula is sweating. Water loss here can range anywhere from a mere 200 milliliters to more than 15 liters (4 gallons). It's no wonder that with all these considerations for how the body can gain and lose water, keeping the human machine properly hydrated, especially under stressful or unusual conditions like diving, can be a considerable challenge.

Given its vital importance, our bodies have evolved highly accurate sensors to monitor our state of hydration and, to some degree, compensate for the loss of water. The two primary mechanisms are through sensing the osmolarity and pressure of the blood. Osmosis refers to the process by which molecules of a solvent — mainly water, in this case — pass through a semipermeable membrane (cell walls) from a less concentrated solution into a more concentrated one, thus equalizing the concentrations on each side of the membrane. The brain contains specialized osmoreceptors within the hypothalamus. The other sensory mechanisms are pressure receptors or baroreceptors located throughout the vasculature of the heart. Low-pressure receptors are contained throughout atrial and pulmonary vessels, while high-pressure receptors are in the carotid sinus and aortic arch. By processing this information our body can monitor its hydration status very accurately.

Drying Up the Reservoir

Dehydration means simply that our body's water content is reduced. The important question is how much water is lost and what are the effects on our safety, health and — when we're engaging in any activity — performance? Several studies have documented exactly how debilitating dehydration can be to athletic performance. For example, a water loss of less than 2 percent can reduce exercise endurance by more than 20 percent, and maximum oxygen use by 10 percent. By the time water loss reaches less than 5 percent — a not-too-uncommon occurrence in many circumstances involving heavy and prolonged exercise — endurance drops nearly 50 percent, and oxygen use by more than 20 percent. These are significant decrements based on dehydration levels that can occur even in diving.

As you may have experienced, dehydration is not an all-or-none situation but a gradual process. For example, a water loss of 5 percent, as just described, is considered mild dehydration, and is normally accompanied by a dry mouth, irritability, fatigue, increased heart rate, decreased urine output, nausea, loss of appetite, constipation and drowsiness. However, it's not always accompanied by thirst, which is why that should be considered a poor indicator of dehydration.

Should dehydration continue to a 5-10 percent water loss, it then moves into the range considered moderate dehydration. The symptoms here are normally dizziness, headache, difficulty breathing and numbness. Severe dehydration occurs with a 10-20 percent water loss and, in addition to the symptoms mentioned previously, visual and auditory hallucinations, delirium and, eventually, death can occur. While mild dehydration can be handled on scene with rest and oral fluid replacement, moderate and severe forms require medical intervention and intravenous fluid replacement.

Of course, our body won't simply continue to lose water without trying to prevent or conserve it. Thirst is one way our body makes us conscious of the need for water, but as mentioned before, this isn't always the case, so it's a poor indicator of our state of water balance. The body's primary response to water loss is to conserve fluid by concentrating urine. (See "The Pee Test" on Page 186.)

The Dried-Up Diver

An irony of scuba diving — an activity in which we're immersed in water — is that it presents lots of circumstances when water loss to the point of significant dehydration is a real and common concern. As mentioned previously, losing a mere 1-5 percent of our body fluid can reduce exercise endurance by a quarter to half. This makes sense when you consider the physiology at hand. As you dehydrate, your core temperature begins to increase. (This happens even before you reach a 1 percent water loss.) In turn, your body responds by redirecting blood to the skin in an attempt to cool off by sweating (which happens even if you're underwater). But if more blood is supplied to the skin, less blood can be supplied to muscles. So, on a dive requiring significant physical effort — and how many don't? — what

Though it may not be something you're used to paying attention to, as a diver you really should. Your pee, that is. Monitoring the color of your urine is a simple and reasonably accurate way to evaluate your hydration status. The yellow color of urine is largely due to the nitrogenous waste product, urea. So, the darker the color, the more concentrated the urine. And the more concentrated the urine, the more dehydrated you are. Of course, the way you dilute your urine is by drinking more nonalcoholic or noncaffeinated fluid. For the diver's pee test, your goal is "clear and copious." And by the way, this advice is also a good way to avoid developing kidney stones. Also, keep in mind that it takes about 30 minutes for your body to fully absorb the fluid you drink. So, slugging down a quick drink of water right before you enter the water does little to improve your state of hydration. Drink water, but drink it early enough to make a difference.

The fact is that, even if you try not to, the mere act of being underwater will make you pee, anyway. Here's why: On emersion, water pressure forces about 750 milliliters of blood that's normally in your arms and legs back into your body core. This increased blood volume to the core is then sensed by the baroreceptors in the heart as an increase in pressure. This is, in turn, interpreted as too much water, even though there's been no change in water content, and the body rids what it perceives as excess water by making more urine. Being cold, too, causes a similar response in blood flow and urine production. The conclusion is that, as divers, we simply can't avoid the fact of increased urine production, so my advice here is pretty clear and unequivocal: Get over it. After all, when it comes to peeing in a wet suit, there are only two types of divers — those who do it and those who lie about it. Peeing is exactly what you want to do, not avoid, and a lot of it, too.

Another factor under our control is not only how much but what we drink. Though it's hard to believe, some bonehead divers do drink alcohol before diving. Aside from the fact that it interferes with mental and motor control, reduces reaction time, enhances the effect of narcosis, and reduces the output of glucose by the liver, alcohol is a diuretic; it makes you pee. In fact, with alcohol, you can actually lose more fluid from urine output than the amount of fluid you took in by drinking. Enough said; don't do it.

Aside from alcohol, caffeinated drinks can be a concern as well. Most of us think of coffee when it comes to caffeine, but caffeine is contained in many soft drinks and nonprescription medications such as decongestants. Among its many complex interactions discussed in Chapter 19 caffeine increases urine production, which can significantly contribute to dehydration. Frankly, it's often difficult to avoid caffeine completely, but you should at least attempt to limit its intake when diving.

Now, what about the uncontrollable factors affecting dehydration? Almost all diving requires wearing some form of exposure protection. There are few things aside from a sauna that can induce water loss through sweating more than wearing a dry suit, wet suit or — depending on circumstance — even a dive skin on a hot, sunny day. But, depending on your activity level, significant water loss still can occur even

seems like a relatively small fluid loss could mean the difference between ending a dive without incident, or becoming an accident statistic. In some cases, you might even pass out from low blood pressure. And all for no other reason than water loss.

But why exactly would diving subject us to such a high risk of dehydration? The reasons are numerous; some we can control while others we can't. In the control category includes how much we choose to drink. Some divers tend to avoid drinking a lot of fluids before diving as a way to purposely reduce their urine output. That may be understandable when using a dry suit, as having to urinate presents some challenges (though not insurmountable challenges). In the case of wet suit wearers, the reason is usually avoiding what some consider the distasteful practice of "warming their suit internally." Consider, though, that distended bladders can lead to infections and kidney stones.

when wearing an exposure suit on a cloudy and cool day. Cooling off, and reducing water loss through sweating, is the main reason experienced divers try to enter the water as soon as possible after suiting up; and it's a good common-sense practice for every diver.

Something else we can't control is the air we breathe in our tanks. Air fill stations go to great lengths ensuring that the air they supply is as dry as possible. And they succeed at doing this quite well. The air delivered from a properly maintained compressor is almost completely devoid of moisture. There are some deserts with higher humidity than the inside of your scuba tank, which is an important requirement in keeping internal tank corrosion at a minimum. Low humidity also helps prevent regulator freeze-up in cold-water conditions. The problem is that your airway (mouth, throat and lungs) need to humidify that air to 100 percent before you can breathe it efficiently and avoid lung damage. In the process, breathing a single standard-size tank saps from your body about 250 milliliters (about a cup) of water. No wonder we often complain of dry mouth after a dive.

A final consideration for dehydration is one that can have a dramatic effect for divers traveling to exotic locations. A common problem that many of us encounter in our journeys is the dreaded "Montezuma's revenge" — travelers' diarrhea. We often forget that this can sap our fluid reserves faster than any other single factor. So, if you do decide to dive when suffering from a mild bout of diarrhea, be sure to increase your fluid intake dramatically.

Dehydration and Decompression

Dehydration creates a potentially greater concern for divers than a compromised exercise tolerance, headache or nausea. It can have a real effect on nitrogen elimination. While it has long been a speculative risk, compelling evidence has come to light recently from scientific studies that seem to back up the theory that dehydration can significantly increase the risk of getting the bends. (See "Dehydration and DCS: What Science Is Finding Out" on Page 184.)

The reason why dehydration is such a concern with respect to decompression is that water loss reduces the circulating blood volume, and increases the blood's viscosity (thickness). This means that blood

flow — what physiologists call perfusion — is also reduced. Therefore, the amount of nitrogen eliminated from our tissues could be less than our computer or tables assumes. Adding yet another factor to complicate the matter is that their similarity in symptoms makes dehydration easily confused with decompression illness.

In the final analysis, perhaps the safest assumption to make is that virtually every diver will be, to some degree, dehydrated at some time during a normal day of diving — before, during or after. It just comes with the territory. So our objective should be to take whatever actions we can to prevent or reduce its effects. Most of all, don't listen to your thirst as an indicator of dehydration; drink plenty of water — more than you think you need — even if you aren't thirsty. It's clear that whoever first said that "water is life" really knew what he was talking about.

Plain-old water works just fine for hydration purposes, but sports drinks like Gatorade® and its competitors may have some advantage. First, for any recreational dive — and contrary to what sports drink marketing tells us — you do not need to replace electrolytes (salts that conduct electricity). Their loss in such a short-duration activity as diving is inconsequential. However, the addition of electrolytes does help the body retain the water in the drink. So if you're one of those "pee avoiders," this may reduce the call of nature. More importantly, the salty taste of sports drinks — like the pretzels or peanuts you'll find on the bar at your local watering hole — will make you want to drink more. And that's the ultimate goal in avoiding dehydration.

What About Sports Drinks?

CHAPTER 25

The Gender Question:
Does Sex Really Matter?

I learned to dive

in the mid-1960s when crew cuts, muscle cars and Camel cigarettes were the norm, and the sport was almost the exclusive domain of men. In fact, I was a diver for almost four years before I even encountered my first "lady diver" (the only descriptor used at the time that I can remember that wasn't offensive). Sure, there were a few well-known females with the chutzpah to don a scuba tank, like Zale Parry and Dr. Eugenie Clark, but we wrote them off as anomalies who possessed some special capability not common to others of their gender.

The overwhelming consensus of opinion at the time — of men, anyway — was that the dark and dangerous underwater world was just no place for the fairer sex. In our wildest imaginings we certainly never thought that someday females would account for nearly 40 percent of all recreational divers, let alone that they'd join the ranks of commercial and military divers.

Clearly, diving is now a far more egalitarian pursuit than when I began. Today, not only women but children, senior citizens and any group you care to name are so common that they don't even turn a head when encountered on dive boats. Yet, while the short answer is no to the question of whether gender is a significant factor in scuba diving, it would be wrong to assume that there aren't some physiologic differences worthy of consideration in the interest of safety. Likewise, there are also some myths that have grown up around the gender issue worthy of dispelling.

Vive la Difference

Women were long thought to be poor candidates for diving for several reasons, such as having smaller lungs, a lower aerobic capacity, greater percentage of body fat and less body strength than men. However, as it turns out, these differences have either minimal effect on diving, or are actually advantageous. Smaller lungs, for example, account for perhaps the biggest advantage most women divers have over men — reduced air consumption. But getting more time out of a tank can be explained by more than just small lung capacity. Studies of swimmers have shown that the way fat deposits are distributed in women allow them to float more horizontally in the water. This provides for better horizontal trim, requiring less energy to move through the water. This more efficient movement, in turn, means less oxygen demand.

Another issue often cited as making women inferior diving candidates is that, on average, they lack the same maximum strength capacity as men. While that's certainly true, in an activity like diving maximum physical exertion is rarely if ever necessary. Yet, when it comes down to matters of strength and endurance, gender differences aren't really the issue. The important factor, regardless of sex, is physical conditioning and training.

Next, the fact that women have, on average, about 10 percent more subcutaneous fat than men has long been touted as a factor that may make them more susceptible to decompression sickness than men. But is this really true? Most studies, as well as accident analyses, have found no gender difference in DCS (decompression sickness) risk in diving or any other hyperbaric exposures. Diving physiologist Dr. Jolie Bookspan says, "Early studies that showed differences compared out-of-shape women with in-shape men, and studied too few women to draw sure conclusions." She explains that many of the early studies purporting an increased risk among women were based on questionnaires. This, she contends, can be problematic because questionnaires rely on voluntary participation, and so have an inherent bias of including more participants who have had DCS than those who haven't.

Bookspan uses an example to explain what is perhaps the ultimate flaw in the "more body fat" theory. A 120-pound (55 kg) woman with 20 percent fat carries a total of 24 pounds (11 kg). However, a 180-pound (82 kg) man with only 15 percent would carry 27 pounds (12.3 kg), and a 200-pound (91 kg) man with the same percentage carries 30 pounds (13.5 kg) of fat. So why would the woman, who actually has less total body fat, have a greater DCS risk?

More important is whether fat tissue is truly a concern when it comes to DCS, anyway. Without a doubt, fat (adipose tissue) can absorb more than four times more nitrogen than tissues composed primarily of water, and it also takes longer for fat tissues to off-gas than nitrogen after a dive. Conceptually, then, the idea seems valid that, due to the affinity of fat tissue for nitrogen, women or anyone who is obese should be more prone to DCS. Certainly, because our tissues are saturated at surface pressure (1 atmosphere), those with more fat have more nitrogen in their bodies before they start diving. However, in DCS risk, the concern is for the excess nitrogen absorbed while at depth. While fat loves nitrogen, fat also has a relatively poor blood supply, and therefore requires more time to become fully saturated with nitrogen at depth. Essentially, recreational (no-decompression) dives are simply too short for fat tissue to accumulate a significant amount of nitrogen to where it controls our decompression status. While obesity may still be problematic when it comes to DCS, it's for reasons unrelated to the "fat affinity" argument. However, so far one thing does seem clear from both scientific studies and common experience: Gender alone apparently has no effect on whether someone gets the bends. Or, as Bookspan puts it, "It seems likely that any difference in risk that may exist between men and women would be far smaller than the variability of risk among men or among women, or even from dive to dive in the same person."

A Difference That Does Matter

While in most instances we can ignore gender difference when it comes to diving, there is one area where sex clearly does make a difference: pregnancy. In most instances, pregnant women can and should carry on with their normal life activities, just as they have for thousands of years in premodern societies. However, while pregnancy shouldn't interfere with many other physical activities, one thing that the human machine wasn't designed to do was survive underwater. And make no mistake; there are some very serious concerns about diving while pregnant.

Issues of ethics preclude medical experiments involving pregnant subjects in studies that purposely expose them to risk, so we're unlikely to ever have a full understanding of the effects of diving. However, we can draw cautious insights from studies involving sheep. (Sheep are an especially good animal model because their placenta is like that of humans.) In this case, research suggests that diving increases the risk of spontaneous abortion; and the risk seems to be greater closer to term. Studies of animals subjected to hyperbaric environments also show an increased risk of fetal abnormalities.

Probably the insight from animal studies that's most alarming to medical experts is that intravenous bubbles can be transferred from mom to the fetus. In addition, fetuses can develop bubbles even when mom doesn't. What's more, when this happens, a fetus is at greater risk than mom because it is yet unborn. Here's why. In divers, as venous blood makes its way back to the lungs, most intravascular bubbles that develop are filtered out by the minute pulmonary blood vessels. There, the bubbles harmlessly defuse. This is why some decompression researchers refer to the lungs as a "bubble trap." However, this safety mechanism isn't present in a fetus because its lungs do not function. Instead, it survives on the blood system provided by mom through the umbilical cord. In fact, most of the venous blood bypasses the fetal lungs via a structure that's become of great interest to divers — the foramen ovale. This bypass mechanism in the upper chambers of the fetal heart means that every bubble becomes an arterial bubble and, therefore, every bubble could likely create a blockage (embolism), probably in the brain. Again, we learned this from animal studies, which by their nature don't always represent exactly what happens in humans. Even so, the possibility seems plausible enough in humans to view diving while pregnant as an extremely bad idea.

Still another concern, though also theoretical, is the risk of exposing a fetus to an elevated oxygen partial pressure (pO_2). The theory goes like this: A fetus develops in a relatively low oxygen environment. It's only when it's born, and the baby takes its first breath, that the rapid elevation in oxygen partial pressure causes blood to shift and start flowing through the lungs.

Divers, of course, are exposed to an elevated pO_2 every time they dive, and even more so when using enriched-air nitrox. Furthermore, if the mother requires recompression treatment for decompression illness, she will have to breathe pure oxygen during some phases of the therapy, exposing the fetus to a very high pO_2. The concern is that the elevated oxygen level could initiate the changes in blood flow described previously while the fetus is still inside the uterus. While blood flow reverts back to normal when the pO_2 is reduced, no one knows what effect these temporary changes might have on fetal development. However, balancing out this theoretical risk is the fact that there are case records of hyperbaric oxygen treatment given to pregnant mothers suffering from carbon monoxide poisoning without adverse effect on the fetus.

Other insight comes from survey-based studies of women who have engaged in scuba and didn't yet know they were pregnant, or were unaware that pregnancy could be harmful to the developing fetus. Studies have also been done involving pregnant women who continue to dive because they have to make a living, like the Ama pearl divers of Japan. In the case of the Ama, who are breath-hold divers, they frequently dive up until a few days before childbirth. Here, studies have documented that 45 percent of Ama diver babies are born premature and weigh less than 5.5 pounds (2.5 kg) compared with only 15 percent in a matched nondiving population

from the same region. This should give serious pause to any women who believes that, unlike scuba diving, breath-hold diving is OK while pregnant.

Other studies involving pregnant scuba divers also raise serious concerns. In 1980, a survey of 208 pregnant divers (of which 134 continued to dive while pregnant) found that those who continued diving had a greater number of fetal abnormalities than the mothers who didn't. Similarly, in 1986 a paper presented at a symposium of the American Academy of Underwater Sciences reported that stillbirths were higher for women commercial divers than that of the general population.

SECTION III TAKING THE HUMAN MACHINE UNDERWATER

In 1989, there was a Scandinavian study involving 100 women divers, 34 of whom dived during pregnancy. Here there was a 15 percent incidence of birth defects compared with 1.5 percent in the nondiving group. None of the divers had DCS and the incidence of other pregnancy-related problems was the same in both groups.

In 1995, Great Britain's Diving Diseases Research Centre surveyed 116 women who had dived while pregnant. They found that, although the spontaneous abortion rate between the women who had dived while pregnant and those who had not dived while pregnant did not differ, the women who had engaged in what the study termed "holiday style" diving (consecutive, multiday diving) reported more spontaneous abortions as compared with those who had not.

As medical researchers emphasize, none of these studies are conclusive — and some not even statistically valid — but they are highly suggestive. So, it's hardly surprising that in 2003 the American College of Obstetricians and Gynecologists issued these guidelines: "...scuba diving should be avoided throughout pregnancy because the fetus is at increased risk of decompression sickness secondary to the inability of the fetal pulmonary circulation to filter bubble formation."

What About Before You Know?

The issue seems clear that women should avoid diving during pregnancy, but in the very early stages, many don't know that they're pregnant and may engage in diving inadvertently. So, what's the risk in this case? Probably very little, if any, according to Dr. Martin Quigley. A specialist in obstetrics and gynecology as well as reproductive endocrinology, and consultant for Diving Medicine Online, Quigley says that an embryo doesn't actually attach to the uterine wall for about seven days, and it's even later in pregnancy (at least another week to 10 days) before there's any effective maternal-placental blood circulation. So, until then, there's no mechanism for transfer of intravascular bubbles from mother to fetus.

Quigley also emphasizes that many thousands of women have been diving unknowingly around the time of conception, and there is no evidence of an increase in miscarriages or other problems. "The zygote is simply a ball of cells," Quigley says. "There is no placenta, no fetal circulation, and no fetal structure at all."

However, not all sources agree with Quigley. Citing studies of pregnant animals that indicate cardiac malformations, the Divers Alert Network (DAN) takes a more conservative approach. They advise that, if a woman dives inadvertently before pregnancy is diagnosed during the first trimester of pregnancy, a second trimester ultrasound (sonogram) be performed with emphasis on limb and spinal development and with good detailing of the cardiac structures and the configuration of the great vessels around the heart.

What About Afterward?

Returning to diving after giving birth, in part, depends on the situation. After a vaginal delivery, DAN advises that women generally can resume diving three to four weeks after giving birth. However, this depends on several factors, including the prior level of conditioning, the level of exercise and conditioning maintained during pregnancy and the lack of any significant pregnancy-related complications, postpartum fatigue or anemia.

After a cesarean delivery, most obstetricians advise waiting at least four to six weeks before resuming full activity. However, given the need to regain some measure of lost conditioning, coupled with wound healing, and the significant weight-bearing load of carrying dive gear, DAN advises waiting at least eight weeks after a C-section before returning to diving. These same guidelines are advised for a hysterectomy, and an even further delay if the procedure is complicated by infection, anemia or other serious issues.

Lastly, for women who have had deliveries with medical complications, a full medical screening and clearance are advisable before returning to diving. There are also no contraindications to diving while breast feeding, provided there is no infection or inflammation of the breast.

With respect to pregnancy, the medical consensus is clear: Women should avoid diving if they're trying to conceive, think they might be or know that they're pregnant. However, child bearing seems to be the only issue in which there's any significant difference between men and women when it comes to diving. In the final analysis, what it comes down to is the individual. "Anyone who goes scuba diving brings different combinations of body attributes and skills to the sport," Bookspan says. "Great overlap in abilities exists between male and female divers. Common attempts to attribute specific characteristics … as gender generalities should be questioned skeptically. Predisposition of one gender to a particular problem is often inconsequential relative to other factors. Compared with the major factors of physical fitness, experience and skill, gender merits little attention and does not seem to be important in diving." Boy, we've sure come a long way since the 1960s.

Find Out More

A comprehensive article, "DAN Explores Fitness and Diving Issues for Women," is available from the Divers Alert Network website at:

www.diversalertnetwork.org/medical/articles/article.asp?articleid=9.

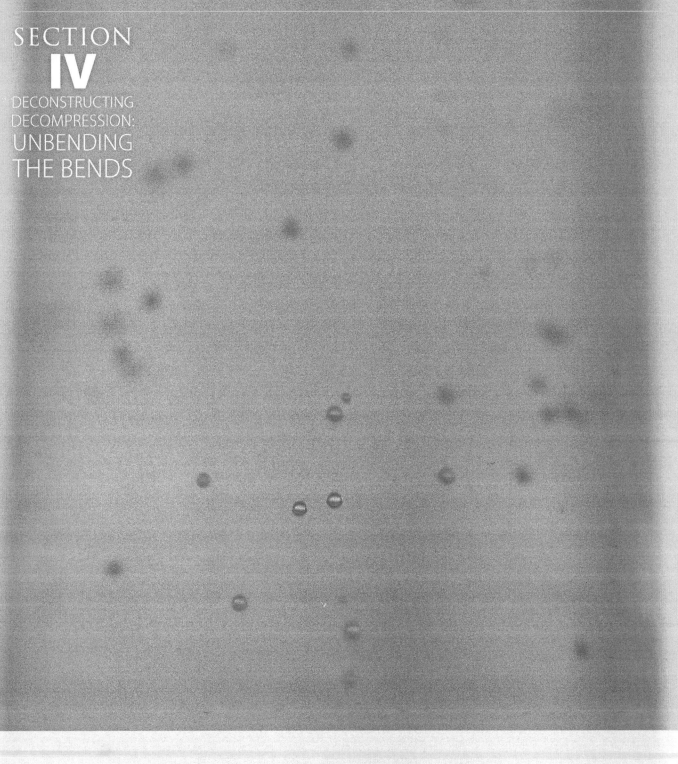

CHAPTER 26

Bends:
The Whole Story

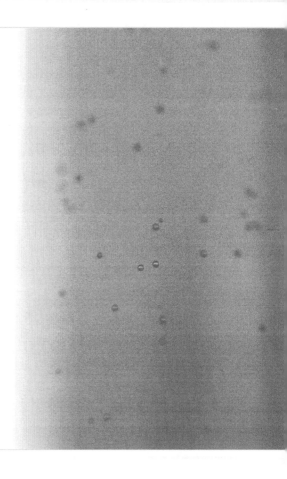

To most people, scuba diving is an activity surrounded by mystery and danger. It's a world closed to all but those who hold a c-card. We communicate with our own technical jargon, and discuss as commonplace experiences that most people on Earth can't even imagine. But there is one aspect of diving that's as well-known as hot dogs and beans. Ask almost anyone on the street what might happen to a diver who remains underwater for too long, or goes too deep, and you're almost certain to hear about the "bends."

Of course, the fact that something called the bends may occur is about as much as a nondiver could probably tell you. Ask him why it happens, and the only response you'll likely get is shrugged shoulders. Divers, of course, know why it happens because it's a significant part of our training. Yet, just how deep of an understanding do most divers really have about what's more correctly termed decompression sickness (DCS)? Sure, you've no doubt learned how, after spending enough time underwater and absorbing enough inert gas (nitrogen or helium), that gas can come out of solution and form bubbles — just like carbonated beverages release dissolved gas when the lid or cap is removed and pressure is released. And under the right circumstances, nitrogen bubbles can come pouring out of our blood-clogging veins and squeezing nerves. To avoid this, we follow certain guidelines and procedures as detailed in our training or by our dive computers. But that's pretty much the extent of what most certified divers know or do to prevent DCS.

While such a cursory understanding may be sufficient to keep you out of trouble in most instances, it's not enough to comprehend what's really going on inside your body. So, for those who'd like to go beyond the "carbonated beverage" understanding of DCS, let's take a closer look at how science now views this all-important phenomenon of diving.

The Gas In the Blood Goes Round and Round

If you haven't read about the gas laws in Chapter 6, let's begin with a quick review of gas absorption into liquids. From common experience, we know that liquids can absorb gas. That's what happens when drinks are carbonated — the liquid absorbs pressurized carbon dioxide. The difference between DCS and a bottle of soda is that the former involves nitrogen (and in technical diving may include helium) instead of carbon dioxide. Still, the concept is the same: High pressure drives gas into a liquid, and when the pressure is reduced on ascent, some of the dissolved gas can come out of solution and form bubbles. While the example of a carbonated soda goes a long ways toward explaining gas absorption and elimination, it doesn't tell the whole story about bubble formation within our bodies. To understand this, we must begin by exploring the differences between the common analogy of a bottle of soda and the human body.

First, forming bubbles in pure water is a lot harder than you might imagine. This is because water molecules are attracted to one another by a phenomenon known as "polar bonding." The strength of the bonds between hydrogen and oxygen within each water molecule as well as between hydrogen atoms of adjacent molecules, makes separating them to achieve spontaneous bubble formation very difficult. How difficult, you say? You could pressurize pure water to more than 200 atmospheres — that's almost 300 psi — and, provided you didn't shake it, immediately decompress it without forming a single bubble.

But if that's true, why does a bottle of soda — with pressure far less than 200 atmospheres — fizz when it's opened? And, more importantly, why then can a diver ascend from as little as 2 ATA (33 feet [10 m]) and risk developing DCS? The answers to these questions go to the heart of current theories on exactly why DCS occurs.

The fact that pure water has such incredible resistance to bubble formation tells us that there's something else besides pressure reduction that produces bubbles. Otherwise, it couldn't tolerate the incredible decompression from more than 200 atmospheres. But notice that I said pure water, meaning that it contains no other substances.

Why are substances in the water so important? In a sense, it can be explained by how clouds are formed. We've all known from childhood that rain comes from clouds, which are made up of water vapor. But it's how a raindrop evolves from the water vapor that's important here. At the core of every rain drop is a particle of dust, salt or some other type of "seed." This acts as a focal point around which the water vapor collects and grows into a drop. Let's now take this idea and apply it to bubble formation.

If we take a liquid containing other substances or particles along with water molecules, we'll see a big difference from the pure water experiment. Just like raindrops, foreign particles in the water seed or enable the production of gas bubble precursors known as micronuclei. The presence of bubble micronuclei is also influenced by other factors to include predive activity and pressure differentials that promote bubble formation. The point is, the seeds make the difference. You can confirm this prediction by sprinkling a pinch of salt into a glass of soda left standing in a glass for days. Even

though it has gone "flat," this will produce more bubbles because something — in this case, the salt crystals — act as seeds for bubble formation.

But exactly how do experiments with soda and salt relate to humans and DCS? In essence, like the flat soda, our bodies can be "seeded" to form bubbles. These seeds are actually called gas micronuclei, which are microscopic pockets of gas caused by various factors such as movement. (You'll learn more about the movement part in the next chapter on exercise and DCS.) Note that in the initial experiment I qualified the conditions by saying that the water couldn't be shaken. This is because, as it turns out, the turbulence caused by shaking the water could generate micronuclei, which would, in turn, seed the formation of bubbles.

Of course, our bodies move all the time, as does the blood in our circulatory system. This continual movement, combined with the normal turbulence of blood flow, is one current theory behind how gas seeds form in humans. During an ascent, nitrogen diffuses into these seeds (which are actually areas of low pressure), forming tiny microbubbles — the precursor of larger bubbles that may lead to DCS.

Researchers speculate that this phenomenon occurs primarily in the capillaries — the smallest structures of the circulatory system. From there, many of the bubbles enter the venous circulation and flow back to the heart. Since they're very tiny bubbles, they normally don't cause blood vessel blockage or impede flow or significant inflammation to cause DCS. From the heart, blood travels to the lungs. When the bubbles reach the extremely fine capillary bed of the alveoli, dissolved gas and small bubbles diffuse into the alveoli and are expired as part of the normal respiratory process. Since these bubbles have no effect on us, they're called subclinical or asymptomatic. Divers call them "silent bubbles." But what about the bubbles that don't make their way back to the lungs?

To understand the next aspect of bubble formation, let's go back to that glass of soda. In addition to adding a pinch of salt, you can also form bubbles by placing a candle in the glass. This happens because the surface of the candle (paraffin wax) is what's called a hydrophobic or nonwettable surface. Bubbles occur quickly on nonwettable surfaces because they require less energy to form than on a wettable (or hydrophilic) surface. But what does this have to do with bubble formation in humans? According to some researchers, everything.

One hydrophobic surface in our bodies is interior lining of our blood vessels, which are composed of endothelial cells. The contour of endothelial cells differs in different parts of the body. In some areas it is smooth and cells are tightly connected. In other areas they are less tightly joined and allow for the passage of molecules. All cell membranes are composed of a bilipid layer. Endothelial cell membranes contain lipids (fats), which make these surfaces hydrophobic. Like the example of the candle noted earlier, this quality may explain the formation of intravascular (within blood vessels) micronuclei and bubbles.

When a diver ascends, the nitrogen built up in the body starts being released in what's called "offgassing." (Remember, only the nitrogen or other inert gas is at issue because oxygen is used up in the metabolic process.) The excess nitrogen now coalesces around the gas seeds and microbubbles form. The more nitrogen that's released, the more the bubbles grow. But here's something interesting: These bubbles tend not to form the familiar spherical shape we see in our soda. Instead, they become elongated — a shape that increases their surface area and resistance to movement. Of course, if they're big enough, bubbles in blood vessels can stop or interfere with normal blood flow, and cause local inflammation. This may contribute to the development of symptomatic DCS, as more gas comes out of solution and coalesces to form larger bubbles.

Some researchers have described this phenomenon as the "bottleneck effect." The dissolved nitrogen tries to escape, but the localized bubble formation slows the flow of blood that would otherwise carry away the dissolved nitrogen. Blood flow also slows due to the inflammatory response caused by the bubbles. In turn, intravascular inflammation can promote clotting and sludging of blood that impedes flow still further. The nitrogen has to go somewhere, so it diffuses into the newly formed bubbles, causing them to grow even larger. This explanation for how inert gas accumulates may explain certain types of DCS that affect particular body areas, for example the spine.

Unfortunately, bubbles don't just form within the blood vessels. Nitrogen can diffuse either from or into tissue compartments and as bubbles grow or the mass of dissolved gas increases, tissue trauma, felt as pain, may occur. As they grow, the bubbles also compress nerves. This type of bubble formation is called extravascular, meaning "outside the vessel." Aqueous (watery) tissues — the type

that make up ligaments and joints — are especially prone to developing these types of bubbles; and it's one reason some researchers believe that extravascular bubbling is the primary cause of the classic symptoms of DCS, joint pain or what's termed "Type I" decompression sickness.

But there are other pain-related symptoms common to DCS. In some cases, victims complain of what's termed a "deep pain," which is difficult to describe and unaffected by movement. Theory holds that this pain is caused by bubbles in the circulation of the bone resulting in either a reduced blood supply — a condition called ischemia — or by increasing pressure inside the bone cavity.

Fat (lipid) tissue has an affinity for forming extravascular bubbles, as well. In fact, because fatty tissues can hold five times the amount of nitrogen than an equal quantity of aqueous tissue, it's thought that lipid tissues might act as reservoirs for extravascular bubbles. It has been shown experimentally that high enough quantities of bubbles can cause vascular hemorrhage, thus forcing both bubbles and fat tissue into the bloodstream. It is interesting to note that most of the cases of "skin bends," in fact, occur in fatty areas, especially the breasts, abdomen, buttocks and thighs.

Decompression Stress

Decompression sickness differs from other diving emergencies, like lung expansion or other forms of traumatic injury, in that the latter are "all or none" events — tissue damage occurs or it doesn't — while DCS symptom onset is gradual. In fact, you can view the risk of DCS on a continuum based on how close a diver is to the no-decompression limits. But it's important to understand that these so-called limits are not, and will never be, the same for all people. People get the bends even when they don't exceed no-decompression limits. The reason is that no theoretical limit can ever fully take into account the nuances of an individual's physiology and diving conditions.

It's also inaccurate to view the decompression continuum entirely as one based on time because an individual's susceptibility to the bends involves many factors in addition to bottom time and depth (although these are the primary determinants). For this reason experts in the field now use a different approach to describe this continuum of risk from a predive state to a point where DCS occurs. That concept is termed "decompression stress."

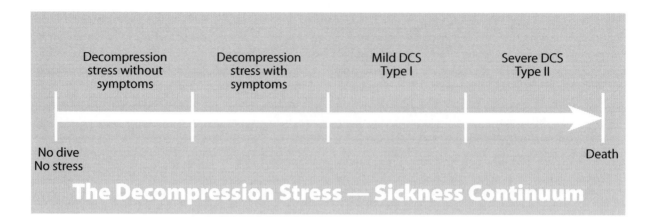

The dictionary defines stress as "pressure or tension exerted on a material object," which isn't a half-bad definition when we consider that material object, the human body. Take, for example, two short 10-minute dives, one to a mere 10 feet (3 m) and another to 100 feet (30 m). While both dives involve the same duration, they differ in pressure exposure. Still, while both result in nitrogen absorption, they each subject a diver to very different degrees of decompression stress. But time and pressure aren't the only factors contributing to decompression stress. And to comprehend this requires a bit more insight into the mechanisms at work.

A pioneering advocate of the decompression stress continuum concept is Dr. David Sawatzky. He uses the analogy of how stretching a balloon is akin to tissue damage done by bubble formation. For example, you can stress an inflated balloon by squeezing it, yet it will return to normal once you release your grip. But if you squeeze harder — or inflate it repeatedly — the balloon will begin to weaken. Eventually, the weakened state could result in a failure, and the balloon pops. In a sense, the same thing happens with the cells of our body. If a mild stress is placed on a cell, it will undergo both physical and — unlike the balloon — biochemical changes, but will return to normal when the stress is removed. However, if the stress is increased or continued, tissue injury may occur.

Continual or significant decompression stress, over time, could at some level cause cell damage; and this may occur even though no obvious signs or symptoms are present. Of course, as the decompression stress increases, so might the level of cell damage, as well as the severity of any DCS symptoms. And even if the signs and symptoms are resolved through treatment, there's still a strong possibility that permanent cell damage may have occured.

In Sawatzky's model, the decompression stress continuum is divided into four categories, as illustrated. Though not intended as a clinical tool, the model nonetheless provides a novel way of viewing the phenomenon of decompression.

The first category is in the range in which the diver emerges from a dive and has no DCS signs or symptoms. Moving up to the second category range, a diver may notice some subtle symptoms such as skin itching or unwarranted fatigue, but no cell damage occurs nor is recompression therapy indicated or any treatment required. Moving into the next category range, the diver demonstrates clear signs and symptoms and cell damage occurs. This warrants treatment — either supplemental oxygen and fluids or recompression — to minimize the amount of damage. The fourth category range is where the diver has severe signs and symptoms, and without treatment the amount of damage could become severe and permanent. Finally, while categorizing symptoms (or no symptoms) in this way may be useful in understanding the concept of decompression stress, it should not imply that symptoms can't evolve from one category to another; and even those in category one are not immune to developing DCS over time.

The uncertain nature of decompression sickness is perhaps the most frustrating part of trying to prevent the disorder. People like things that can be described as right or wrong, positive or negative and black or white. But in the case of DCS, that's not always possible. People get the bends even when they do everything right, and some avoid it even when they do everything wrong. All we can do is try to put into practice everything we think might help us prevent it. And one of the most important preventive measures is not viewing the risk as an all-or-nothing event, but on a continuum of stress. The objective is to reduce the stress — and hopefully the likelihood of symptoms — but also to recognize that, as in all aspects of life, there just are no guarantees.

Bubbles Aren't Everything

A common misconception held by most divers, including those who think they have a pretty firm grounding in decompression theory, is that bubbles are the sole cause of DCS. In reality, while bubble formation may be the factor that gets the ball rolling, new research is showing that DCS is actually a highly complex interplay of both bubbles and biochemistry. A fairly recent discovery about hyperbaric oxygen therapy is that the combination of both pressure and oxygen helps minimize bubbles as well as reduce the associated biochemical cascade associated with inflammation.

One aspect of DCS that most never consider is that, to our body, bubbles are foreign invaders; and our body has evolved a sophisticated means of fighting off invaders, called the immune system. DCS bubbles have been shown to activate a specific part of the immune response termed the complement system (so called because it helps or "complements" the ability of antibodies and phagocytic cells to clear pathogens from your body). This system includes more than 25 different proteins and protein fragments. This is important because the immune response has a domino effect on blood chemistry, leading to marked changes in tissues long after bubbles have disappeared. The presence of complement proteins also causes the release of histamines and other chemicals that cause fluid to leak from the capillaries into the surrounding tissues. Additionally, and perhaps equally important, the presence of bubbles also activates the body's inflammatory response.

Bubbles also stimulate platelets, the blood component responsible for initiating clot formation. When activated, they become sticky, attach themselves to each other and cause blood thickening (sludging). This may be associated with inflammation, but not necessarily from platelet activation. Inflammation can cause loss of blood vessel integrity, reduce blood flow and slow inert gas removal. Eventually, the blood vessels themselves begin losing their integrity and start breaking down. This may result in the release of ad-

ditional cellular debris and lipid particles, which then can act as new micronuclei.

Research into the immune response to DCS has emphasized the importance of early treatment, demonstrating that the longer the delay in treatment, the more blood chemistry changes occur and the greater the damage done to tissues. Furthermore, research has shown that repeated activation of the complement system may acclimate divers to the effects of DCS. Dr. Ernest Campbell, a highly regarded diving medical authority, said, "This might suggest a 'using up' process of multiple shallow dives with subclinical bubbling causing complement activation and having little or none present when a subsequent deeper dive is done." He hypothesizes further, "This same process might be the explanation of the excessive fatigue that many divers describe after diving — the fatigue actually being the complement activation damage that is known to occur distant from local bubble sites and the hemoconcentration that occurs."

Another implication of this line of research is that individuals who have greater sensitivity to complement activation may be at greater risk for DCS, and manifest more severe symptoms. Divers with chronically "used up" complement, such as those with conditions like chronic asthma or allergic sensitivity or perhaps those who dive frequently, may be at a reduced DCS risk.

There is a relationship between decompression stress and the presence or elevation of certain chemical substances within the blood. One example is smooth muscle activating factor (SMAF). When mice were injected with SMAF and subsequently exposed to minimal decompression stress, unexpectedly high rates of DCS were seen. Of note, DCS symptoms were not seen in the control group that did not receive SMAF. Similarly, another substance called anti-smooth muscle activating factor had just the opposite effect. Symptoms in mice purposely induced with DCS resolved the symptoms when this blood factor was injected. These findings led to other exciting studies into the biochemical involvement of DCS.

The overall effect of this biochemical activity is like a snowball rolling downhill. The blood thickens, becomes sticky and cannot move as efficiently through the vessels. This decreases circulatory efficiency and the efficient release of nitrogen. More bubbles form, and bubbles that already exist grow. The blood flow slows even further, and in an cascading downward cycle, the condition gets worse.

Maybe It's Not Bubbles At All

A relatively new line of research, supported by several studies, maintains that much of what we associate with symptoms of decompression sickness may be an inflammatory response, rather than any direct effects of the bubbles. Furthermore, this inflammatory response may persist even after the bubbles are gone (and by the time most recreational divers present for treatment, their bubbles are long gone). This is important because treatment is focused on enhancing tissue oxygen supply and reducing inflammation (a unique function of hyberbaric oxygen therapy).

There's even a more compelling and radical theory. While much of what science tells us about decompression may be unproven or speculative, there's one aspect of the disorder that's rarely questioned, and that's that bends is caused by bubbles. Well, hold on to your hat because I'm about to turn your world upside down: DCS may not be caused by bubbles, after all. In case your head just exploded, let me repeat that: DCS is not just about bubbles.

The no-bubble theory, known as the "at-depth endothelial dysfunction hypothesis," maintains that gas bubbles are not the cause of DCS, only an exacerbating factor. Writing in the journal *Medical Hypotheses*, British researchers Leigh Madden and Gerard Laden assert that DCS is possibly the result of "endothelial dysfunction caused by a temporary loss of haemostasis due to increased total oxidant status." (Hemostasis is a process that causes bleeding to stop — the opposite of hemorrhage.) Their theory holds that breathing oxygen at any pressure increases the number of oxidants in circulation, causing vasoconstriction. This, in turn, sets in play a complex and cascading process in which microparticles are released from cells causing inflammation, leakage of fluid from the blood vessels and cell damage. And it's this physiologic dysfunction that actually causes DCS; bubbles merely make matters worse.

One proposed mechanism for what may cause the dysfunction has to do with something known as "microparticles" (not to be confused with microbubbles). Microparticles are pieces of cells that circulate in the bloodstream. They can be remnants of cells such erythrocytes (red blood cells), leukocytes (white blood cells), platelets or endothelial cells (cells that line the inside of blood vessels). They range in size from 0.01 to 1.0 micron (a micron is one-thousandth of a millimeter or about 0.000039 of an inch). Although circulating microparticles can be found in the blood of healthy individuals, they're also a feature of several conditions, including diabetes, various coronary and vascular diseases, hypertension, pre-eclampsia, rheumatoid arthritis and sepsis.

The presence of microparticles can lead to degeneration of and leakage of fluid from the blood vessels. Very recent research has shown that decompression can enlarge the microparticles by three times or greater, which could be a result of gas expansion within them. This hypothesis is supported by the fact that recompression can shirk the microparticles.

While most of the studies conducted regarding the role of microparticles have been conducted on animals, a more recent study has been published involving recreational scuba divers. Consistent with the animal studies, researchers found that decompression stress did indeed contribute substantially to microparticle development, and the molecular marker found on the microparticles showed that the cells releasing the particles were themselves under stress.

The implications of this new way of viewing DCS may be profound. For example, perhaps antioxidants might be effective in reducing decompression stress. In addition, in animal studies microparticles have been reduced or virtually eliminated by a number of therapeutic interventions, including injection of polyethylene glycol surfactants. So, perhaps a similar approach may be used with humans as an adjunct or even alternative to traditional recompression treatment. There has been at least one study involving U.S. Navy SEALs in which they were injected with polyethylene glycol surfactant to determine its effectiveness in preventing DCS.

With a fuller understanding of the complexity of decompression sickness, it's easy to see how difficult it is to develop reliable models that predict and prevent DCS across the vast array of variables. And while we're far from understanding all the intricacies of DCS, our appreciation for this unique disorder certainly extends beyond the useful, but simplistic model of bottled soda. Then again, it's a lot more interesting, too.

CHAPTER 27

The Exercise Factor:
The Role of Physical Activity and Decompression Sickness

With a full one-third of Americans

now considered obese, advice about adopting a healthier lifestyle is rampant. Opinions and details differ on what exactly a "healthy lifestyle" means, but every definition includes three components: stop (or don't start) smoking, eat right and exercise regularly. This advice is doubly important to divers because, even when it may not seem especially strenuous, the stress we expose our bodies to underwater requires that we not only be healthy, but reasonably fit. In fact, according to recent accident data, heart disease is now a major contributor to diving fatalities, making fitness an even more significant factor in diving than we once realized. (This should come as no surprise given that the age of the average diver is now about 45.) Some even believe that the single biggest step we can take toward making diving safer isn't more training but simply getting into better shape.

But here's where diving shows itself once again to be unlike most other recreational endeavors. Unlike running or swimming or biking or virtually any other activity you can name, when it comes to diving, exercise can have a downside. We're all familiar with the overzealous athlete who takes his or her workout a bit too far and suffers some form of injury. In fact, this is a common outcome among older athletes who refuse to count the number of candles on their birthday cake, and insist that the only difference between them now and back in high school are a few gray hairs. However, in diving it's different … quite a bit different. It's not that too much or too rigorous exercise is a problem; it's that, depending on the timing and nature of the activity, any exercise may be harmful. (Notice I said exercise, not fitness.) Additionally, some recent studies have brought the conventional wisdom about diving and exercise into serious question. So what gives with this seemingly schizophrenic relationship between exercise and diving?

Why Exercise Matters

Just why the issue of exercise is important to decompression has to do with what it affects: blood flow.

While we normally emphasize depth and duration when it comes to what determines the amount of nitrogen in our tissues, another determinant is the amount of blood passing through the lungs and body tissues. So, as exercise increases blood flow, exercise also increases the amount of nitrogen absorbed. What's less obvious is how exercise might affect us before or after diving.

Understanding the effect of exercise first requires a deeper insight into the phenomenon of decompression sickness (DCS); and as you saw in the last chapter it's far more complicated than we're often led to believe. One important point to recall from the last chapter is how we think bubbles form from micronuclei or gas "seeds." (If you didn't read Chapter 26, you may want to do so before proceeding any further.)

Research has shown that micronuclei generated by exercise will last about four to six hours after exercise. This, combined with the fact that strenuous exercise will mean an elevated heart rate for several hours, is why it's advised that divers avoid strenuous exercise for several hours before diving. Furthermore, the greater the decompression stress, the more important it becomes to avoid strenuous exercise. What accounts for great decompression stress are factors such as deeper and longer dives, multiple repetitive dives, and decompression dives.

Now, here's the rub.

Research on animals indicates that humans might lower their risk of DCS by improving their general state of fitness. The reason appears to be that greater fitness translates into fewer micronuclei. There's even evidence from animal studies that, if it occurs, the severity of DCS is less for those who are in better shape. So, how do you achieve and maintain a good state of fitness if the mere act of exercising may increase the risk of DCS? More to the point, how long before diving is it safe to exercise? The answer is that no one really knows, but some important new research appears to be pointing us in the right direction. And it seems like in diving, as in life, timing is everything.

What Science Says

Just how exercise affects decompression has been examined by scientists for some time. Recently some of these scientific studies have made their way into the recreational diving community. In the process, some studies have been misinterpreted, or generalizations have been made that really aren't warranted from the conclusions. Probably the most talked-about study appeared in a 2004 issue of *The Journal of Physiology*. (One reason for its popularity is that it was the subject of several articles in nontechnical publications such as *New Scientist* and the online WebMD.) The study appeared to demonstrate that strenuous exercise might actually reduce, not increase, the likelihood of developing both large quantities of silent bubbles and DCS. But it wasn't quite as straightforward as some who heard the results assumed.

Previous studies on mice, pigs and rats by the same research group revealed that several weeks of daily aerobic training could dramatically reduce the incidence of severe DCS. The authors postulated that it was due to some unknown change in the flow dynamics of blood, brought about by physical training, that altered the susceptibility to DCS (probably through modified tissue perfusion and reduced body fat, which is a nitrogen store). But what they determined subsequently — quite by accident, it turns out — changed their minds. In a later study they found that a single bout of exercise was equally effective to a longer training regimen in producing a short-term (one to two days) reduction in decompression-induced bubble formation.

In an even more recent study with humans (the one that got all the press), the researchers took 12 fit men, all experienced divers, age 22-38 (mean age of 30). The subjects first did a very strenuous five-minute workout, with the first three minutes at a 90 percent maximum heart rate, and then reduced it to 50 percent for the final two minutes. They repeated this pattern eight times for a total exercise session of 40 minutes. Then, 24 hours afterward they were taken to 60 feet (18 m) in a chamber on air. After a bottom time of 80 minutes they were decompressed at 10 feet (3 m) for seven minutes, and then surfaced. (From previous research it's known that this profile normally generates large quantities of silent bubbles in most divers.) The divers also did another identical dive one week apart, but preceded by no exercise.

For 80 minutes after the dive the subjects were monitored at 20-minute intervals for silent bubbles through echocardiography. Episodes of silent bubbling were graded according to a well-established system. The result showed that both the number and the size of bubbles decreased significantly, compared with diving without exercise beforehand; and none of the divers developed symptoms of DCS. It appears as well that the level of exercise must be strenuous. Other studies have found that low-intensity exercise does not appear to be effective. Furthermore, exercising strenuously within 10 hours before diving does not seem to help, and may be harmful. However, exercising strenuously 48 hours before diving also does not help reduce bubble formation.

How Come?

The contradictory research results from various exercise studies seem to point to more than exercise as the mechanism for the lack of bubble formation. Many, including the group involved in the studies mentioned, are looking at a biochemical explanation involving nitric oxide. (Note: That's nitric oxide [NO], not nitrous oxide [N_2O], which is laughing gas.)

It turns out that strenuous exercise boosts the nitric oxide levels in the lining of artery walls (endothelium). As you might recall, this is a prime location for bubble formation. Nitric oxide is crucial in regulating breathing and blood flow. More to the point, there's also evidence that it prevents red blood cells from sticking together — aggregating — and attaching to the vessel wall. This makes the endothelium more slippery, and therefore harder for bubbles to form. In experiments in which nitric oxide is blocked by the administration of certain drugs, a substantial increase in bubble formation is observed. Still, nitric oxide alone doesn't seem to be the entire answer because, even when it's blocked, exercise still has a positive effect on reducing bubble formation. So, it appears that as in all areas of cutting-edge science, the complete picture isn't yet in focus.

So Where Do We Go From Here?

As with all scientific studies, it's difficult for the average Joe to make any practical sense out of the often tentative and obtuse conclusions. It complicates matters even further when there are contradictory studies (sometimes by the same groups who found the opposite conclusions). So, aside from keeping abreast of what scientists are up to, it's also helpful to seek advice from those knowledgeable in science but who also have an understanding of recreational diving practice. It's equally important to remember the limitations of the tools we use to predict DCS, dive tables and computers. Both merely estimate inert gas exchange; they can't actually know what's going on inside your body. This means that any calculation made by tables and computers is, at best, speculative — it's what the mathematics of time and pressure tell it to say.

As to what scientists say who are in the know about diving practice, their advice is cautionary. Neal Pollock, an exercise physiologist at the Center for Hyperbaric Medicine and Environmental Physiology at Duke Medical Center, and Research Director at the Divers Alert Network, is a good example. Aside from his scientific qualifications, Pollock also has a great deal of "street cred" in both recreational and technical diving. He summed up his perspective quite well in a recent article that addressed the effect of exercise before, during and after diving. "We do not yet have sufficient data to quantify the difference between beneficial and potentially harmful exercise," he said. "Understanding the various issues and applying common sense confer the best protection."

Regarding exercise while at depth, Pollock stresses that moderation is the key. In other words, be conservative with your dive profiles; never dive to the limit of any

table or computer. He describes any consideration of exercise as providing only a "secondary defense." "In terms of the secondary defense, though, the compression and bottom phases are best associated with the lightest exercise possible." And, he says, "Ascent and stop phases are best associated with mild, low-intensity exercise. Exercise that is aggressive and/or stimulates substantial joint-loading is almost always undesirable at any point near or during a dive."

Pollock also emphasizes the importance of physical fitness for divers. However, he says that, "Regular exercise training is best scheduled to separate intense exercise and diving. Intense physical training should be avoided 24 hours on either side of diving activity. Any exercise within 24 hours of diving should involve the lowest possible joint forces." He also advises an even longer time interval with more extreme dives.

Insights regarding post-dive exercise are well-addressed by another well-respected medical authority with an extensive cave diving background, Dr. David Sawatzky. "Adding to the problem is the fact that we also know it is not safe to exercise immediately after diving," he says. "If you have done a dive that has generated intravascular bubbles, exercise while you are bubbling will dramatically increase the number of intravascular bubbles as you increase the blood flow through the muscles, and this will dramatically increase your risk of developing DCS." Therefore, Sawatzky says that divers should not exercise after diving until all intravascular bubbles have been eliminated. While this is generally thought to take at least six hours, Sawatzky says, "How long this takes is influenced by the dive profile [and] is also highly variable for different divers and even for the same diver diving the same dive profile on different days." Like Pollock, he recommends a longer period, particularly for extreme exposures such as multiple repetitive dives and, especially, long deep dives.

Finally, there's the advice of Dr. Richard Moon, an anesthesiologist and diving medical expert at Duke University. In reviewing several studies on the effect of exercise on decompression illness (DCI) (both those addressed in this article and others) he draws the following conclusions: One, the effect of exercise before, during or after a dive probably depends on the level of exertion and exact timing. Two, appropriately timed exercise before a dive may protect against DCI; and, most important, three, these data are from small numbers of observations and provide limited information, so it is premature to use them to make general recommendations.

The take-home message from the exercise and decompression discussion seems clear: While there are many exciting research findings, there's currently no prudent rationale to alter the current recommendations. So, it's best to avoid rigorous exercise before, during and immediately after diving. As far as exercise is concerned, leave it for the gym.

CHAPTER 28

Avoiding a Day at the Chamber:
Preventing Decompression Illness

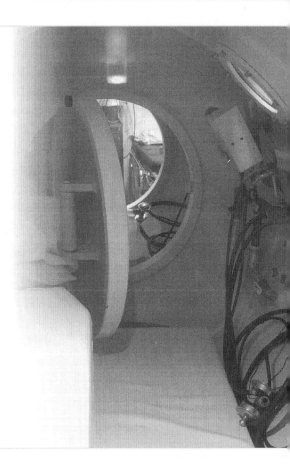

Those who know me will attest that my sense of humor is, to put it kindly, a little

offbeat. Others might say it's downright sick. This probably explains my favorite scuba T-shirt. While on a dive boat many years ago, I noticed that one of the passengers was wearing a rather plain-looking tee with the word "SCUBA" emblazoned on the front. I paid little further attention until later that afternoon when I got a look at the back. There, the acronym was explained, but it wasn't "self-contained underwater breathing apparatus." Instead, it read, "some come up bubbling alot!"

As I said, sick, but funny.

Over the years I've used the joke more times than I can remember in teaching divers and dive professionals about the nuances of decompression because, twisted as it may be, there's a modicum of truth to the point. It reminds us that, with all the new theories and advances we've made over the years, there's still an awful lot that we don't know about decompression sickness (DCS) and how to avoid it.

But this is not to say that we can't do something to even the odds of becoming a victim. In fact, there's quite a lot that we can do. So let's explore some of the behaviors that might make the difference between a trip home versus a trip to the recompression chamber.

The Art and Science of Ascending

The first step in solving a problem is to better understand its nature. This was drolly summarized long ago by one of my scientist friends. As he explains in his lectures, there's absolutely no problem in avoiding DCS with complete and absolute certainty: Just don't come up. Of course, what he means is that the problem isn't going down, but returning to atmospheric pressure. This is why so much attention has been given to the issue of ascents.

Understanding the importance of ascents requires correcting a common misnomer, and that's the term "no-decompression" diving. In reality, there's no such animal because all divers must allow their body to slowly release — decompress — the excess nitrogen or other inert gas as they return to the surface. So, all dives are, quite literally, decompression dives; it's only that some dives require a stop before proceeding to the surface and some don't. A term preferable to no-decompression dive is "no-stop" dive. But as we shall see, even that term isn't — or shouldn't be — entirely accurate.

These definitions are more than mere semantics. How we think of an ascent often dictates how we perform an ascent. And probably more than any other practice, with the possible exception of purposely violating your tables or computer, how you ascend will be the single greatest determinant in whether you'll get the bends. However, it's only been in the last decade or so that we've put such emphasis on ascents. Until then, recreational divers paid little attention to this final phase of the dive. It's why some come up bubbling a lot.

One purpose of this section of *The Complete Diver* is to provide a historical perspective on decompression issues. So, to understand where we are today, let's take a look at how we got here.

The Evolution of Ascending and Stopping

For those of you trained back in the 1980s or earlier, you probably learned to ascend no faster than 60 feet (18 m) per minute (fpm). It was one of those almost-holy admonitions divers lived by, as though the scuba police would arrest you if you went any faster. Moreover, most assumed that this vital safety tenet was derived from a solid theoretical basis and rigorous testing. Not so. In fact, the story of the 60-foot-per rate is quite interesting, as it illustrates how many supposed immutable rules have been determined in ways that are less than scientific.

Initially, when the Royal Navy adopted Haldane's decompression tables they also implemented an ascent rate of 60 fpm. This was apparently because of the ease with which they could haul a diver up and avoid missing his first decompression stop. (Haldane's original tables did not have a specific ascent rate, only total time for ascent, which included decompression time.) As the U.S. Navy adopted the Royal Navy tables with little change, it also instituted the 60 fpm rule. So, it became the ascent rate specified back in 1916 for the original U.S. Navy Bureau of Construction Tables. Somehow, for reasons no one seems to remember or, at least, documented, The *USN Diving Manual* of 1943 changed this rate to 25 fpm. Perhaps it was another accommodation to the poor tenders with the back-breaking task of hauling hundreds of pounds up and down a line all day.

In the mid-1950s a set of new U.S. Navy tables was under development. One important ingredient of the tables was the rate at which they allow the diver to ascend. A meeting was called to discuss the issue. Attending the meeting were representatives from both the Navy's hard-hat divers and their new "frogmen" (scuba divers). As it was a comfortable rate to haul up a surface-supplied diver, the deep-sea contingent wanted the then-current 25 fpm standard retained. The scuba diving contingent objected, saying that this was an impossibly slow rate of ascent for a free-swimming diver. They advocated a 100 fpm rate. As a practical human compromise — having no particular scientific basis — the group settled for 60 fpm.

By the 1970s, with the development of the Doppler Bubble Detector, scientists began conducting studies on the Navy tables. Each found a high incidence of silent bubbles present in divers after surfacing from dives defined as no-decompression. Alarmed by these results, some researchers advocated slowing the decompression rate by slowing the ascent rate. This, they reasoned, would reduce silent bubbling and — they hoped — the likelihood of DCS. Satisfied, however, with the performance of their tables in preventing DCS, the Navy did not see any need to officially amend their 60 fpm ascent rate. But the story doesn't end there.

Based on these silent bubble findings, researchers began warning recreational divers to exercise caution in their decompression practices. One practice they advocated was what we've come to know as a "safety stop." As this is sometimes a confusing issue, let's begin by looking at the difference between a *safety* stop and a *decompression* stop.

A decompression stop is a required delay in the diver's ascent before surfacing. This occurs when the diver exceeds the no-stop limit provided in the decompression model (table or computer) in use. Without such a stop, the diver will exceed the maximum allowable nitrogen level, making DCS a likely outcome (though not a certainty).

Conversely, decompression models do *not* require safety stops to reduce nitrogen levels below a critical threshold. A safety stop is merely a way of incorporating an added margin of protection. By delaying his ascent, the diver accomplishes a slower and safer elimination of nitrogen than ascending immediately to the surface.

A diver could opt not to make a safety stop — ascend directly to the surface — and not violate the decompression model. There are, however, compelling reasons you should still make a safety stop.

The first clear evidence supporting the effectiveness of safety stops was published in the 1970s. It involved two groups of volunteer recreational divers and a profile of 100 feet (30 m) for 25 minutes. (Many readers may recognize this profile as requiring a decompression stop with the table or computer they use today, but under the U.S. Navy tables it's a no-stop dive.) One group of divers ascended directly to the surface. Another group made a two-minute stop at 10 feet (3 m) before surfacing. Still a third group stopped for one minute at 20 feet (6 m) and then four minutes at 10 feet before surfacing. All divers were monitored for silent bubbles for two hours after surfacing.

The results showed a very high incidence of silent bubbles in the no-stop group. Even more striking is that the one-stop group drastically reduced their silent bubbles, and the two-stop group almost completely eliminated them. While that sounds like unequivocal support for safety stops, here's the rub. There has never been a clear causal relationship made between silent bubbles and DCS. It's merely a logical conclusion that if you reduce silent bubbles, you're likely to reduce bends. But from a purely scientific perspective, the jury is still out.

Still, even without a clear association between silent bubbles and DCS, there's still a solid reason to include such a delay in every dive you make. The reason is that safety stops make you *think* about your ascent. Frankly, before all the attention to safety stops, divers blithely ascended to the surface with little or no consideration for how fast they were going. This absentmindedness was documented in a classic study by Dr. Glen Egstrom, professor emeritus at UCLA. He demonstrated that, on average, divers ascend more on the order of 120-160 feet (36-48 m) rather than 60 feet (18 m) per minute. If you plan to make a safety stop, however, it's unlikely you'll ascend so thoughtlessly. By planning to stop before surfacing you must ascend in a very controlled, deliberate manner. This gives you an added benefit as you approach shallow water.

Initially, the advice for making a safety stop suggested that it take place at a depth of from 10 to 20 feet (3 to 6 m) for three to five minutes. If you remember back to your entry-level course, the greatest change in volume in a flexible, air-filled container — like your lungs — occurs between 2 atmospheres absolute (33 feet [10 m]) and 1 atmosphere (the surface). So, the greatest danger from a lung overexpansion injury is in shallow water. Your rate of ascent — particularly in shallow water — then becomes an important factor not only in avoiding DCS, but lung overexpansion, too. Even if you are breathing normally, shutting off your airway by an innocuous action like swallowing, combined with an innocuous action like swallowing while ascending in shallow water, could result in a lung overexpansion injury. Slowing your ascent as you approach the surface reduces the likelihood of such an accident.

However, there has been a great deal of experience and research into the ascent rate/safety stop issue in the past 15 or so years. For one thing, most authorities today agree that an ascent should not exceed 30 fpm, and many advocate an even slower rate. This advice has been built into current dive computers, which now provide both monitoring and warning when the ascent rate of their decompression model is violated.

A New Perspective

The issue of ascent rates and safety stops has become a common feature in diving safety procedures since the advent of dive computers. It has also been a critical factor in the various decompression models — and refinements of models — over the past several years. It has become an especially important component of the recent Reduced Gradient Bubble Model (RGBM) addressed in Chapter 4. Not surprisingly, the implications of ascent rates and safety stops to dive safety has not escaped the interest of the pre-eminent dive safety organization: the Divers Alert Network (DAN). DAN's former executive director, Dr. Peter Bennett, along with his colleagues Drs. Alessandro Marroni and Frans Cronje, have taken a long, hard look at the matter.

In a recent paper the researchers reflected on a fact that few have noticed: While decompression models have supposedly improved over the past two decades, and dive computers are now a standard part of the diving ensemble, *the incidence of DCS remains essentially unchanged*. Furthermore, the nature and form of DCS has remained the same. According to DAN statistics, "pain-only" (Type I) DCS accounts for about a quarter of all reported cases. Another 9.8 percent of the accident cases are arterial gas embolism, not the bends. As has been the case since such statistics were first compiled, the vast majority — 64.95 percent — of DCS cases are the more serious neurological (Type II) form of the disorder. Most of these involve the spinal cord.

In the article, the authors go on to demonstrate how this finding makes sense when one considers the kind of profiles done by recreational divers. In no-stop diving, particularly below 80 feet (24 m), fast rather than medium or slow tissues control the dive. (In this case, "control" means that they reach their critical load of nitrogen first.) Most importantly, they showed that in deep dives, tissues often have insufficient time to offload to safe levels *even if the diver makes the currently recommended safety stop of 2-3 minutes at 10-20 feet (3-6 m)*. With the fast tissues, (such as the spinal cord) so full of nitrogen, the

Bennett study contends, it's no wonder that significant post-dive silent bubbling occurs, and that Type II bends is the most common form. In another study involving almost 1,500 profiles, in which the divers wore "black box" computers that didn't permit them to know the nature of the data collected, the results were significant. After repetitive dives, 85 percent of the divers showed silent bubbles 30-40 minutes after surfacing. More troubling was that 67 percent showed high grades of bubbling, which are much more associated with the likelihood of DCS. But when a deeper safety stop was added, silent bubbling was eliminated. While the efficacy of a deep stop is still far from proven, there is evidence that making such stops might be helpful, and certainly not harmful.

A follow-up study conducted by International DAN has confirmed these results in a more controlled setting. Here, 15 divers dove eight profiles with differing combinations of ascent rates, some without a stop, some with only a shallow stop and some with both a shallow and deep stop. The profile dived was 80 feet (24 m) for 25 minutes with a three-and-a-half-hour surface interval, followed by another 80-foot dive for 20 minutes. Once again, the addition of a deep stop showed a clear advantage in having both a lower nitrogen tissue load and lowest silent bubble scores. According to the Bennett paper, the concept of deeper safety stops really represents a paradigm shift from the idea of "treating the bubble" to "beating the bubble." That is, preventing bubbles from forming in the first place, rather than attempting to minimize their size.

For those who like original sources — and aren't afraid to wade through scientific literature — a copy of the paper explaining these issues along with supporting references is available from DAN (Marroni, P. B. Bennett, F. J. Cronje, R. Cali-Corleo, P. Germonpre, M. Pieri, C. Bonuccelli1, C. Balestra. 2004. *A deep stop during decompression from 82 fsw (25 m) significantly reduces bubbles and fast tissue gas tensions. Undersea and Hyperbaric Medicine*, Vol. 31, No. 2, pp. 223-243.)

Turning Theory Into Practice

While today most divers understand that they should make safety stops, it's often a different matter when it comes to actually doing them. So, to help you turn desire into practice, here are a few suggestions on how to make this vital safety practice an easy part of every dive. By practicing these techniques as part of every dive you'll develop good diving habits, and the procedures will become second nature.

Never take the elevator. An effective safety stop begins with a proper ascent. Start giving thought to this as soon as you leave the bottom. One bad habit to get into is adding air to your buoyancy compensator (BC) as an aid, using the positive buoyancy to "take the elevator" to the surface. You should never do this. A positively buoyant ascent is not a controlled ascent. Some air in your BC can help offset the effect of excessive negative buoyancy at depth. But, it's your effort of kicking that should dictate the speed of your ascent. Your buoyancy is correct only if you stop ascending when you stop kicking. If you don't stop when you cease kicking, you should let some air out of your BC.

Ascend hand-over-hand when possible. You'll often have a rope or line to aid your ascent, particularly if you're diving from a boat. If you do have an ascent line, use it. Ascending hand-over-hand on a line, without kicking, is an excellent way of controlling your ascent rate and conserving energy. It also helps avoid kicking the mask off any diver below you. When in rough seas, however, be very careful using the anchor line of a boat. Severe pitching of the boat can make the anchor line difficult or even dangerous to handle. It could also pull you up several feet through the water at a rapid, uncontrolled rate.

Practice controlled ascents often. It's sometimes difficult to learn what a proper ascent rate should feel like. A good way to judge this is by using a mechanical aid. Practice ascending while closely monitoring your computer. All current devices will let you know visually or audibly if you're ascending too fast. If you want to really master the technique, have your buddy time you in an unaided ascent. Continue practicing until the proper rate becomes second nature. Remember, your ascent rate should be no faster than 30 fpm or *one foot every two seconds*.

Empty your BC before reaching your first stop. Too much air in your BC sometimes makes it difficult to halt your ascent as you reach shallow water. Prepare to stop by letting out air from your BC as you near your stop depth. By the time you reach that depth, you should have little if any air left in your BC. Once at your safety stop, you can then add a small amount of air to offset any negative buoyancy. Again, this is where a descent line comes in handy.

Practice 'hovering' often. You won't always have the aid of an ascent line to help you. When you don't, you'll have to maintain your position at the safety stop using only your buoyancy control skills. This requires the ability to remain in midwater by using your BC and breathing patterns, and is called "hovering." It's an essential skill for making effective safety stops. If you can't hover well, the struggle to maintain your position can cause you to exert a lot of energy. Good hovering skills allow you to relax and avoid exertion while at your safety stop.

Be careful to maintain your depth. If you're diving below 40 feet (12 m), consider taking a deep stop at half of whatever was your deepest depth. That means that after an 80-foot (24 m) dive, you have to be prepared to stop at 40 feet. So don't get complacent or distracted. Give your full attention to your ascent (but don't lose track of your buddy, of course). On shallower dives, or as you move on to your second ascent, you'll want to stop at about 15 feet (4.5 m). But maintaining a precise point at such a shallow depth can be difficult in open water when the sea state is anything but calm. In controlling your depth, err to below rather than above 15 feet (4.5 m). Getting deeper in the water column makes you less subject to the effects of surge and gives you a margin of error in case you begin to ascend inadvertently. It also helps you avoid being hit by boats that might pass overhead. Keep a constant eye on your depth gauge to make sure you're not slowly descending or ascending.

Remain at the stop for an appropriate amount of time. For the deeper stop, one minute is all you need. At the shallower stop spend at least two minutes. However, some authorities have suggested remaining at the shallower stop for a period equal to 10 percent of the bottom time. The point is you can't spend too long at this shallow depth.

Too Much of a Good Thing

Ascending and stopping aren't the only issues that have been explored and revised in the last two decades. The most important benefit of dive computers is that they allow us to dive longer and more often. But, as with all good things, this comes with a price. Some contend that technology may now actually allow us to do too much diving, period. The reason is that no current decompression model so far — and thus no dive computer

— was designed and tested conclusively for multiple-day, multiple-dive use.

Multiple-day diving is still a very poorly understood aspect of decompression theory, so science has no firm hold on exactly what's too much, or even what precisely we can do to make it safer it (although this is an issue DAN hopes to get a handle on through a multiyear study called Project Dive Exploration). But that hasn't stopped researchers and clinicians from offering some informed advice. For example, to reduce the yet-unqualified risk of multiple-day diving, DAN has long recommended either of two common-sense practices. One is to curtail diving somewhat toward the end of a diving holiday. The second is to consider taking a day off to go sightseeing or just lay on the beach in the middle of a trip. Either practice will help reduce nitrogen levels and, hopefully, the risk of DCS while on an extended diving vacation. There's also some statistical evidence that it may be a good idea to limit the depth of any repetitive dive to a maximum of 80 feet (24 m). Dives deeper than 80 feet ideally should be confined to the initial dive of the day.

Diving, as life does in general, involves risk. For a prudent diver, just as for a prudent person, the trick is determining the degree of acceptable risk, and doing everything reasonable to reduce it. Risk can never be eliminated, and all dives, regardless of the precautions taken, carry with them the possibility of ending in bends. And while there's a lot we can do to hedge our bets, there are no guarantees when it comes to avoiding DCS. Remember, DCS is a probabalistic condition determined by depth, bottom time and gas mixture. Simple steps like limiting depth and bottom times, slow ascents, safety stops, prolonged surface intervals and use of nitrox on air tables are all ways to reduce our risk. Who knows; maybe one day SCUBA will mean "some come up bubbling alittle" — or perhaps not bubbling at all. ꩜

CHAPTER 29

Excuse Me, I Think I'm Bent

I've spent most of my adult life writing and teaching people about the infamous diving disorder, decompression sickness (DCS).

The result has been countless articles, lectures, seminars and even an entire book on the subject. So, it may seem strange to hear that, in nearly a half-century of diving, I've never had — nor even witnessed — a single case of bends.

Not one.

If there was ever a reason to knock on wood, that's certainly a good one. But what it goes to show is that diving accidents are, indeed, very rare events. According to Divers Alert Network (DAN), about two to four cases of bends occur for every 10,000 dives. Most divers who hear that little tidbit think it's a very low number, but I guess it all depends on whether you're one of the two to four victims. To anyone unlucky enough to suffer the disorder, one case is entirely too many. This chapter addresses the topic of DCS from the perspective of commonly presented symptoms, appropriate first aid and case management — to include use of expert resources like DAN, and goes on to describe treatment.

No diver can receive certification without learning the signs and symptoms of DCS. The question is, however, just how much of this knowledge do they retain? And in discussing the issue with colleagues in the diving medical community, apparently, not much. Furthermore, even those who should know better often fall victim to the old adage, "denial ain't just a river in Egypt." Indeed, it seems that recognizing signs and symptoms is

one thing; but believing one has actually succumbed to DCS can be quite another.

Experience shows that divers will evoke a plethora of excuses, ranging from "strain from carrying tanks" to "partying too hard last night," rather than accept the more serious probability of DCS. Like with any potentially serious medical condition, when it comes to the bends, the it-just-can't-happen-to-me syndrome is alive and well. Amazingly, this refusal to believe something is wrong is so strong that, according to DAN statistics, 20 percent of injured divers continue to dive, even after noticing their symptoms. This has led many in the diving medical field to consider denial one of the most common symptoms of DCS, and one DAN official to remark, "Many injured divers call us not because they have symptoms, but because their symptoms won't go away."

Once all doors to denial are closed, however, it's time to get down to dealing with the matter. The first step is determining the severity. The most severe cases of DCS appear within about an hour of surfacing. Here, you're dealing with a true medical emergency.

DCS symptoms that occur soon after surfacing (within about an hour) tend to progress rapidly, affect the nervous system and are at risk of becoming severe. Such cases are true medical emergencies. Signs and symptoms may include abnormal gait, muscular weakness, urinary retention and loss of sensation. By contrast, symptoms that present much later, say 12-24 hours after surfacing, tend to be milder, and thus may get ignored or downplayed — a time when prompt treatment may have resulted in resolution.

Most recreational divers who suffer DCS experience mild symptoms that occur many hours (less than 24) after surfacing. Initially, the victim may not appear to be in distress, and some neurological signs (what you can observe) and symptoms (what the victim feels) may not be obvious without a careful history and examination.

Regardless of severity, all DCS victims should be placed immediately on 100 percent oxygen and given fluids by mouth. Do not give any pain medication unless advised to do so by medical personnel. Continue supplying oxygen until supplies are exhausted or the diver arrives at a medical treatment facility.

In dealing with conscious and alert victims, have them assume a position of comfort. This can include sitting upright or lying on their back. If the victim is not fully alert, or may vomit, place the diver in what's known as the "recovery position." This involves having them lie to one side (usually left) with the head supported at a low angle and upper leg bent at the knee. If vomiting occurs in this position, gravity will assist in keeping the airway clear. For you old mossbacks out there, the old Trendelenburg position — head low with the diver's feet elevated or body on an incline — is no longer used in cases of DCI, as it sometimes causes breathing difficulty, wastes time and complicates movement of the patient. Studies have also shown that the procedure increases intracranial pressure and adversely affects the blood-brain barrier.

Sometimes recognizing DCS can be difficult when symptoms are either not obvious or have progressed slowly for several days after initial presentation. In this case, the main signs or symptoms are usually vague complaints of pain ("I can't really describe the pain") or abnormal sensation ("I've never felt this way before"). Here, the diagnosis of DCS may be in question, so it's important to get as complete a diving history as you can

and, if possible, a neurological evaluation. Then call DAN or the nearest medical facility for advice.

Unlike cases of arterial gas embolism, in which symptoms are almost immediate, DCS takes time to evolve, sometimes even several hours. Much can happen over this period, and it's easy to forget some of the details. However, treatment will be much more effective if medical personnel know as much as possible about what exactly occurred. This makes a complete diving history an invaluable aid in DCS treatment. So, once you suspect a case of DCS, it's a good idea to start taking some detailed notes about the incident. There's specific information that you should try and collect.

Get a description of all dives made within the last 48 hours preceding the event. Try to determine the injured diver's dive profiles as accurately as possible, along with surface intervals, the type of gas used and any problems or symptoms that arose at any time before, during or after the dives. Note any traumatic injuries before, during or after the dive.

Record the onset times and progression of symptoms after the diver surfaced from his last dive. Describe all first-aid measures taken, including times and method of oxygen delivery, and any effect on the symptoms. Make note of and describe all joint or other pain symptoms, including location, intensity and changes with movement or weight-bearing maneuvers. Include descriptions and distribution of any rashes, and be sure to record the results of any neurological exams.

Part of determining the eventual treatment for DCS is determining the course of treatment. This will be done by medical personnel at the treatment facility, but it can be immeasurably helpful if someone on the scene can conduct a basic field neurological exam as soon as possible after the report of symptoms. Conducting a basic field examination is easy, and training is available from DAN-qualified instructors all over the world. Even if you have no formal training, the basic guidelines are contained in the DAN Pocket Guide to First Aid for Scuba Diving. This small, plastic booklet, along with an oronasal resuscitation mask ("Pocket Mask"), should be a part of every diver's equipment ensemble.

Why Oxygen?

Virtually every diver everywhere knows that the most helpful thing anyone suffering from DCS can do is to breathe pure oxygen. Yet, many don't know exactly why. Oxygen breathing helps injured divers in two primary ways. First, it accelerates removal of nitrogen (or other inert gas) from the body — a process that may also reduce bubble size. Second, it enhances oxygen supply to tissues that may have reduced blood supplies due to local inflammation or vascular blockages. Additional benefits may also include swelling reduction and reduction of respiratory distress in those with pulmonary symptoms.

To be most effective, the oxygen concentration should be as close to 100 percent as possible. The problem is that actually achieving full 100 percent oxygen concentration is almost impossible in the field, so the objective is to get as close as possible. Remember, too, that with the proper equipment and training you can provide supplemental oxygen even while administering rescue breaths or CPR. As mentioned earlier, once oxygen therapy has begun, the goal should be to continue until the diver either reaches a medical facility or emergency oxygen supplies are exhausted. Learning how to deliver oxygen at a maximum concentration is one of the many benefits of taking an Oxygen Provider course.

Sometimes oxygen administration alone can completely resolve DCS symptoms. In fact, in one study, 12 percent of reported DCS victims who received supplemental oxygen were symptom-free by the time they received recompression therapy; but that fell to a mere 3 percent for those who did not receive supplemental oxygen. In another study, 14 percent of victims receiving supplemental oxygen experienced complete relief, with 51 percent showing at least some improvement. Furthermore, those who had received oxygen before recompression therapy — even if it was many hours earlier — had better treatment outcomes.

These are reassuring statistics, but the problem is that only about one-third of all DCS victims receive supplemental oxygen (though there is a much higher percentage in emergency cases). Clearly, there's still a lot of room for improvement in the first aid DCS victims are given on the scene.

While oxygen administration is a priority in any case of DCS, it's ironic that its effectiveness can also pose a problem. Because oxygen breathing can reduce or eliminate signs and symptoms, some have used this as a rationale to delay or not call for medical assistance. They wrongly assume "everything is OK" or "it's getting better on its own." This is a wrong conclusion because, without medical consultation, you can never know to what degree an injured diver has recovered or be certain he may not relapse. Without exception, medical evaluation is necessary whenever bends is suspected, even if the situation appears to be getting better or if signs and symptoms have resolved with emergency oxygen therapy.

An unfortunate misconception among many divers is that, when bends occurs, you should rush the victim off to the nearest recompression chamber. This is understandable, given that recompression is most often the ultimate treatment for DCS. However, while a chamber may be the victim's eventual destination, it's not the first priority. From a practical standpoint, how do you know that the nearest chamber is working or is available to receive patients? Are you even sure that what you think is the nearest chamber is, in fact, the nearest chamber? In reality, in severe cases, immediate medical support in the form of oxygen and IV fluid may be even more vital to the injured diver than recompression. The point is, you're in no position to make these assessments. That's why, as in all medical emergencies, the first step is to activate the emergency medical service (EMS) and seek medical evacuation.

Once emergency services are activated, contact DAN. DAN medical staff are available to talk with you at the scene and with treating physicians at the medical facility once the patient arrives. DAN can also help if transportation requires air evacuation or coordination with remote chambers. Don't try to coordinate evacuations yourself, as this requires expertise that the folks at DAN have.

Medical Intervention

Victims of DCS often arrive at the emergency room of their own accord or are brought in by fellow divers. Although severe cases require urgent recompression, it's essential that the injured diver first be stabilized at the nearest medical facility before medically supervised transportation to a chamber.

In areas where diving is popular, EMS personnel may be well-versed in the management of diving accidents. In this case, there may be little to do other than provide the medical professionals with as complete a history of the event as possible. However, in regions where diving isn't very popular, your role may be much more direct. In some cases, EMTs or paramedics may not be aware of the nature of DCS, or the importance of emergency oxygen.

For example, in cases in which divers have recovered from a reported unconscious or unresponsive episode, EMTs may stop oxygen administration, not realiz-

The U.S. Navy has set rules for returning to diving after treatment. For pain-only DCS involving no neurological symptoms, divers may begin diving two to seven days after treatment, depending on the treatment table used.

If there are neurological symptoms, the diver may resume diving two to four weeks after treatment, depending on symptom severity. For very severe symptoms, the diver must be re-evaluated three months after treatment and cleared by a diving medical officer.

Of course, the Navy's guidelines are for professionals, whose time off must be minimized so operations are not compromised. For recreational divers, whose diving is not a livelihood, a more conservative approach is called for to further minimize the chance that a diving injury will recur.

With "pain-only" DCS (absence of *any* neurological symptoms) the diver may resume diving two weeks after complete symptom resolution.

If there are even minor neurological symptoms, a minimum of six weeks without diving after symptom resolution is recommended.

If there are severe neurological symptoms or any residual symptoms, no further diving is recommended.

Again, these are recommendations for military personnel. Most diving medical authorities recommend that recreational divers wait to resume diving at least six weeks after all symptoms have subsided; and do so only after a complete medical evaluation.

Even those with a history of severe neurological DCS can dive again based on their clinical condition. However, a cautious approach is recommended to include an alteration of diving practices such as shorter bottom times, shallower dives, the use of nitrox on air tables and longer surface intervals. These people should also consider not diving more than twice a day. There isn't data to support these recommendations, but they all add up to enhanced safety.

Even if symptoms were not severe and resolved completely, a diver who has had frequent bouts of DCS-like symptoms should take special precautions. DCS is a probabilistic process that may occur in a diver, even when others in the group are symptom-free. Such occurrences may represent normal variations in susceptibility, but may also indicate an underlying condition that increases the chances of DCS in that individual — especially if DCS hits occur repeatedly in nonprovocative dive profiles. Such divers may have increased susceptibility to DCS; and in these instances a diving medical specialist should be consulted to determine if diving can be resumed safely.

Source: Divers Alert Network

ing that it should continue until a physician can make an assessment and diagnosis. Don't be hesitant to emphasize that they should not curtail oxygen administration once the patient becomes alert and responsive. Sometimes this is even necessary with treating physicians who aren't familiar with DCS. If you face resistance from medical personnel, it may help to recommend that they call DAN to speak with medical personnel familiar with diving accidents.

During transport, especially with unconscious patients, EMS personnel are likely to begin intravenous (IV) infusion. This is to begin correcting any dehydration and reduce hemoconcentration (thickening of the blood). The process to correct fluid imbalances in the diver is begun immediately to help slow the progression of symptoms. In spinal cord cases, a urinary catheter may also be necessary.

Definitive treatment of DCI (both DCS and air embolism) is performed in a hyperbaric chamber, which enables both the administration of high oxygen concentrations and increased ambient pressure. The combination of oxygen and pressure help to reduce bubble formation, reduce systemic inflammation, speed inert gas removal and symptom resolution.

Prompt treatment initiation is always preferred, but in most cases of mild-to-moderate DCS, moderate delays don't seem to affect treatment effectiveness. Current case series data gathered by DAN from treated harvesting divers in Honduras also suggest that even after several days, treatment can still result in symptom reduction.

Treatment of DCS is usually done in accordance with tables developed and published by the U.S. Navy.

Comparison of Symptoms Presented by DCS Victims

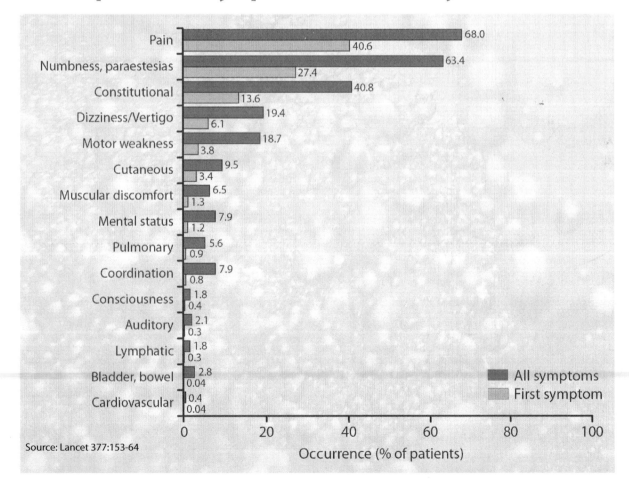

Symptom	All symptoms	First symptom
Pain	68.0	40.6
Numbness, paraestesias	63.4	27.4
Constitutional	40.8	13.6
Dizziness/Vertigo	19.4	6.1
Motor weakness	18.7	3.8
Cutaneous	9.5	3.4
Muscular discomfort	6.5	1.3
Mental status	7.9	1.2
Pulmonary	5.6	0.9
Coordination	7.9	0.8
Consciousness	1.8	0.4
Auditory	2.1	0.3
Lymphatic	1.8	0.3
Bladder, bowel	2.8	0.04
Cardiovascular	0.4	0.04

Source: Lancet 377:153-64

Occurrence (% of patients)

The most frequently used protocol is the U.S. Navy Treatment Table 6 and consists of compression to the depth of 60 feet (18 m) seawater with the patient on oxygen. The diver is later decompressed to 30 feet (9 m) on oxygen then slowly pushed (1 foot [0.3 m] per minute) to surface pressure. This table typically takes about five hours, but may take longer. U.S. Navy Treatment Table 5 is similar to Table 6 but is shorter in duration. It is typically used as a follow-up treatment when mild symptoms remain after initial therapy. Table 9 involves compression to 45 feet (14 m) seawater with the patient on oxygen, with later decompression to surface pressure. This table is often used as a follow-up treatment as well as for wound care unrelated to a diving accident — a common use for hyperbaric oxygen therapy.

While the vast majority of DCS patients recover fully by the end of therapy, in some cases there may be residual symptoms. In severe DCS cases, significant residual neurological dysfunction may be present, even after the most aggressive treatment. The patient may also require numerous follow-up treatments, as well as physical therapy. Still, provided a diver seeks prompt treatment, the outcome is most often complete symptom relief.

Any form of bends is a serious matter, and even when staying within the no-decompression limits, DCS can still occur. Knowing the signs of DCS and how to provide oxygen first aid can make a big difference. In the event that DCS does occur or is suspected, place the person on oxygen and activate EMS. Even if the injured person isn't a DAN member, they can still provide information, describe first-aid procedures and talk with treating physicians. Hopefully, like me, you'll never see a case of DCS, but if you do, knowing how to respond can make all the difference in the outcome. ♺

You can reach the Divers Alert Network Emergency Hotline by calling 919-684-9111 to talk to an expert in diving medicine. DAN medics are on call 24 hours a day to provide information and assistance to injured divers.

When calling tell the operator you have a diving emergency. They will either connect you directly with a DAN medic or have someone from the medical staff call you back at the earliest possible moment. DAN asks that you do not use the emergency line for fitness-to-dive issues or general diving and health issues, or for DAN membership, insurance and product questions and purchases.

All calls are triaged by DAN medical services staff. They also have hyperbaric/diving physicians from the University of California at San Diego or University of Pennsylvania on call for consultation.

If the situation is life-threatening, call EMS immediately. Call DAN once EMS has been activated, as they may be able to provide guidance and assistance.

CHAPTER 30

Bending the Mind:
The Psychology of Decompression Sickness

Regardless of our capacity for abstract reasoning, most humans are very concrete

thinkers. We like definitive answers — right or wrong, yes or no. Shades of gray, or any sort of uncertainty, is just not what we like to hear or even accept. While the idea of certainty is comforting, it's not really the way life works. Few aspects of our lives — at least, the important stuff — tend to fall into neat categories of black or white.

Definitive answers are exactly what people expect when it comes, particularly, to science and medicine. Yet the very nature of these fields defies certainty. That's why many consider medicine as much an art as a science. And it's why, as every true scientist knows, absolute certainty regarding any phenomenon in nature is a virtual impossibility.

In the diving realm, when dealing with medical issues like decompression sickness (DCS), we often forget or ignore the uncertain nature of science and speak unjustifiably in terms of certainty. For example, how often have you heard statements like these? "Bends happens because bubbles form." "Drinking plenty of water will help you avoid DCS." "Your risk of decompression sickness will increase if you're obese." "The computer says that for this depth the no-decompression limit is 30 minutes." These are statements you might encounter in any discussion of DCS and, as a result, divers can come away with the impression that our understanding of the phenomenon is as certain as Newton's laws of motion. The reality is that we don't know for sure whether any of these statements are really true. They're merely theo-

retical assumptions based on a model of decompression that scientists use until something better comes along.

An unintended result of viewing the science of decompression as certitude is that it can lead to serious misconceptions. It can also result in some negative psychological consequences, and even encourage some to deny very clear and obvious symptoms of bends.

What We Know and What We Don't

I've had lots of opportunities to speak with audiences about dive safety issues, and it has become abundantly clear to me that divers harbor many beliefs and assumptions that are completely unfounded by science, medicine or even practical experience. Much of this, I believe, stems from the impression of certainty that we instructors convey about the subject of decompression during training. But what can we really say with any certainty? Surprisingly, not much. We think — though it's unproven — that DCS results from bubble formation; and we've developed some pretty elaborate theories — none yet confirmed — about why bubbles form. We can also make some generally reliable estimates — that work most but not all of the time — about how long divers can remain at depth without a "significant chance" of getting the bends.

Likewise, we often hear of the "risk factors" that supposedly predispose us to bends. But as you read about earlier in this section on decompression, not only are most of these accepted risk factors supported by very little scientific evidence, every diving medical expert has his or her own set of risk factors and a different opinion on the relative importance of each. Clearly, if you're someone who demands clear and unequivocal answers, the subject of decompression theory is not one that will make you feel all warm and fuzzy.

Scientists even have a term for the fundamental uncertainty of decompression sickness, calling it a "probabilistic risk." In other words, sometimes it just happens. The one and only absolute certain fact about DCS is this: You can do everything right, and follow every rule there is, was or ever will be, yet still get the bends.

Denial:
An Unintended Consequence

I've had this discussion with many dive professionals about the negative consequences of implying more certainty concerning DCS than is warranted. Some have countered my opinion, claiming that the more confidence we express in what we tell divers about the subject, the more likely they are to follow the rules and guidelines. This approach may, in fact, work as long as nothing goes wrong. But, when bends occurs unexpectedly — when it happens when it supposedly should not — there can be serious psychological and attitudinal consequences. Take this scenario, for example: A diver assumes, based on what he's been told by his instructors and other experienced divers, that his computer will keep him safe as long as he doesn't violate its dictates and follows all the guidelines like staying warm, remaining well hydrated and avoiding vigorous exercise. Then, one day after a modest dive well within the limits, he experiences some minor joint pain that progressively grows worse over time.

It's often said that the first symptom of the bends isn't pain or paralysis but denial. Indeed, just like folks ignore or deny heart attack symptoms, the last thing that many divers will admit is that they might have the bends. Now, here's where the consequences of certitude come into play. Confronted with a situation he doesn't want to believe in the first place, our injured diver assumes that "this can't be bends because I did nothing wrong." Thus, his case for denial is strengthened, and he writes off the pain as the result of muscle strain from carrying tanks improperly or an aggravated previous injury. Anything but DCS.

In fact, denial of DCS symptoms is so strong that, according to accident statistics from the Divers Alert Network (DAN), 20 percent of divers who seek treatment continued to dive even after experiencing the first signs. If that statistic is hard for you to believe, as it was for me, consider this actual account from a British diver (whom we'll call "Jane") who was thoughtful enough to share her experience and feelings on an Internet blog. "My bends appeared to come out of the blue. A bit like being hit by a bus when you're standing in the middle of a field, it's just not expected. This is how mine felt; forty minutes after surfacing … I developed terrible pains in my chest, I remember being bent double in agony. Partial blindness followed, as did confusion and extreme distress. I had to be helped off the boat, very unwell, but oblivious of what was happening to me. *At the time it didn't occur to me that this was bends. It didn't occur to those around me either,* [author's emphasis] so instead of rushing me to the nearest chamber, I was tucked up in bed to 'sleep it off.'"

Denial took hold so strongly that Jane believed, rather than DCS, she was suffering from the worse migraine of her life. "[F]or the remainder of the week I did further dives, with symptoms after about half of them, including a rash across my stomach, swollen breasts and the beginning of pitching when I walked. My brain was already swollen and damaged; I didn't have the insight to know I had to stop and get help."

An extreme case, you say? The same blog relates another similar story. "Sarah" was on a dive when she began to experience serious pain and numbness down one side of her body. "I was literally dragging my leg as I walked," she writes. "My boyfriend was moaning at me for holding everybody up, so ignoring it and getting on with the diving just seemed the best thing to do." Not a single diver in her party even questioned whether she might have DCS.

Several days later Sarah finally went to the hospital. The result? "At first they wanted to send me away with a painkiller, but I was in agony and was beginning to think I may have the bends so I insisted on being seen. They decided I had DCS and referred me to a recompression chamber." In Sarah's case, she turned out not to have DCS after all but rather a slipped disk. Still, the denial that bends could have even been a possibility, by her and everyone around her, was clear and unequivocal.

One writer has compared this not-uncommon denial scenario with the battling knight in the cult classic comedy, *Monty Python and the Holy Grail*. In it, the knight hops around with a severed leg, repeating, "No, I'm fine! It's just a flesh wound." Sarah adds, "It's simply not polite to point out that someone is dragging their leg and question them about their diving. It's terribly embarrassing to own up to the fact that we cannot lift our arm properly, or that we suspect our murderous headache might need more than an aspirin to sort it out."

Aside from whistling past the graveyard, denial of DCS is also a result of peer pressure because, for many, it somehow implies failure or weakness. Jane's continuing saga is a case in point. "Forty minutes to an hour after surfacing [the pain] started with a sharp stabbing pain in my left shoulder. Next came the very sudden loss of vision followed by shivering and feeling very cold. I went to an experienced diver who was sitting near me and told her what was going on; she said, 'let's get you on oxygen.' I felt a wave of relief that help was on its way, only to have that hope dashed when the Divemaster over-ruled her. My symptoms got much worse. I started to get stabbing pains in the small of my back, then the terrible itching started. I got up and staggered over to a very experienced diver that I trusted. He asked if I had a rash and I told him I didn't know as I couldn't see. The Divemaster suggested that I had a 'heat rash.' I felt like a pest."

Of course, the solution to the problem is obvious; we need a change in attitude. Tom Mount, founder and head of the International Association of Nitrox and Technical Divers and one of the most experienced divers on the planet, sums it up this way: "We need to take the blame factor out of dealing with bends ... a DCI [decompression illness] hit should be viewed as a sports injury. If people feel that they will be condemned as 'bad divers' for suffering a bend, it does nothing to encourage people to speak up when they feel unwell after a dive."

Dealing With Uncertainty

The uncertain nature of DCS has given rise to describing two different phenomena when classifying the disorder; "deserved" and "undeserved" bends. The former refers to situations when tables, rules or guidelines are clearly broken, and the latter where there's been no such violation. But what may not be so obvious is that these terms imply a moral judgment — one either deserves or doesn't deserve to be injured. It also makes possible a defense mechanism whereby others can distance themselves psychologically from someone who gets DCS. By looking only for a logical explanation for the accident, insisting that a diver was injured because he or she violated the tables or broke a rule, we feel more in control and confident that we can alter our own diving practice so we don't make the same mistake.

A more severe reaction than trying to make some sense out of an uncertain situation, and one that's all too common, is actually attacking the victim. By desperately trying to find some mistake, attackers can prove to themselves that their behavior isn't like the victim's. Worse yet, the victim may be viewed as weak or flawed. Rather than acknowledge that they are equally at risk, attackers conclude that they have nothing to worry about, thus restoring an illusion of safety.

The more positive approach is, of course, to avoid attacks and moralizing, and emphasize the truly uncertain nature of DCS. Further, many authorities now advocate using less emotional and value-ridden terms, and describe DCS rather than deserved or undeserved as either "expected" or "unexpected."

The upshot to all this is that, while DCI is clearly a physiological disorder, there are nonetheless important psychological consequences as well. Therefore, dealing with DCS means more than treating what's wrong inside the body; it also requires dealing with what's going on inside the mind. This is especially true when divers feel that they didn't deserve what happened to them.

Studies of injured divers have found that the psychological consequences of DCS can have profound and lasting effects on one's mental health. Often those injured in an "unexpected" case feel that their body has somehow "betrayed" them, as they, after all, did nothing wrong. And mental health professionals have documented in case after case that if this conflict isn't resolved it can lead to more serious mental disorders like depression.

To avoid negative psychological consequences, therapists encourage DCS victims to talk about their feelings. Remaining silent or denying the event is the worst possible course of action. Equally important, if it's an unexpected case, is that the injured diver come to understand that not all cases of bends are preventable — that the only way to avoid the bends with complete certainty is never to dive.

Even after a full recovery, remaining silent is still the wrong approach. Quite often, divers want to use their experiences as object lessons to help others in similar circumstances. This is an especially powerful desire among victims who are instructors. In addition to the practical benefit in educating others, there's a therapeutic role in letting the victim put some positive meaning into an event that he may feel was a mistake. And this was exactly how Jane eventually reacted to her injury. "Telling my story over and over again is good therapy for dealing with what happened," she says. "Every time I tell it, it feels more real. Besides, I hope to share the experiences I made with as many divers as possible. I am still firmly convinced that a large part of all the certified scuba divers in the world very well could end up in the same situation. For this reason I choose not to hold back, but instead tell my story to as many people as possible, even if it exposes my clumsiness to the rest of the world, to some extent."

Another important aspect of the psychology of DCS is how others react to bends victims. Much like the victims of sexually transmitted diseases, divers who get decompression sickness are sometimes stigmatized. They are even ridiculed and reproached by their friends, diving professionals and even — as the example that follows points out — the medical community. This, of course, reinforces the feeling that they did something "wrong."

A case in point comes from British technical diver Natasha Abels, who suffered DCS after a record-breaking 590-foot (179 m) trimix dive several years ago. "I have experienced the bends three times and each time has been different. I always train and plan for my dives, make sure I'm well hydrated and do more than the required stops. But if you dive enough, then decompression sickness is bound to catch up with you at some point."

But what Abels wasn't prepared for was the reaction to her accident. "I was quite horrified at some of the attitudes I came across. People reacted in a very judgmental way, as if I was some silly girl who didn't know what she was doing. When I was in the hospital, the doctor was hastily reading up about DCS and it was apparent that I was far more informed about my symptoms than he was. Yes, I was pushing the limits, but no one turns around to a mountaineer with a broken ankle and goes, 'Well that was a bit stupid, wasn't it?' For some reason, diving has a more moralistic attitude. It's not only unhelpful, it's actually quite harmful to the sport."

What the Pros Tell Us

One researcher who has conducted some compelling research into the social and psychological consequences of DCS is Dr. Jennifer Hunt, a New York-based psychologist and avid diver. She says there are significant negative consequences to the diving community's attitude of making value judgments of bends victims. Hunt says that moralizing serves no useful purpose; and chastising a victim only makes it more likely he or she will hide their symptoms, or make them more reluctant to seek treatment. And, if they do seek treatment, the fear of being branded "bad" or "wrong" makes it likely they'll omit details about their profile or other information that could be vital to a proper diagnosis and resolution. The result could be not just psychological scars, but permanent physical damage from delayed or improper treatment. She says, "In the face of social assault, divers are encouraged to maintain defenses such as denial and self-recrimination, which may minimize some immediate danger but can compromise their long-term psychological welfare."

Summarizing her research, Hunt says DCS is not a moral disease and should not be treated as one. "To do so damages the victim's chance at full physical and psychological recovery and has a negative impact on the diving community. This recognition does not constitute an acceptance of practices that some segments of the dive community feel put divers at risk. It simply acknowledges that divers who are bent suffer a serious physical illness that can have far-reaching consequences. Victims of decompression illness deserve understanding and treatment rather than social ridicule."

A useful perspective is also offered by Dr. David Sawatzky, a Canadian diving medical authority and technical diving enthusiast. He sees benefits in understanding and accepting risk on an individual level, which is something we can do only if we understand the uncertain nature of DCS. "The first step in understanding the real risks in diving," he says, "is to understand our own personal responses to those risks, and try to accept others' responses to those risks. If we can accept that everyone will have a different comfort boundary and if we can see honest admission of our limitations as a strength instead of a weakness, we will empower the individual diver and remove the element of peer-induced risk from the sport. If we stop criticizing and ostracizing accident victims, we will all be far more likely to admit the possibility that we could be bent when we have symptoms, be more likely to seek treatment, and more likely to share our experiences so that others can learn from our mistakes."

One thing is certain, however, and that's that decompression sickness involves a lot more than bubbles. And its consequences also include a lot more than physical symptoms. 🐋

SECTION
IV
DECONSTRUCTING
DECOMPRESSION;
UNBENDING
THE BENDS

CHAPTER 31

Head Games:
The Mental Side of Dive Planning and Performance

I $once$ heard a report that Americans now have the distinction of working more hours than any others on Earth, even the traditionally workaholic Japanese. In a smug, congratulatory tone, the announcer went on to explain that our love affair with our jobs is a primary reason for the unprecedented productivity of our economy. Frankly, my reaction to the report wasn't what I'd term positive. My mama always told me that I was so lazy she was surprised moss didn't grow on me. She mistakenly believed that her comments would shame me into action. I, on the other hand, took her jibes as a compliment. Then, as to this day, I pride myself on working as little as possible.

Another little factoid that piqued my attention was the recent announcement by the U.S. Department of Labor that my generation works, on average, one day per month more than a generation ago. It's strange how all the predictions by futurists of years past have turned out to be so wrong. With all the prepackaged, automatic, ready-to-serve, computerized labor-saving gadgets, we're now working more, not less, than our parents.

While it's great to enjoy the fruits of our success-driven culture, the downside of this equation of happiness is obvious. More work equals more stress and less time to enjoy what we work *for*. In fact, escaping work-related stress is one reason many folks get into diving. And it seems to work well. It would be impossible for me to recount the number of times harried executives, overworked physicians or stressed-out lawyers have told me that nothing is more relaxing and rejuvenating than spending time underwater.

While I'm the first to endorse diving as an escape from the hectic existence of modern-day life, let's not forget that stress, albeit a different form, is still a part of the diving experience. In fact, in the context of div-ing accident analysis, stress is a bigger part of the diving experience than most realize.

To understand where I'm coming from, let's start with a definition. Psychologists define stress as a "state that evokes effort on the part of the individual to maintain or restore equilibrium." At issue is that things somehow are out of balance. But is this necessarily bad? Not at all. In fact, stress is neither good nor bad; what counts is how we handle it.

The assumption by many that stress is always something to avoid is a major misconception. Some stress, believe it or not, is good. Psychologists have long recognized that there's an "optimal level" of stress that will actually enhance performance. Think back to the last time you addressed a group of people. If you did a good job, you probably remember that you weren't totally stressed out about the prospect of speaking in public, but you certainly had some trepidation. That's the good stress keeping you on your toes and helping you strive to do the best job possible. The same thing applies when we dive.

Some assert that whether stress is positive or negative depends on the three C's — choice, control and consequence. Choice is whether an individual elects to be placed under stress, such as by accepting a challenge. Control relates to how much influence the individual can exercise over the situation. Consequence involves the individual's ability to anticipate what may happen as a result of the situation.

What Causes Stress?

Diving psychologists (yes, there are such folks) have determined four categories of stress: physical, psychological, equipment-related and environmental. These may work either independently or in combination. Physical stressors are pretty obvious and include cold water, fatigue and lack of fitness. Physical stress can even be induced by the constriction of movement or breathing impairment caused by your wet suit or buoyancy compensator (BC). These all translate to your brain telling you, "Hold on a minute, I'm not quite happy!"

As diving is highly equipment-intensive, it should come as no surprise that this can induce stress, especially for the inexperienced. Stress can arise from a whole host of equipment-related factors such as poorly maintained or malfunctioning equipment, wearing too much or too little weight, or wearing the wrong equipment for the task at hand (like tanks of inadequate capacity). Other forms of equipment stress might arise from a failure to monitor information (such as air supply, depth or time) or even abrupt loss of equipment, such as a dislodged mask or loss of a dive light when night diving. Given the amount of equipment we wear, the sky's the limit when it comes to the number of potential sources of stress. Again, your mind is telling you, "I'm really not pleased!"

Just when you thought you had a handle on the stress issue, here comes another factor: the environment. Here the problem is twofold because the stressor can be either obvious or subtle. Obvious stressors might be poor conditions such as rough seas, bad weather or low visibility. But factors that induce environmental stress aren't always obvious. For example, even good conditions can be stressful when the environment is unfamiliar. Take night diving. Recognizing that jumping into the ocean at night isn't quite at the top of the list of "things I most want to do," instructors often take great care to select conditions that are as calm and ideal as possible. Yet try as they might, most sane human beings are still more than a bit stressed about the idea of diving in a darkened world. (Go figure.) This is a perfectly natural, healthy human response. In fact, if stress is managed as a way to maintain an alert state, it's good that you feel this way.

The final category of stress — psychological factors — can be the most complex and least obvious. Psychological stress comes from a number of sources, ranging from having to perform too many tasks at once (what's referred to by some as "taskloading") to having to perform within a limited time frame to diving beyond your perceived limits or capabilities. Another common psychological factor seen in dive buddies who are also spouses is the stress induced on the "weaker" or less experienced buddy due to overdependence on their partner. This stress arises from a fear that one's buddy might not be there to lend assistance. And let's not forget that sometimes psychological stress can be chemically induced by drinking alcohol or taking what you might assume to be safe drugs.

A psychological stressor that's always present yet rarely addressed is the potential of encountering danger. Divers often avoid talking or even consciously thinking about this because it may imply that they're wimps. But such reasoning — or lack of reasoning — is nonsense. This time your mind is just telling you that, "I'm not happy because I think something may sting or bite me!" This is a perfectly reasonable response for anyone about to enter an alien environment where humans were not meant to survive; and — by the way — an environment that's home to animals most of us have been conditioned to fear. Your mind isn't telling you that you're a wimp, it's just taking the collective experience of 4 million years of evolution and saying, "Hold the phone, there could be some problems here."

If you think the psychological stress of diving is confined to actually being in the water, think again. The social nature of diving makes for another form of stress we deal with all the time: peer pressure. We all want the respect of others, and will at times go to great lengths to avoid situations in which this respect might be compromised. The problem is that diving sometimes places us in situations where failure — or not living up to what we perceive to be expectations of the others — is a real possibility. This is what psychologists term "ego threat," and it can be one of the most significant causes of stress.

Psychologists who study the intricacies of stress have learned that, like some kind of perpetual motion machine, stress can perpetuate itself in what's termed a "stress feedback loop." It works like this: An initial stress reaction — seeing a shark, for example — causes increased heart and breathing rates along with other physical responses. This reaction itself fosters even more stress, which, in turn, causes still further increases in physical responses.

The result is like a snowball rolling downhill. If not dealt with quickly, stress will continue to feed on itself until you're eventually unable to function. Therefore, the trick in dealing with stress effectively — both in yourself and in others — is recognizing it at its earliest stages.

What to Look For

Because they're such a common part of the human experience, there's no need to belabor the signs of stress. But to quickly review, they can include things such as nausea, muscle tension or shaking, a wide-eyed look, rapid heart rate, and shortness of breath. When living our normal lives, such manifestations usually result in little more than some embarrassment or inconvenience. But for divers trying to survive in an environment not meant for us, they can quickly lead to hypoxia, fatigue, hyperventilation and exhaustion. In other words, disaster.

The ultimate result of stress — the monster of all mind games — is panic. This is a state of overpowering fear in which we abandon all reason and return to an instinctual "fight or flight" reaction. Some diving psychologists have aptly termed panic as the equivalent of an "emotional air embolism," because, indeed, it's the most potentially life-threatening psychological condition that a diver will ever encounter. All other problems we face can be dealt with by reason, planning and practice; but not panic. By definition, panic is the utter lack of reason, and not being able to think can kill you faster than any exotic diving disorder like decompression sickness or a real air embolism.

An almost limitless number of factors determine one's susceptibility and response to stress. And the degree of susceptibility varies among individuals. But research has clearly demonstrated that certain personality types are especially vulnerable to stress. Interestingly, these types tend to be at opposite ends of a spectrum. The first is what psychologists term the "anxious-dependent" personality. These individuals are particularly susceptible to stress due to a lack of control, and dependence on others for guidance. Such individuals usually lack self-confidence, tend to be nervous and often maintain a poor level of physical fitness.

On the opposite end of the continuum is a personality type termed the "competitive-perfectionist." This person tends to be aggressive and controlling; and they often get into trouble by underestimating a challenge. And when they do experience problems, they have trouble asking for assistance. These are the folks for which peer pressure and ego threat are particular stressors. But learning to deal with stress requires more than a quick lesson on pop psychology. You must begin by understanding its more subtle signs.

Before You Enter the Water

As any experienced instructor or divemaster knows, those experiencing predive stress exhibit a whole range of signs. And at times the signs are at the complete ends of the continuum. For example, stressed divers may appear either preoccupied or inattentive. It's also not uncommon for them to exhibit signs of tardiness or procrastination; and to make mistakes involving what under normal circumstances may be simple, matter-of-fact tasks. Excuse making is also a common reaction.

Yet stress reactions in humans are very complex behaviors, and impossible to predict with accuracy. As a result, those under extreme stress could display almost complete introversion and withdrawal from the group. Then again, they may become boastful or uncharacteristically cocky. But it's important for others, and especially dive buddies, to recognize that these outward signs actually mask an inner conflict.

What to Look for In the Water

In most cases, if stress isn't dealt with before a diver enters the water, problems will not somehow miraculously disappear. To identify stressed behaviors, look for inefficient or erratic movements. Stressed divers tend to use their arms to assist them in swimming. At the surface, instead of remembering to use their BC for flotation, they'll often tread water, and try to keep themselves further out of the water than they need to be. If things begin to go wrong, and the opportunity arises, they'll hang tenaciously on a line or, if near panic, even attempt to climb onto a surface float. These are, of course, futile efforts that lead to nothing more than additional stress; the snowball is back on course.

Strange as it sounds, stressed divers often reject their equipment. This is one of the reasons instructors emphasize during training that students never remove their mask while still in the water. Besides making it more difficult to function, a maskless diver is a classic sign of that ultimate stress: panic. Much the same goes for the regulator or, when at the surface, snorkel. The diver's complaint typically is, "I can't get enough air" or "my regulator isn't working right." But in reality, rejecting the regulator or snorkel is actually a sign of stress and accomplishes nothing except making it more difficult to breathe. Yet, another common sign of a stressed diver is fixation, which is often manifested by continual attention to or readjusting equipment without any apparent reason.

While you might assume that the signs of stress are always active and more or less obvious, this clearly isn't the case. Some respond to stress by complete withdrawal from the situation, showing signs of lethargy or apathy. This is actually an extreme case of what psychologists who study stress term "perceptual narrowing." While this defense mechanism may have little consequence on dry land, underwater it can quickly lead to trouble. Divers in such a state of stress are highly prone to making errors in judgment or forget such simple but vital tasks as keeping track of their air supply, bottom time or depth. And, of course, anyone in such a state is either incapable or highly compromised in their ability to render assistance to someone else should the need arise.

Perhaps the most insidious aspect of diver stress is what we've already called the "snowball effect." This is where minor problems quickly mushroom into serious life-threatening situations. While a relaxed, comfortable diver will be able to handle a multitude of small problems, the same situations could easily send a stressed diver into a state of panic.

Although stress is a common part of life, important differences exist between the stress we feel in our jobs or at home versus that which occurs in diving. Unlike most situations we experience every day, the consequences of even mild stress to a diver can easily snowball into circumstances in which lives are in danger. But like the gurus who churn out the multitude of self-help books tell us, you can deal with stress by applying some simple and common-sense techniques. Remember, simplicity and control are not only the keys to a happy, stress-free life, but to a safe dive as well.

Dealing with stress safely and effectively requires breaking the cycle of the stress-response-stress feedback loop. To do this, psychologists offer some useful advice.

1. Begin by talking. Never feel reluctant nor ashamed to talk about your fears and apprehensions. One of the best ways to reduce stress from ego threat and peer pressure is by letting others know what you're feeling. You'll probably find that everyone else is experiencing similar feelings. In helping others deal with stress, provide lots of information and encouragement, not judgment. Emphasize the positive; many people stress themselves out merely by dwelling on negative aspects of a dive (poor visibility, sharks, current), while overlooking the positive (the possibility of seeing something they've never witnessed before).

2. Stay occupied. This helps maintain focus and may even distract you from being nervous. But remember that having too much to do could be just another cause of stress. Strive for balance.

3. Dive with an experienced buddy. If you're feeling a bit stressed, find a buddy who is confident in his or her own abilities and willing to spend the extra time with you. Often, all that's needed is a little patience and empathy. The right companion can make all the difference.

4. Take it easy. There's never any reason to rush. Diving is, after all, only a sport, and there will always be another time to go diving. And don't allow your buddy to rush you. (It's good to mention this in your predive discussion.) Once you are in the water, proceed slowly, keeping an eye on your partner. Make sure that your buddy is paying attention to you, too. If you find that your stress level is not decreasing, stop, calm down and regain a comfortable breathing pattern before continuing the dive.

5. Stop, rest, think, then act. This is the most important thing you can remember any time you feel stressed. From a safety perspective, it's as important as remembering to never hold your breath.

CHAPTER 32

A Wing and a Prayer:
How to Evaluate Conditions

Have you ever asked yourself what makes the difference between a great dive and one you'd

rather forget? Sometimes it may be the person you're with. Few things are more aggravating than a bad buddy. Other times it may be your state of mind. Diving when you really didn't want to, or when some pressing problem or concern is distracting you, usually isn't a recipe for a fun time. Yet, while bad buddies and mental distractions may be at the root of some of your less-than-spectacular undersea excursions, the more common reason for those "dives from hell" is usually the environment. Bad vis, screaming winds and gut-emptying seas are the real bane of all divers.

But it's foolish to blame diving conditions for a bad experience. After all, we make the choice to dive, not the environment. The crux of the problem isn't the diving conditions, but how adept we are at interpreting and understanding those conditions. In other words, when we have a bad day, we often have no one to blame but ourselves.

Unfortunately, some divers never make much of an attempt to properly evaluate environmental conditions: If the ocean's wet and the boat's running, they're gone. But diving should be more than a form of a maritime poker game in which you "pays your money and takes your chances." Evaluating dive conditions must mean more than making sure there's beer in the cooler or consulting a Ouija board. So let's see what should go into a well-planned dive.

Praying to the Weather Gods

Weather is perhaps the most important consideration in evaluating diving conditions because it affects conditions both above and below the water. In fact, few other leisure activities are as much at the mercy of the weather as diving. But to properly evaluate weather conditions and their suitability for diving, you must first have at least a rudimentary knowledge of how the atmosphere behaves.

The first step in making an informed decision about weather is getting accurate information. That means a forecast. With the Internet, or even a smartphone, that's a no-brainer. It's also simple if you have a VHF-FM marine radio, as channels set aside as "WX" continuously broadcast updated marine weather reports. You can also purchase a dedicated weather radio at your local electronics supply store. These inexpensive devices are designed to receive National Weather Service broadcasts exclusively, and even have an activator switch that turns them on automatically when severe weather warnings are announced. There are also a number of Internet sites devoted to marine weather, such as the National Weather Service marine forecast and "unofficial" sites like the Weather Underground.

What we call "weather" is really changes in atmospheric conditions caused by warm equatorial air masses interacting with colder polar air. The driving force of these air masses is the Earth's rotation, and uneven heating and cooling of the Earth by the sun. High-pressure areas — associated with stable weather — can hold vast amounts of moisture. As air pressure falls, however, the air cools and moisture condenses into clouds, rain or fog. Although it may sound relatively simple and straightforward, predicting weather is enormously complex and — as anyone knows who watches TV weather reports regularly — not terribly accurate.

Divers need to know a bit more about weather than where to get the latest forecast because weather patterns in coastal regions often differ from forecasts for inland areas. This is why a marine-oriented forecast is vital when you plan a dive along the coast. For example, calm wind conditions in the early morning hours is a typical summertime weather pattern. But, as the sun heats landmasses much faster than water, the land quickly warms and forms an upward convection current. This pulls cooler air in from the sea and creates a sea breeze. The wind usually intensifies until late afternoon, when it begins to dissipate. Nighttime often brings very little or no wind. Using this knowledge, you can normally assume that morning will bring the calmest wind conditions in coastal regions. But the wind will build gradually throughout the day. This is not, however, an absolute rule. Weather patterns are influenced by many different factors and can behave very differently from what's been described. So, regardless of your knowledge of how weather happens, there's still no substitute for an in-depth forecast of the area where you plan to dive.

Another aspect of coastal weather makes even a marine weather report at times less than accurate. This normally occurs when offshore winds (blowing from shore) are forecast. An excellent example of this discrepancy between a forecast and reality occurs regularly along Florida's east coast. Primarily in winter and spring, cold fronts blow into the region, causing strong westerly winds. Under such conditions marine advisories are often posted because these winds can create dangerous sea conditions. But, as it's blowing from shore, the wind doesn't have time to affect the seas very close to shore. The result is calm seas within a few miles of the beach, even though seas may be raging only a few more miles east. But as prime dive sites are close to shore, I've often experienced excellent diving conditions even though small-craft advisories were in effect, and the local TV weatherman was warning people not to consider going

out in a boat. This points up the need to have not only accurate information, but a lot of local knowledge as well when assessing diving conditions.

The Motion of the Ocean

When planning a dive in the ocean, currents are another environmental concern. Often, when they're severe, currents are caused by tidal exchange. So, to predict current, you must be able to read a tide chart. In assessing their effect, take special note on days when there is a great variation between tides. When this occurs, vast amounts of water must flow between the high and low tide, creating local currents that are much stronger than on days with minimal tidal exchange. Under most circumstances, diving at high tide yields the best visibility because it brings with it fresh, clear water.

If you think current may be a factor in your dive plan, the ideal time to enter the water is on what's termed a slack tide. This is the point when tidal currents cease in preparation for the change in the opposite direction (high to low or low to high). Logically, the greatest water flow takes place midway between the tidal exchange. For example, if a low tides occurs at 10 a.m. and a high at 4:50 p.m., then the current is likely to be at its worst at around 1:30 p.m., halfway between the two. A slack high tide will occur sometime around 4:50 p.m., as the water reaches it crest. But, tides can be influenced by a wide variety of factors, such as physical obstructions, bays or even bottom topography. This makes determining the precise time of a slack tide in some locations very tricky. If you need to be dead-accurate in an area where you're unfamiliar, consult local watermen or use information from the Tidal Current Charts published by the National Oceanic and Atmospheric Administration. This publication is available in any marine supply store and provides virtual worldwide coverage, as well as instructions for use.

In addition to tides, local currents can be influenced by major oceanic currents. Especially when these major currents interact with localized near-shore currents, predicting the behavior of water movement can be next to impossible. For example, as the Gulf Stream flows from south to north along the U.S. East Coast, it's logical to assume that all long-shore currents on the eastern U.S. coastline flow unalterably in a northerly direction. But, as anyone who has ever dived off that coast can tell you, that's just not true. Indeed, at times the current does flow north. But just as often it flows south, and sometimes there is no current at all near shore.

This doesn't mean the Gulf Stream has ceased its flow or changed direction. These variations in local currents are caused because major ocean currents aren't stable; they meander and undulate like snakes slithering across the ground. Sometimes they move shoreward, and at other times they move seaward. Under the right circumstances, countercurrents called "eddies" spin off and cause localized currents in a direction opposite the oceanic current. And, just as with tides, local physical features have an influence as well. In the final analysis, understanding and predicting local currents takes extensive experience. And if you lack that experience, it's often best to leave this aspect of dive planning to professionals. This is only one of the many advantages of diving with organized groups such as those sponsored by dive clubs or dive centers. Learning under the tutelage of more experienced divers is both safer and less stressful than going it alone.

If you insist on planning your own dive, make sure that you assess the sea conditions from the best vantage point. In determining the direction and strength of the current, watch for either boats at anchor or flotsam on the water's surface. And make sure it's the current moving the objects in the water, and not the wind. Strong wind can push floating objects — even boats — against a mild current. Although uncommon, also be aware that a subsurface current might flow in a different direction than the surface current (sometimes by as much as 90 degrees or more). This occurs in open, deep water — such as what you might encounter while diving from a boat.

When you must dive in a current, remember it's the ocean that controls things, not you. For instance, you can only swim against the slightest current (usually a knot or less) and even then only for a short distance. So instead of fighting the ocean, use it. Plan your dive so the current is an aid, not an enemy. Consider drift diving if the current is especially strong. Or, if you must anchor dive or dive from shore, plan to end your dive upcurrent of your entry point. This let's you use the current to bring you home; and it's at the end of the dive when you'll be most tired. Equally important, never assume that because the current is flowing one way when you enter the water, that it won't change direction. During

your dive pay close attention to anything that might indicate a change in the direction or speed of the current such as aquatic weeds, soft corals, plankton or other particles suspended in the water column.

If you screw up and get caught in a strong current, don't try to fight it. In any fight with the ocean, you will lose. Inflate your buoyancy compensator, drift with the current and signal for assistance. Hopefully, if you're diving from a boat, it will have a drift line trailing from its stern for just this type of situation. Although it may be embarrassing, you can always get back to your exit point somehow. But exhausting yourself by fruitlessly battling a current could be deadly.

Seeing Is Believing

The reason we dive is to see what's down there, so visibility is an extremely important factor in selecting a dive site. How calm the sea is, or how little current we have to contend with, is irrelevant if we can't see our hand in front of our face once we're underwater.

There are myriad factors that influence visibility, including weather, seasonal variation, bottom composition, water motion and even the time of day. All of these affect either how much particulate is in the water (turbidity), or the amount of light that can penetrate underwater (absorption).

Weather and seasonal variation have a significant effect on visibility. Near shore, rain causes runoff, which can greatly increase light-robbing particles in the water. But normally this is a near-shore problem. Both nearshore and off-shore warm temperatures and increased sunlight during summer can produce explosive "plankton blooms." (This is one reason that in cold-water regions like the Pacific Northwest, visibility tends to be better in the winter than summer.) In fresh water particularly, changes in subsurface thermal stratification caused by seasonal changes greatly affect visibility. Predicting visibility in fresh water often requires special knowledge and a great deal of experience.

The most obvious factors affecting visibility are the composition of the bottom and water movement. Severe surface chop or wave action decreases the amount of light that can penetrate the water. Bottom composition, on the other hand, affects turbidity. As a rule, the finer the substrate the easier it is for it to be disturbed and become suspended in the water. And the easier the substrate can be disrupted, the easier visibility is affected by water motion such as waves or surge.

Bottom compositions such as mud and silt are most prone to the effects of water motion. Rock, hard-packed earth, course sand, or coral are much less affected. Aquatic weeds also help to keep the bottom more stable and less susceptible to water motion. This means that when planning a dive you should select a site with consolidated bottom materials — rock, course sand, coral — whenever possible. If you are not sure what kind of substrate to expect, consult a nautical chart. In addition to telling you what kind of bottom topography to expect, they also indicate the bottom composition. If you must dive on a muddy or silty bottom, maintain good buoyancy control and make sure you keep your fins away from the bottom. (Anti-silting procedures are important skills in cavern diving, and mastering these techniques is an excellent reason to take a Cavern Diving specialty course even if you don't intend to do a lot of diving in caverns.)

Although rarely considered — except by underwa-

Before you arrive at the dive site:

■ Get accurate weather information. Call the dive off immediately if severe weather is forecast. Take into account that it takes time for weather to influence sea conditions, and time for sea conditions to respond once severe weather dissipates. And make sure the forecast you use applies to the area you'll be diving.

■ Consult tide charts and try to schedule your dive to take place at a slack high tide. If diving on a commercial charter boat, however, this may be meaningless because the boat will probably operate on a fixed schedule regardless of the tide.

Once on site:

■ Carefully observe the sea state and evidence of current. Take several minutes to do a thorough assessment. Sometimes the effects of current are subtle, and an oversight or bad decision can mean a bad dive or worse.

■ Evaluate the visibility. How does it appear? Remember that vertical visibility is often better than horizontal, so don't overestimate. Determine if there are any conditions present that might cause a change in visibility such as building wind, changing tides or threatening weather. Is the visibility sufficient to fulfill your dive objective and plan? In poor or deteriorating visibility, make sure you review what to do if buddies separate. Also consider what effect the bottom composition will have on visibility.

■ What kind of marine life will you encounter? This can depend not only on locale but the season, too. For example, some fish species are migratory, and some forms of jellyfish proliferate at certain times of the year in many locations. You should also have a field guide for the local marine life when possible.

ter photographers — the time of day you make a dive can also be a significant factor in the quality of underwater visibility. A physical property of light is that when it strikes the surface of the water at an angle of less that 48 degrees, most of it is deflected. The higher the angle, the more light can penetrate. Taking this to a practical level, the highest light penetration, and the best visibility, normally occurs when the sun is at an optimal angle — between 10 a.m. and 2 p.m.

I Ain't Afraid of No Shark

The influence of marine life presents the most unusual challenge to evaluating dive conditions because its effect can be both positive and negative. On one hand, few things are more frightening to divers than their unrealistic perceptions of the creatures that live underwater. The "jaws mentality" seems to hold that if something can eat you, it will — or at least try. Yet, on the other hand, the main reason most of us dive is to experience the unique world that houses the same critters that foster our fear. How do we deal with this paradox? By striking a balance between reason and fantasy. Certainly, there is always some risk from interacting with wild animals in their own environment. But the risk must be put into perspective. After all, the vast majority of injuries from marine life are a result of defensive action on the part of the animal rather than aggression.

Most enlightened divers today believe that what we should concentrate on is not protecting ourselves from marine critters, but protecting them from us. It seems that fear and education are inversely proportional; the more you gain of one the more you lose of the other. So the answer lies in learning more about what's down there. To do this, consider taking a course or attending a seminar to round out your knowledge of the environment. If you really get hooked, then you might think about a formal course at a local college. And if that's not possible, you still have the ultimate educational resource — the Internet. Whether you're interested in coral reefs or diving more frigid but no less spectacular waters, information abounds. All that you need is a desire to learn.

Learning how to accurately assess diving conditions takes time. While the basics are pretty simple, the intricacies of how environmental conditions interact can be confusing and even — as we saw in the analysis of weather — misleading. That's why it's best to gain experience under a more seasoned buddy or by continuing your education. But even experienced divers aren't immune to mistakes, particularly when they dive an unfamiliar site. Whether you're a novice right out of certification course or an experienced instructor, get assistance when diving a new area for the first time. Many training organizations have special programs just for this purpose. Consult a local dive center in the area you plan to dive for advice. Remember, it's not the environment that causes problems, it's the decisions you make in evaluating the environment.

SECTION
V
DOING THE
RIGHT THING:
DIVING TECHNIQUES
RE-EXAMINED

CHAPTER 33

Running On Empty:
Why Divers Run Out of Air

One of my greatest joys is tooling

around the Florida Keys in my trusty little 17-foot (5 m) Boston Whaler. The gas gauge rarely works, and when it does, I don't really trust it. But it makes no difference because it has a bigger fuel tank than I can exhaust in one day's adventures. My lack of concern for the status of my fuel supply, however, is valid only if I follow one important caveat: Refill the tank every time I take the boat out.

One day, after a long hiatus, I was so eager to get out on the water that I neglected to top off the tank. I was certain that I had used so little gas during my previous outing that there would surely be enough for the day. I was, of course, wrong; and as I waited for the friendly Sea Tow man to rectify my predicament, I had ample time to ponder and regret my decision. I had the gauge fixed the very next day.

While bouncing aimlessly for hours — and watching with envy the passing boats that actually had gas — it struck me that in any endeavor in which I'm at the mercy of a fuel supply, I'm never far from trouble. Usually this is because I, like many other males of the species, absolutely refuse to refuel any mechanical device when the fuel gauge doesn't indicate that the tank is completely empty. My wife is often less than amused by my attitude, especially considering that I once ran out of gas while driving our RV in the middle of Alaska's Kenai Peninsula. Clearly, it's a good thing that I'm not a pilot.

Fortunately, however, as a diver I'm much more conscientious about another fuel supply — my air. Inconvenience is one thing, but death is entirely another.

Still, not all divers maintain such vigilance in managing their air supply, which amazes me, considering the potential consequences.

As I sat there that day waiting for fuel to arrive, I thought of every out-of-air circumstance I had ever witnessed. Then I tried to analyze what factors lead to the problem. After several hours I had identified four common reasons for causality: laziness, failure to plan, poor maintenance and cockiness.

What the Data Says

Investigations by Divers Alert Network (DAN) have revealed some very interesting trends regarding out-of-air emergencies. DAN's analysis of more than 1,000 fatal accidents involving recreational divers found that 41 percent were the result of running out of air. And in case you think that deep diving was a factor, 70 percent of the accidents occurred at depths shallower than 100 feet (30 m). Forty percent happened at the depth range of 60-99 feet (18-30 m), and 30 percent shallower than 60 feet (18 m). That's 3 in 10 deaths happening at a depth at which even novices should feel comfortable, and within easy reach of the surface. Of course, the act of running out of air alone doesn't kill; it's the diver's reaction to the situation. And, like most emergencies, they're much easier to avoid than to survive. Overall, had it not been for running out of air, 410 divers would still be alive today.

A major contributing factor to death involving out-of-air emergencies — and one that probably comes as no surprise — is buoyancy control. Buoyancy problems were reported in 39 percent of the deaths. In 22 percent of the cases, rough seas were an associated factor, and in just over 10 percent of the cases some other equipment-related problem was reported.

For those of you looking for trends involving gender, the data showed that women made up only 20 percent of all diving fatalities (well below the one-third they comprise of the recreational diving population), and only 13 percent of the deaths resulted from running out of air. Score one for the ladies.

The Challenge of Underwater Breathing

Aside from inattentiveness, another reason many divers run out of air, I think, is that they retain the mentality of a landlubber. Here's what I mean. On land, the issue of breathing resistance is virtually irrelevant because, provided we're in good health, our breathing is unrestricted. In addition, there are no situations in which we're likely to breathe gas under pressure and, therefore, the density of the air breathed doesn't change to any important degree. Underwater, however, the situation is completely different.

As explained way back in Chapter 9, immersion in water causes dramatic changes in our breathing even if we're not breathing from a scuba tank. Compression of the chest by hydrostatic pressure causes a reduction in tidal volume (the volume of air that moves in and out with each breath) by as much as 20 percent. That means merely by being in water up to your neck, your respiratory efficiency is significantly reduced. Additionally for divers on descent, as the pressure of the air we breathe from a tank increases, so does the density of the air. The "thicker" air causes significant breathing resistance from friction. How much resistance? In one study of divers at 100 feet (30 m) in a recompression chamber, breathing resistance doubled and maximum ventilation rate was reduced as much as 50 percent. By the time the study

subjects reached 150 feet (45 m), the maximum rate was down to only 33 percent of the surface rate. Noteworthy is that these tests were done under dry conditions using subjects who were at rest, and using apparatus that's a lot more efficient than standard scuba equipment. One can imagine what happens to breathing efficiency when we add the increased resistance of scuba equipment, and the constriction of the chest and abdomen from a wet suit, buoyancy compensator (BC) and weight belt. But what does this have to do with running out of air?

The point to all this is that, even if you aren't exerting yourself, the mere act of breathing underwater is a physiologic issue requiring that you use more oxygen than under comparable conditions on land. So, for a comparable workload, increased breathing resistance makes us use much more air when breathing underwater than on land. The result is that you use your air supply much faster than you might assume or realize because your perception is based on your experience breathing in the atmosphere, not underwater. Just ask yourself, how many times have you assumed you had plenty of air only to be shocked into reality when you got around to checking your submersible pressure gauge (SPG)? The reason is because you were still thinking like a landlubber.

Laziness Can Be Deadly

A lot of out-of-air situations occur because of bad habits or outright laziness. Although divers tend to do more exhaustive predive checks when they dive with someone new for the first time, as familiarity grows, the thoroughness of their predive routine diminishes. This is a serious mistake; a cursory predive safety check can mean starting the dive without a full tank. Regardless of your experience or familiarity with your buddy, you never outgrow the need for a thorough predive safety check.

During the safety check, confirm that both you and your buddy have full tanks, and that both valves are in the full open position. (Turn the valve until it's completely open, then turn back a quarter to half rotation.) A tank valve that is only partially open might deliver air normally while you're at the surface, but cannot give you sufficient air as you descend. As you go deeper you'll experience the sensation of getting some, but not enough, air. Another telltale sign of a partially opened valve is indicated by your SPG. In such an instance the needle on the gauge will deviate radically from full to zero with each breath.

Once in the water bad habits can continue. One of the worst, from an air management perspective, is not checking your air supply frequently enough. SPGs are great devices, but they are *passive*. You have to remember to read them.

It's important to develop the habit of monitoring your air supply at frequent, regular intervals. Also, consider securing your gauge console in a way that reading it requires little thought or effort. To accomplish this some divers thread the SPG hose through the left armhole of their buoyancy compensator (BC). This positions the console securely in the midchest area where you can easily see it. Personally, I keep my console clipped to the front of my BC so that it's impossible to ignore, and easily seen without having to use my hands. Regardless of the technique, the idea is to make the console so prominent that you can't forget to look at it.

The cause of these bad habits is poor buddy interaction. The buddy system is not something you had to learn only to pass your certification course; it's a vital aspect of safety. Good buddies communicate frequently, continually reminding each other of their air supply status. In fact, if you dive with the same buddy often enough, you'll eventually be able to tell how much air he has based on your own air supply. Still, even in this case you should never *assume* you know how much air your buddy has. Always confirm it.

Yet another factor that can lead to running out of air is poor buoyancy control. Wearing too little weight requires that you continually fight to stay down. This causes you to use far more air than if you're properly weighted; and the continual attention to your buoyancy can easily distract you from keeping track of your air supply.

While diving without enough weight can be a problem, it's not nearly as common as diving with too much. Aside from the environmental destruction an overweighted diver can inflict on a coral reef, it also can lead to unexpectedly running out of air. There's probably no faster way of using up your air supply than constantly fighting to stay off the bottom. Being overweighted also means you'll probably need to add air to your BC to begin an ascent. This creates a dual problem: Less air to breathe *and* to put in your BC.

The answer to the buoyancy problem — and the out-of-air problem — is simple. Wear only the amount of weight you need to maintain neutral buoyancy. Never overweight yourself to make descending easier. It only

shortens your dive in the long run. Also, reduce the amount of weight you wear when conditions warrant, such as when you're wearing less exposure protection than normal, or go from salt water to fresh water.

Failure to Plan
Is Failure to Learn

Like forming bad habits, the consequences of failing to plan begin before you even enter the water. It's easy to become distracted in the predive phase of planning. You could be sidetracked by the excitement or anxiety over making the dive. You could be overcome by seasickness. Or you could have so many tasks to perform that forgetting something is almost a certainty. To prevent this, develop a consistent predive procedure that includes an "air check," and *never* alter the routine.

A second problem we can lay at the feet of poor planning is not having enough air for the dive objective. It really doesn't matter if your tank is full if you aren't carrying enough air in the first place. The deeper or longer you dive the more air you'll need; and you'll also use more air than usual if you're diving in water that's colder than you normally experience.

Still another reason divers run out of air is because they develop an "expectation" of how long a tank will last. As divers gain experience, they begin to form a mental perception of how much time they can get out of a tank of air. This may be an accurate estimate *as long as they're diving similar depth profiles and all other conditions are generally the same*. Over time, they come to expect this amount of air every time they dive. The problem arises when the diver makes a dive outside his usual realm of experience, but still assumes his tank will last as long as it did under normal circumstances. The result is often a very short dive, if not an out-of-air emergency. The reality is that different conditions can radically alter air consumption rates, causing you to run out of air long before you assume you will. The lesson is, never assume anything.

Once, on a dive to the Channel Islands of Southern California, I watched a diver strap a 50-cubic-foot tank to his back. I asked him, "Where do you think you're going with that? This dive is to over 60 feet [18 m] and the current is really ripping." He replied, "Don't worry, I know what I'm doing. I dive with 50s where I dive

[Florida] all the time, and the current gets worse than this. I've never run out of air yet."

Unfortunately, he hadn't taken into account the increased effort required by the heavy exposure suit or the colder water. Fifteen minutes later he was back at the surface complaining about "what a terrible dive it was." His buddy, who still had over a half tank of air, was not amused by his poor planning. On the second dive I noticed my friend was wearing an 80-cubic-foot tank.

Tanks today are available in a wide variety of sizes, some in excess of 100 cubic feet. Just as a golfer chooses the right club for a particular shot, the diver must choose the right tank for a particular dive. It's, of course, always better to have too much air than not enough. High-capacity steel tanks also have another advantage. Because they're heavier than standard aluminum tanks, they let you take some lead off your weight belt.

The final, and probably most common, result of poor planning is not knowing when to head for home. Here, too, early experience isn't necessarily the best teacher. Take, for example, a diver who has learned to dive in a quarry or lake. He has never had to contend with current or finding his way back to a boat. So, planning his dive in terms of his air supply is simple: Swim out until he uses half his air, then swim back using the other half. Providing nothing out of the ordinary occurs, this technique seems to work well. Or does it?

One day in the future our quarry diver is on a dive vacation, and during his first boat dive he mistakenly comes up 200 yards (182 m) astern. Equally unfortunate, he was using the "half out/half back" rule that served him so well back home. He now has a real problem because his remaining air supply is probably insufficient to allow him to fight the current as he returns to the boat. The result is he will likely run out of air before reaching the boat, and have to make a lengthy — and potentially exhausting — surface swim.

In many situations, what's known as the "one half plus two" rule is acceptable. This means that your turnaround point should be when your air supply falls to 200 psi more than half of your starting air pressure, i.e., 1,700 psi if starting with 3,000 psi. While that gives you some margin for error, it sometimes isn't enough. For situations in which lots of exertion is likely, the better rule for air management comes to us from the cave diving community — the "rule of thirds." You should plan only one-third of your air supply for the trip out, then another third for the trip back. The final third is held in reserve for unforeseen circumstances, like getting lost or caught downcurrent of the exit.

Running out of air underwater isn't exactly like my running out of gas in my boat. You can't just call for help and wait patiently for a response. The better analogy is flying. To a pilot, running out of fuel is a real big problem. And no pilot would ever plan a trip without factoring in a reserve fuel supply. The same advice holds true for divers, and the rule of thirds is a good way of doing just that.

1. Always conduct a thorough predive safety check, confirming that your tank is full and valve is fully turned on.

2. In calm, familiar conditions where current isn't a factor, manage your air supply using the "half plus two" rule. In more challenging, unfamiliar conditions — or any time you may have to swim against a strong current — consider using the "rule of thirds."

3. Communicate with your buddy often, inquiring frequently about air supply status.

4. Secure your submersible pressure gauge in a location where you can see it easily.

5. Carry enough air — use tanks of appropriate capacity.

6. Dive properly weighted — not too much nor too little.

7. Avoid using a maladjusted regulator — have it serviced annually.

8. Don't get cocky — follow the rules regardless of how much experience you have.

Take Care of Your Gear and It Will Take Care of You

Though many divers never think of it — at least until it's too late — poor equipment maintenance can be yet another reason for running out of air without warning. One way this can happen is by using a maladjusted regulator. I once had a diver tell me that he didn't want his regulator to breathe too easily because he'd use his air too quickly. His logic was certainly flawed.

A regulator with a lot of breathing resistance makes you work harder than if it were adjusted to breathe easily. The more difficult it is to breathe, the more oxygen you'll need and, in turn, the more air you'll use. So, one way to optimize your air consumption is by keeping your regulator in tip-top shape. Have it serviced annually.

There is one instance in which a regulator can be too finely adjusted — when it's an octopus. On more than one occasion I've seen divers run out of air early in their dive because they didn't realize their alternate air source was free flowing. (So much for an attentive buddy!) One way you can be certain that the octopus doesn't freeflow is to have it adjusted to breathe slightly harder than your primary, and make sure it's secured properly. Ideally, your octopus should be attached to your BC somewhere in the area of your chest. This not only makes it easier for your buddy to find in an emergency, it also lets you know immediately if it's free flowing. Never let your octopus dangle freely at your side.

Although rare, another out-of-air problem can result from an SPG that gives an inaccurate reading. A faulty gauge will show air remaining even though the tank is virtually empty. I once had an SPG that read 500 psi even when it wasn't attached to a tank. This could lead to disaster and points up yet another reason for vigilant equipment maintenance.

It Can't Happen to Me

It's an interesting phenomenon that, in my experience, bad attitudes are most often seen among experienced divers rather than novices. That probably makes sense. New divers usually know that they don't know everything and, therefore, tend to follow the rules. If they run out of air, it's usually because of an oversight or lack of diligence. On the other hand, experienced divers sometimes run out of air simply because they think "the rules don't apply to me anymore."

My theory, incidentally, isn't entirely based on conjecture. Accident statistics compiled by DAN tend to back it up. In analyzing when divers are most likely to become accident statistics and plotting the result on a graph, the line shows two spikes. One is, as you might expect, when the diver has very little experience — fewer than 30 dives. Interestingly, the other spike is for those who have extensive experience — hundreds, even thousands, of dives.

The conclusion is inescapable: The rules apply to *everybody*. Get cocky and you'll pay the price. No level of experience makes us infallible. The situation reminds me of an old adage used by U.S. Navy divers and it sums up very well the "it can't happen to me" crowd. It goes, "there are old divers and there are bold divers, but there are no old, bold divers." It's a good thing to remember the next time you check your air.

CHAPTER 34

Separation Anxiety:
The Art of Becoming a Good Buddy

"**Never** hold your breath" and "never dive alone." If there was an aquatic Moses these two admonitions would certainly be chiseled on the top rows of his tablet of Diving's Ten Commandments. In fact, even today it's tough to decide which should hold the singular honor of "the first rule of scuba diving." Frankly, my vote's for the breathing issues, because not having a buddy isn't likely to be as immediately catastrophic as holding one's breath. Remembering to breathe normally is also, I believe, at the top of the list because, unlike the buddy issue, in most circumstances it's a no-brainer. After all, we can dive without a buddy, but we can't do much of anything without breathing.

My comments about the relative degree of impunity by which we can violate diving's two sacred laws is not meant to be glib. (OK, maybe a little.) But instead, it's to point out that, when we can turn a blind eye to the rules, we often do. Although it's most often unintentional, the buddy system rule is broken almost as much as New Year's resolutions.

As an instructor for nearly a half-century, I can anticipate the behavior of scuba students pretty well. I know, for example, how they become particularly attentive during the final pool session before their open-water training dives. And I know that the day after they purchase a dive computer, everything they ever learned about the dive tables is zapped from their memory as if they experienced some sort of a mental power surge. That's why I can always anticipate the rolling eyes and glossed-over looks when I announce that it's time to talk about the buddy system.

It has always interested me why students often have this less-than-enthusiastic attitude toward learning to be a good buddy, but I finally think that I understand the reason. The buddy system is one of those subjects —

like wearing your seat belt getting a flu shot — divers know is important, but just can't muster a great deal of enthusiasm over.

Psychological Considerations

Too often we base discussions regarding the buddy system solely on practical issues, such as suiting up, remaining together or knowing what to do when problems occur. While these are certainly vital considerations, I believe that the most important aspect of the buddy system isn't what we do but how we think. For example, the buddy system is doomed from the outset if the pair doesn't share a common concern for each other. It doesn't take a degree in psychology to understand that unless you care about the person you're diving with, a buddy team isn't likely to maintain the vigilance required to remain together and be prepared to help each other.

Certainly, for psychological and practical reasons, problems are much more likely when two unfamiliar partners dive together. But with a little foresight you can decrease the chances of something going wrong even when you're buddied with a stranger. First, if you know you'll be diving with someone you've never met, don't wait until you're ready to enter the water before you introduce yourself. And do more than a simple, "Hi, my name is...." Take a few minutes to get to know your new partner. Find out how much diving he or she has done, when they dove last and if they ever made a dive like the one you're about to make.

Also, don't confine your conversation to planning your dive. Try to learn something personal about your buddy. Where's he or she from? What do they do for a living? Explore their background and try to find some common experience or aptitude. What you're trying to do, of course, is form some kind of bond. This mutual empathy will go a long way in maintaining an effective buddy system once you hit the water.

But there can also be a downside when partners are on *very* close terms, and one is overly dependent on the other. Without any intent of sounding sexist, this occurs most often in male/female buddy teams. A buddy system truly exists only when the team has the desire and capability of looking out for each other. If this mutual relationship doesn't exist, it's just two people diving together. For the buddy system to work, you must first ask yourself an important question: "Even if I *want* to help my buddy, will I be able to?"

An effective buddy system also has important psychological consequences. Regardless of how good a diver you are, diving causes some degree of stress and anxiety in all of us. A good buddy gives his or her partner the reassurance of knowing that someone else is looking out for them; a poor buddy just causes more stress. Their lack of caring or attentiveness can increase the anxiety of diving to a point where some might consider it *less* stressful to dive alone. A good buddy is a "worry-wart." He lives by the creed of Murphy's Law: What can go wrong *will*. Most importantly, a good buddy is ready, able and willing to do something about it.

Another consideration often overlooked is that we're talking about a buddy *system*. A system is defined as, "A group of interacting elements operating as a complex whole." This means that a buddy team is more than merely two people diving together in the same ocean on the same day. To work, the team must function as a single interacting unit, continually taking in and relaying input to each other. In short, the buddy system is an *interactive process*, not a thing; and there's no such thing as a "passive" buddy system.

Perhaps the most important psychological benefit of an effective buddy system is also the most overlooked — it's just more fun to dive with a partner. Shared experiences are usually the best; they're what make a relationship. When reminiscing about past diving experiences, you're likely to remember as much about *who* you dove with as what you did or saw.

Practical Considerations

While one can make an argument that it's the psychological side of the buddy system that's the key to it working, this doesn't mean that we can ignore the practical end. If the nuts and bolts aren't in place, then the system will certainly fall apart. One of the first practical issues a buddy team must decide is what they're going to do on a dive. Without a common objective, there's little probability you'll remain together, let alone enjoy your shared experience.

Likewise, it helps if you agree on who will direct the dive. Confusion over whose job it is to lead the way is a very common — perhaps the most common — reason for buddy team separation. Finally, there's the issue of how long and how deep to dive. Air supplies are not unlimited, nor is no-decompression time. If we adhere to the idea that diving is a shared experience — as well as a shared responsibility — you must address these two considerations before, not during, the dive.

It's said that two heads are better than one. In reality, two heads are worthless if neither is thinking. The benefit lies not in two heads, but in two *brains*. As in most situations, the problems we're likely to encounter while diving are predictable. If they're predictable, then they're also avoidable. This is why a predive safety check is so essential to effective buddy diving. It's amazing how often we think we're ready to enter the water only to have an astute buddy turn on our air, connect a low-pressure hose, fasten an unsecured strap or buckle or remind you that you forgot to put on your weight belt.

I once was teamed with a diver from Europe who spoke very little English. Halfway into the dive he began making a gesture that I had never seen — appearing to hit himself in the head. Upon investigating the situation more closely, I discovered he was very low on air, and was signaling to use my octopus regulator. The moral of the story: Anytime you dive with a new buddy, review communications as part of your predive plan. Although most divers learn the same signals to deal with the most common or significant problems, not all do. Confirm your assumptions before you take the plunge, not after.

A prime time for buddy system failure is during descents and ascents. When we descend, we're often distracted by anxiety, adjusting equipment or dealing with equalization problems. Buddies sometimes unintentionally become a secondary priority, and we arrive at the bottom alone. During ascents, we often begin our return to the surface assuming that our buddy saw us, or is probably ascending as well because his air is low, too. If you've ever reached the surface without your buddy, you know how wrong this assumption can be. Proper descent and ascent procedures require that we maintain buddy awareness, and confirm that both partners understand and agree to each other's intentions. The key is to pay attention at all times, not just when you're on the bottom.

While you are on the bottom, consider that your position relative to your buddy will make it either easy or hard to keep an eye on each other. Try to remain side by side rather than play "follow the leader." It's easier to see someone that way. And the easier you make it for your buddy to keep an eye on you, the more likely it is that he will. The best advice is to try to select a dive objective that involves both of you. Remember what we said about the buddy system being an interactive process. If you interact, then it's unlikely you'll lose sight of one another. For example, you might develop the habit of showing your buddy items of interest such as marine life. Another technique is to frequently ask him questions, such as, "Which way do you want to go?" or "Where's the boat?" or "How much air do you have?"

Still another way to make the buddy system an interactive process is by practicing important skills such as out-of-air emergencies or buoyancy control. Some of the best buddy teams I've ever seen are those who regularly practice alternate air source use or "hovering" (remaining absolutely motionless in midwater without kicking or sculling). Doing so enables them to maintain a very high level of skill proficiency, and generates a feeling of confidence. Each buddy knows that in the event of an emergency — or if things just get tough — his partner can handle whatever arises. After all, the real test of the buddy system is how well the team can handle problems.

Hopefully, you'll avoid the need to ever use out-of-air procedures by practicing good air management.

This, too, is part of becoming a good buddy. The status of each other's air supply is one of the most important pieces of information a buddy team shares. Get in the habit of exchanging air supply status often. As you dive deeper, you'll use air more quickly. You should, therefore, check each other's air supply even more frequently. Also, never assume that your buddy uses air at the same rate as you. Although he or she may have a similar air consumption rate as you under normal conditions, you might encounter situations that drastically alter how fast they use their air. The only way to know how much air your buddy has is to check it.

The most important factor affecting air consumption is, of course, your level of exertion. Good buddies keep a close eye out not only to see where their buddy is, but also so they can evaluate his physical and psychological state. Is your buddy's breathing rate comfortable and regular? Is his motion slow and purposeful? Is he attentive to you and the task at hand? If you answer "no" to any of these questions, it's time to do something. Most often the answer lies in having him slow down or stop all activity completely. If that doesn't resolve the problem, then it's time to calmly head for the surface. Diving is great, but it's not worth risking your life. You can always dive another day.

One advantage of diving regularly with the same buddy is that you're able to establish a baseline for normal behavior. This helps you evaluate his or her reaction to situations as they change. Any changes to what you know as "normal" behavior, of course, deserves close attention. For example, let's assume your buddy is usually attentive and stays close by you. One day while deep diving you notice that he's paying little attention and tends to wander off. This could be an early sign of a problem such as narcosis. Yet, if you didn't have this insight into his behavior based on experience, you might not realize that a problem was occurring until much later — perhaps too late.

The ultimate breakdown of the buddy system is when divers separate and cannot find their way back together. This isn't necessarily a serious problem, if it's handled properly. "Properly" means that you realize very quickly that your buddy is gone and that you react appropriately. Unfortunately, divers often don't even realize their buddy is nowhere to be found for quite some

1. **Discuss and agree on an objective for the dive.** Try to avoid conflicting objectives, such as one diver spearfishing while the other takes photos.

2. **Often there is no objective except to sightsee**. In this case, determine who will lead the dive, how deep you'll go and how much time you'll spend at depth. Also, decide exactly how you plan to stay together (swimming formation, buddy line, etc.), and how often you'll exchange information.

3. **Sometimes, regardless of your plan, it's your air supply that dictates when your dive is over.** So, in addition to planning your bottom time, also agree at what minimum air pressure you'll terminate the dive. (Don't forget: This part of the plan is worthless unless you check each other's air supply regularly.)

4. **Always review the meaning of hand signals.** Some signals are standard, others aren't. And even the standard ones can be forgotten. Be sure you agree on communicating for all possible situations. This is particularly important if you are diving with someone for the first time.

5. **Review emergency procedures.** Confirm that both of you have some form of alternate air source device, and know how it's used. (You might consider practicing for a few minutes after you enter the water.) Discuss the possibility of entanglement and how you'd deal with it. Also, buddy separation should be considered an emergency procedure, even though it might not be life-threatening. Decide what to do about it before it happens.

time; sometimes, not until they're ready to surface. This is a sure sign of a very "noninteractive" buddy team.

Appropriate action for a missing buddy is simple: Find him! This is sometimes easier said than done. The most common rule is to search for one minute, then ascend and wait. (Be sure to look up and around; it's amazing how often a "lost" buddy is just above your head or right behind you.) If your buddy, in turn, does the same, he should either be at the surface already, or should join you shortly. On deeper dives, buddy awareness becomes even more crucial. For optimal decompression safety you don't want to ascend to search for a lost buddy, then descend again. Stay closer together than normal and monitor your air supply even more frequently.

Another useful deep-diving technique to deal with buddy separation is to use a descent line. Agree that if separated you will both return to the descent line and wait a few minutes before surfacing. Hopefully, if your buddy does the same thing you'll be able to find each other and continue the dive, rather than have to ascend. But this works only in relatively good visibility. The best advice is still to remain attentive and stay close to each other at all times, particularly when deep diving.

Taking on the role of a dive buddy is a heavy responsibility. To agree to be someone's buddy, but not properly fulfill the role is irresponsible, and could be life-threatening. Exercise your duty seriously and with appropriate planning. Follow the guidelines I've addressed, and continue your diving education. Probably the best thing you can do is to take what I consider the "ultimate dive buddy course" — a Rescue Diver course. Your buddy will appreciate it.

CHAPTER 35

O' Solo Mio:
A Unbiased Look at Diving Alone

Humans are interesting creatures because we're such contradictions. On one hand, we're among the most gregarious species on the planet. In no small way, our culture has evolved to where it is today precisely because of the human desire to be around others. We call it society. Yet, in stark contrast, there are times when we need to be alone. Striving for the right balance between membership in a pack and the desire to be a lone wolf is, according to many mental health professionals, critical to a happy life. In fact, our very personalities are often defined as being either a "people person" or a "loner." We even take this dichotomy of the team player versus the rugged individualist with us underwater.

On dry land, our preference to be apart from the crowd rather than a part of the crowd brings little consequence except the risk of being thought of as a bit odd. But underwater the preference to be left alone can have very direct and immediate consequences that can mean the difference between life or death.

Until recently, violating that great credo to "never dive alone" would have branded someone in our community as a fool or worse. However, in recent years that attitude has been changing. Not only is solo diving being discussed more broadly and openly than in the past, it has received official sanction by some diver training organizations. Is solo diving destined to become, like nitrox, a once-taboo practice that's now as common as neoprene rubber? Or is it just the controversy de jour that will eventually reassume its black sheep role in the diving family? Only time will tell, but given its growing notoriety, diving alone is worthy of discussion whether you agree with it or not.

Is the Buddy System Unsafe?

The recent interest in solo diving was, in part, sparked by claims by some that the time-honored te-net of safety diving, the buddy system, is actually dangerous. Specifically, the allegation is that the buddy system fosters a false sense of security. Actually, such claims run counter to a long history of experience and accident analysis.

Since 1989, the Divers Alert Network statistics have shown that nearly half of all fatalities involved divers who were alone at the time of their accident (either by choice or circumstance). Indeed, having a buddy may have made little or no difference in the outcome of some of these unfortunate events. But it's reasonable to assume that an extra set of eyes and hands would have lessened the likelihood or degree of a bad outcome in many others. To claim otherwise seems foolish, and blaming the buddy system as a cause of accidents can in no way be supported by the data. The conclusion seems obvious: In an accident, diving without a buddy reduces one's chance of survival, regardless of the problem. If nothing else, diving with someone else gives the diver a safety redundancy that going solo simply cannot provide. But this is not to say that there aren't problems with the buddy system, or at least with the way it's practiced.

Circumstances often arise in which divers, who think they are buddy diving, find themselves on their own. Lack of attentiveness or distraction is probably the most common reason. The result is either a miserable dive spent looking for each other, or an ill-prepared and unintended solo experience.

In some situations, divers can be lulled into a false sense of security by believing they're safe just because they're in the water with someone else. Just because someone is diving with you doesn't mean he's your buddy. Unless the dive team members are attentive, willing and able to help each other, for all intents and purposes, they're actually diving alone. They merely happen to be in the water at the same time.

To illustrate the point, consider the classic example you can see on any dive boat any weekend. You arrive with no partner for a trip and are told that you must dive with a buddy. So, you're paired with someone else who is in the same predicament. With only a cursory exchange of names and pleasantries, you and your new buddy enter the water reassured by the fact you are "following the buddy system." As nothing remarkable happens — which is the case on the vast majority of dives — you exit the water becoming further proof of "how well the buddy system works."

The question is, does such an experience really constitute proof that the buddy system works? Or, is it that because diving is an essentially safe endeavor, the buddy system is rarely tested? From our scenario we have no way of knowing if either diver had the capability or intention of acting as a true buddy. All that we're sure of is that the divers were in the same ocean at the same time, and remained close enough together to exit the water together. We can never know what might have happened if one of them needed help from the other.

Another common example of what I call a "false buddy system" is played out all the time during training dives. When an instructor takes a class into open water, is he buddy diving or solo diving? Even though he may be with several other student divers, most instructors would say the latter. After all, it's his responsibility to watch his students, but not vice versa.

Another problem the buddy system sometimes presents is its use as a crutch by the incompetent or psychologically insecure. Some divers, who lack the ability or self-confidence to take care of themselves,

assume they'll be safe as long as they're diving with someone who can take care of them. This "dependent buddy syndrome" is one of the most dangerous situations imaginable for several reasons. First, as buddy separation is a common occurrence, one can never assume that a buddy will always be around to offer help. Second, whether it's lack of knowledge or simply an unwillingness to accept responsibility, not all divers can be counted on to help their partner. And finally, what if the assumed "stronger buddy" is the one who needs help? The dependent buddy is then useless and could be responsible for the injury or loss of his partner. Logic dictates that there is simply no place in the water for a dependent buddy except under the direct supervision of a professional. A buddy cannot be a quick fix for incompetence.

As these and countless other similar experiences point out, solo diving happens whether we realize it or not. All of us at some time do it, intentionally or otherwise. So, it seems that the key to safety is not in numbers but in self-reliance. Only when you can take care of yourself can you really be prepared to help someone else.

The Cornerstone: Self-Reliance

While opinions may diverge on whether solo diving is something that the diving community should actively promote, there's no argument over one essential ingredient of diving sans buddy: the need for a high degree of self-reliance. The benefit is obvious; a self-reliant diver is one who can handle problems even if his buddy isn't around or paying attention to him. To a self-reliant diver a buddy is an aid, not a necessity. From a psychological perspective, a self-reliant diver is a self-confident diver because he knows — buddy or no buddy — that he can handle whatever problems might arise. This translates into less apprehension and anxiety. The results are a reduced breathing rate, lower threshold of panic and improved ability to pay attention to the dive and to his buddy.

Achieving self-reliance requires three essential conditions. The first and most obvious is that you possess skill competence. At the minimum you must be able to perform all the skills you learned in your entry-level course in a calm, deliberate manner, and without the need for assistance. You also should be able to do this in an environment typical of the conditions you normally encounter.

Skill competence also implies some familiarity with self-rescue and the ability to offer assistance to others. The willingness to help your buddy is meaningless if you lack the know-how to do it. But such knowledge and skill doesn't just materialize out of thin air, nor are they covered in most entry-level courses. To gain these insights requires training, such as a diver rescue course.

The second element of self-reliance is that you maintain an adequate physical condition. Few doubt the need for good physical condition, but the question is, what's adequate? That answer is highly personal and varies according to circumstance. Start by reviewing the kinds of environmental conditions you usually encounter. Do you normally dive in heavy or moderate currents or surf? At what depths and temperatures? Do you dive in open ocean or in a lake or quarry? And how likely is it that these conditions will change from day to day, or even hour to hour? Your physical condition must match or, better yet, exceed the conditions you dive most often. What this means, of course, is that someone who dives primarily in the cold waters of the north needs more physical stamina than someone who confines his diving to Caribbean holidays.

Third, and perhaps most importantly, a self-reliant diver understands and accepts his limitations. This may be the most difficult element to achieve because it requires a great deal of something many of us lack: self-honesty. We all have an internal vision of ourselves, and sometimes that vision belies reality. Certainly, there's nothing wrong with a positive self-image. Quite the contrary. But, as divers, when that self-image is overblown, the result can be downright dangerous. A truly self-reliant diver understands his strengths and limitations and, as a result, when he decides to dive, it's with a high level of psychological and emotional confidence. This is the final measure of a self-reliant diver.

Let me illustrate what I'm saying with a personal example. I'd like to believe that I possess the same stamina and physical prowess as I did when I was an 18-year-old jock. But realistically, I know I don't. And lying to myself could mean getting into circumstances I can't handle. But as most of you baby boomers with a realistic self-image, I've managed to compensate for the lack of youth and brute strength by learning to use my brain and some basic common sense. This lets me honestly assess diving conditions and make the appropriate decisions. If I believe that I might get in over my head (figuratively, at least), than I'm wise enough not to dive. After all, diving is a recreational endeavor, not a test of muscle and testosterone. The outcome from such a self-assessment is that when you do decide to make a dive, it will be with a high degree of psychological and emotional confidence — the final measure of a self-reliant diver.

Assessing the Decision to Go It Alone

In my experience, the main reason some choose to dive alone isn't because of a belief that buddies are dangerous. It is, rather, that there are some diving activities that simply lend themselves to diving alone. For example, the last thing in the world an underwater photographer wants — unless, of course, he needs a model — is someone else tagging along, scaring the marine life and reducing visibility. Adding credence to this is the fact that virtually all professional underwater photographers dive alone when there is no need for a model. And even in those situations where there's someone else accompanying him, you can rest assured that for all practical purposes the photographer is solo diving. His or her attention is devoted completely to getting pictures, not watching another diver.

Like photographers, underwater hunters often prefer to go it alone. Many lobster divers look at buddies as nothing more than competitors for a limited resource. And having a buddy means that they'll give away the location of their special spots and successful techniques. Spearfishers, likewise, usually feel the same way about buddies. Furthermore, they say, it's a lot safer to dive without a buddy because in limited visibility a partner risks becoming an accidental target.

Another reason some choose to dive alone is simply because they don't want to take responsibility for someone else. While many might consider anyone who would dive solo as totally irresponsible, my experience is that most devoted solo divers are more responsible than many buddy divers that I know. Given all the careful consideration, planning and self-reliance that's needed to become a proficient solo diver, that shouldn't really come as a surprise.

Another big factor that explains solo diving is purely one of practicality — there's just no one else to dive with. We often forget that there are lots of places where diving isn't a popular activity, and not being able to find a buddy can be a serious impediment. This isn't a minor issue, either. One of the primary factors the diving industry points to in explaining why so many people drop out of diving is simply that they can't find anyone to dive with. While it may be difficult to endorse the practice of solo diving for that reason alone, it's also difficult to rebuke those who do. Would you stop diving simply because you couldn't find someone to dive with? To some — myself included — the answer is a resounding no.

The final reason for going it alone may be the most compelling — the solitude. While there's certainly something to be said for sharing the experience, solo divers often feel that diving is best appreciated in isolation from others. It is, after all, *the silent world*; and some feel that the accompaniment of another diver is nothing but an intrusion. While many may not agree with this, we also should remember that as citizens of a free society, it's someone's right to feel that way.

Not so long ago those who wanted to learn about solo diving were limited to Ron von Maier's book, *Solo Diving: The Art of Underwater Self-Sufficiency;* and there was no such thing as a formal course and certification. That changed a few years ago when Scuba Diving International (SDI) introduced the first specialty diver program called Solo Diver. More recently the Professional Association of Diving Instructors (PADI) followed suit with its Self-Reliant Specialty Diver Course. The program is designed with three overarching goals: developing an understanding of the value and application of the buddy system and the philosophy of, and motivation for, diving without a partner; an introduction to the risks, risk management techniques and the need for equipment redundancy in self-reliant diving; and improving self-reliant dive skills, dive planning and gas management abilities. Both programs require extensive diving experience of at least 100 dives, and an advanced diving certification. You can find out more about these programs by contacting an SDI or PADI diving professional or facility.

The Solo Recipe

Solo diving is often misinterpreted to mean nothing more than jumping in the water without a buddy. That's not solo diving; that's just plain stupid diving. Because he has no one else to fall back on in case of a problem, a responsible solo diver must follow a planning routine that is often more rigorous than when buddy diving. In addition to the standard predive preparation, he'll follow a set of special rules and safety considerations.

Perhaps the most important rule for solo diving is that the diver have experience in similar diving conditions. In other words, the dive isn't beyond his level of experience and his personal comfort zone. This applies not only to the conditions present at the time he enters the water, but also consideration for how those conditions might change during the course of the dive. It's one thing to enter the water on a bright calm day with no current, but if the weather or tide changes there won't be anyone around to help. If in the planning process the diver determines that he can handle the dive only if conditions remain stable, then that's a good indication that he should abandon his solo plan and make that dive with an experienced buddy. This is an excellent illustration of the need for the unflinching self-honesty mentioned previously.

Once in the water, perhaps the most important consideration is air management. Some suggest that solo divers take the time to meticulously calculate their air requirements and probable air usage. My experience tells me that, except for mission-oriented technical dives, divers rarely are willing to do this. A simpler and more practical planning guideline is to use the "rule of thirds." This simple rule says that you should plan to use only one-third of your air supply for the trip out, then another third for the trip back. The final third is a reserve for unforeseen circumstances which, when diving without a buddy, can be a particularly vital consideration. (The need for this air management technique is also why some view solo diving as a form of technical diving.)

Some solo divers advocate an alternate air management guideline to the rule of thirds. They suggest calculating your returning air pressure in consideration of your depth. To do this, round off your actual depth to the next greater increment of 10, then add a zero to that figure. The result is the air pressure at which you should begin your ascent. For example, assume you're making a dive to 57 feet (17 m). Round that up to 60 and by adding a zero you have 600. You should then begin your ascent when you reach an air pressure of 600 psi.

The next consideration is probably the most important. What if you screw up your air management plan and run out of air? There will, of course, be no one around to give you a spare regulator. The only out-of-air contingency that will work for a solo diver is a completely redundant air supply, such as a Spare Air® or pony bottle. When making deeper dives, larger-capacity pony bottles or dual tanks with independent valves or separate regulators are essential. (Learning how to use this is yet another reason technical training is a good idea for would-be solo divers.)

Ron von Maier, author of *Solo Diving: The Art of Underwater Self-Sufficiency*, advocates two other common-sense rules for solo diving. The first is that one should never solo dive deeper than twice the depth to which he can freedive. This tends to impose a reasonable and personalized depth limit. Personally, as an often-solo diver myself, my guideline is a little different. As relatively few folks do much freediving, it might be difficult for some to see von Maier's suggestion as a usable guideline. My guide has always been to limit my solo excursions to a depth no greater than that from which I'm comfortable performing a controlled emergency swimming ascent. That way I have the self-confidence of knowing that even without air I can make it to the surface because I've done it before.

Von Maier's second rule is another sensible and practical one: A solo diver's underwater distance from his exit point should not exceed the distance he can comfortably swim in full scuba while at the surface. Remember, getting to the surface is only half the battle. You also have to get out of the water, and there won't be anybody to help you.

Making the Choice

From an analysis of the weaknesses in how the buddy system is practiced, and in what's truly necessary for safe solo diving, one can conclude that safety doesn't necessarily lie in numbers but in preparation and attitude. Although safety may be enhanced through a cooperative process, in the end it depends on the individual.

All diver training organizations place great emphasis on the buddy system, and require adherence to it during any training-related activity. Most dive operators and charter boats, likewise, insist that divers operate in pairs. These, I believe, are wise practices given that many — perhaps most — divers aren't self-reliant to the degree I described earlier. So, I cannot in good conscience advocate doing away with the buddy system. I believe it will, and should, continue to be a vital safety procedure for the vast majority of divers. And I certainly wouldn't want to suggest to those who just like sharing the diving experience with others to do otherwise.

But we should also not lose sight of the fact that we live in a free society. And as there isn't any governmental regulation of diving, there are no "scuba police" to enforce buddy diving or any other practice. If someone wants to solo dive, neither I nor anyone else can stop them. Even if they're forced to enter the water with a partner, no one can control their behavior once they're on the bottom. This issue is not black and white. Solo diving isn't necessarily dangerous and irresponsible, nor is it the panacea for all the problems divers face. Equally, I believe the buddy system has saved numerous lives when it's practiced properly; but I'm not blind to the fact that when it's put to the test, it doesn't always work.

An alarming trend in our society is the reluctance to accept personal responsibility for our actions. The credo seems to be this: When something goes wrong, blame anyone or anything but ourselves. In reality, it's not our government, not our mothers, not our instructors, and not even our buddies who are responsible for our safety. In the final analysis, the buck stops with us — individuals with free will to make a decision and accept the consequences.

If you choose to dive solo, please do so only if you're truly self-reliant and follow the appropriate guidelines. To do otherwise is foolish. If you choose to dive with a buddy, then don't fall into the trap of assuming all is well just because someone is accompanying you. No procedure nor any technology on the face of the earth can replace a functioning human brain. Use it and dive safely.

CHAPTER 36

No Klutzes Allowed:
The Fine Art of Buoyancy Control

Years ago while on a dive trip I witnessed a heated exchange between two dive buddies. Apparently one of them had run low on air long before the other; and the more air-efficient partner was less than pleased that he had to exit the water with more than 1,500 psi remaining. Colorful expletives and less-than-complimentary words filled the air until, finally, the divemaster intervened and the duo retired to neutral corners.

While most onboard were satisfied that the altercation ended without violence, it struck me as remarkable for reasons other than the ugly scene it created. Both combatants were of about the same age and size and, by their sculpted physiques, obviously spent more time in a gym in one week than I've ever seen in a lifetime. Indeed, they were poster boys for the Perfect Diver, and I was intrigued to learn why one used so much air. So, I decided to spend a few minutes observing the kids from Muscle Beach on the next dive. In watching them suit up I noticed nothing remarkable, except that the "air hog" donned a weight belt that could have been used as an auxiliary anchor for the dive boat. Even his well-toned muscles quivered as he lifted it into position. (I later found that it weighed 28 pounds [13 kg], yet the diver was wearing only a 3-millimeter shorty wet suit.)

Confident that I had determined the cause of the air consumption discrepancy, I entered the water to confirm my suspicions. As if on cue, the divers played out what could have been a scene from a video called "The Dos and Don'ts of Buoyancy Control." One diver looked like a chambered nautilus, gliding effortlessly through the

water as a small stream of bubbles periodically pulsed from his second stage. This was in stark contrast to his heavily overweighted buddy, who looked more like a human yo-yo or a marionette whose puppeteer was having a spastic fit. Air poured from his regulator as if it were free flowing. Twenty minutes later, the pair was back on board and the war resumed.

The event made me reflect on the importance of buoyancy control and the unique character of scuba diving. In most sporting activities, those who can exert the most energy are normally the most proficient. Yet, in diving the exact opposite is true. Heavy exertion means that you're doing something wrong; it means you're reducing the amount of time you can spend underwater, and perhaps even risking your well-being by overbreathing your regulator or possibly increasing your susceptibility to decompression sickness.

Clearly, one can make a convincing argument that buoyancy control is the most critical skill in a diver's repertoire. Even the most cursory review of diving fatalities reports demonstrates that what kills divers more often than getting trapped in caves or shipwrecks or succumbing to catastrophic diving diseases is something much less exotic. More often than not, divers die from drowning due to panic, exhaustion or running out of air — problems that are easily prevented or overcome by good buoyancy control.

Another reason buoyancy control is the diver's most important skill is demonstrated by the growing concern for environmentally responsible diving. While some divers with poor buoyancy control may never experience problems from panic or exhaustion, they will certainly wreak havoc on the environment. Like the infamous bull in a china shop, the damage done by divers who cannot control their buoyancy can be devastating to the fragile coral reef and its inhabitants. Evidence has proven the seriousness of the problem in numerous diver impact studies on coral reefs around the world.

The ironic part of all this is that divers wear hundreds of dollars worth of equipment designed to help control their buoyancy. And, they normally train for several hours learning how to do it. Furthermore, most of the damage done to the environment by divers isn't intentional. So why is there a problem? The answer is twofold: Many divers have an inadequate understanding of what constitutes good buoyancy control and they lack either the commitment or know-how to develop and practice good techniques.

For your own safety and enjoyment, as well as concern for the environment, let's assume that you *want* to improve your buoyancy control skills. But, how do you do this? Essentially, there are three factors critical to maintaining good buoyancy control, which include proper weighting, effective use of the buoyancy compensator (BC), and awareness and control of breathing.

Proper Use of Weights

The oldest and simplest form of buoyancy control is merely adding weight to the diver. This is, at best, a gross adjustment. Its primary effect is in achieving negative buoyancy. While that's important, it's not sufficient. The proper use of weight means more than wearing enough to make you sink. Using weights wisely requires some careful consideration. Here's some advice:

Use only the amount of weight you absolutely need. Excess lead should never be used as a quick way to reach the bottom. A proper descent means a *controlled* descent, but if you're overweighted it's difficult to control the speed of your descent. This risks in-

jury from ear squeeze, exhaustion and exceeding your planned depth. Think of your weights as an aid to diving, not a crutch. Set a personal goal to dive with as little lead on your weight belt as possible. To make sure you're properly weighted, conduct a buoyancy check with a near-empty tank at 10-20 feet (3-6 m). That way you'll be sure to have sufficient buoyancy control to make a safety stop at the end of the dive. As you reduce weight from your belt, you'll find that diving becomes more enjoyable because it requires less effort. And with the decreased effort, your breathing rate will also decrease, enabling you to get more time out of every tank of air.

Another way of reducing the amount of lead you wear involves the kind of tank you use. Instead of using the more common aluminum tanks, some divers prefer to use steel. The added weight and decreased displacement of steel tanks allow divers to take lead off their belt. Especially with the newer high-capacity steel tanks now on the market, some divers can get away with only a minimal amount of lead around their waists.

Check periodically to make sure that you don't dive overweighted. Many divers learn to dive with too much lead. And, unfortunately, instructors often contribute to this problem by intentionally overweighting their students. Their rationale is that it's easier to handle overweighted students because they stay securely on the bottom. The problem is that once students leave the course, they continue to use the same amount of weight their instructor advised. I have often witnessed new divers showing up at a dive resort demanding a 20-plus-pound (9 kg) weight belt because "it's what my instructor said I needed."

To confirm that you're not using too much, periodically check the amount of lead you use, and make a record of it in your logbook for future reference. Divers are often surprised to learn that as their experience grows, and diving conditions change, so will the amount of weight they need. (This is because as divers gain experience, they develop a more relaxed breathing cycle, resulting in less fluctuation in displacement from the expansion and contraction of their chest.) Never assume that the amount of lead your instructor said you needed was correct or will never change. Check it to make sure. With a little effort, it's not uncommon for divers to sometimes drop half the amount of weight they used when they were in training.

The problem with diving overweighted is that it gives you only two options. The first is to spend your dive continually bouncing off the bottom. This damages both the reef and your exposure suit, and subjects you to injury from scrapes and bottom-dwelling critters such as sea urchins. It also destroys visibility by silting up the bottom. What diver hasn't watched with contempt the "wandering dust clouds" created by thoughtless or incompetent divers who can't stay off the bottom?

Your other option, of course, when diving overweighted is to inflate your buoyancy compensator (BC) to stay off the bottom. The problem is that excessive weight will require an excessive amount of air in the BC to compensate. The result is that your upper body tends to float, while your lower body tends to sink. This is both an inefficient and uncomfortable position to maintain. You present more surface area while swimming and exert more energy due to the increased drag. In addition, you'll still damage the reef because the downward angle of your fins will make you kick whatever's beneath you. The use of ankle weights makes the situation even worse. While they are sometimes useful when wearing a dry suit, you should avoid wearing ankle weights — especially when diving on a coral reef.

Use the most appropriate type and configuration of weights. For many years molded lead weights were the standard for divers, but recently there's been a trend toward lead shot encased in vinyl or nylon mesh bags. These shot weights are usually a better choice because they conform more comfortably to your body. In addition, they won't cause injury if you drop them on your foot. They also won't injure someone beneath you should you ever have to jettison your weight belt at or near the surface (and they won't damage the bottom of swimming pools, either).

Regardless of the type of weights you use, make sure you distribute them evenly around your body. Uneven distribution will throw off your center of buoyancy and, like an unstable boat, cause you to list to the side as you swim. Continually trying to correct your position to swim level requires a needless expenditure of energy, which can lead to poor buoyancy control or exhaustion.

Recognize the effect of changing environments or equipment. You obviously need more weight when you go from diving in fresh water to seawater. The problem is that divers often add more than is necessary. Add only as much lead as you need to maintain neutral buoy-

ancy — no more and no less. This is why it's a good idea to routinely conduct a buoyancy check during the first dive in any new environment or after a period of inactivity. Also be careful when you go from seawater to fresh. Some divers ignore this advice, reasoning that, as their seawater weight belt will overweight them in fresh water, there won't be any problem descending. So, they conclude, there's no real need to change the amount of weight. The result is probably a grossly overweighted diver.

Archimedes' principle says that your buoyancy changes according to the amount of water you displace. Keep this in mind when you add or subtract *any* item of equipment, not just weights. When you dive with a new or altered equipment configuration, spend some time after entering the water evaluating any changes in your trim or buoyancy characteristics. That 25-pound (11.25 kg) weight belt you wear with a full 7-millimeter wet suit back in New Jersey won't be necessary — and could be dangerous — when you dive in the Caribbean with only a Lycra™ suit.

One of the biggest equipment factors affecting buoyancy involves underwater photography. A camera, complete with an underwater strobe, will have a big effect on both your buoyancy and trim. Unfortunately many photographers never take this into account. When you use an underwater camera system you must be especially careful of how your equipment — and picture-taking habits — affect your buoyancy. Destroying the reef in the interest of getting the perfect picture is selfish and irresponsible.

The Buoyancy Compensator

While you make gross buoyancy adjustments by adding weights, you begin to refine your buoyancy control with the addition of the BC. Here are some important considerations for using your BC to its greatest effect.

Be sure you are using the right BC. The *right* BC is one that fits. Most of us learned to dive using rental equipment. This means the BC you trained with might not have been the best one for you. Your BC should fit snugly, but not interfere with movement or restrict your breathing. But, be careful not to use a BC that's too big. An oversized device can cause excessive drag when you swim, and not support you in a comfortable position either underwater or at the surface. To avoid these problems, seek the advice of your instructor or your local retailer when buying your own BC.

Your style of BC should reflect the type of diving you do. The color or the way it looks on you shouldn't be the most important criterion in selecting a BC. Instead, choose your BC according to the kind of diving you do most often. Divers who primarily frequent warm, tropical water often prefer a low-profile or even very low-profile BCs. Their reduced size and smaller buoyancy chambers give them minimal drag (but also minimum lift). They're generally more comfortable than the larger-sized models — particularly if you're wearing only a dive skin or no exposure suit at all.

Recently, some BC manufacturers have introduced systems with interchangeable bladders, allowing the diver to customize the size and style of bladder to local conditions. For instance, a diver who lives in a cold-water environment might use a larger-capacity bladder for local diving, and switch to a low-volume style when going on vacation to a tropical resort.

Dry suit divers, on the other hand, often opt for back-floatation models. Because dry suit manufacturers usually mount the inflator/deflator valves in the chest area of the suit, back floatation devices give easier access to the suit valves. In addition, many BC manufacturers are giving special consideration to female divers. For women divers, BCs designed for female proportions can often make a significant difference in both comfort and stability in the water.

The Importance of Proper Breathing

The last component of buoyancy control is the most overlooked, and stressed the least during training. We've seen so far that gross control of buoyancy is achieved by adding weights. Then, you refine the process with the BC. But that's not enough. To fine-tune your buoyancy control you must learn to use appropriate *breathing techniques*. As you breathe, your chest expands and contracts, causing the amount of water you displace to change. This results in small but continual changes in your buoyancy throughout the dive. Recognizing this, and using your breathing pattern as a tool, enables you to achieve the buoyancy control expected of an experienced diver. Here are some ways you can take your breathing patterns into account.

Recognize that your psychological state will affect your breathing pattern. A physiological response to stress is to increase your respiration rate. This will make a big difference in your buoyancy. You will find it harder to maintain position because of the constant and rapid changes in displacement. Believe it or not, good buoyancy control begins *before* you enter the water. If you start your dive stressed out, you're likely to have buoyancy problems that can often lead to exhaustion. Take a few minutes to rest, calm down and get your breathing pattern under control before entering the water.

If you find that you're breathing still isn't under control even after you enter the water, then stop and rest before proceeding with the dive. A few minutes spent regaining your composure could make all the difference between an unforgettable dive and one you'd rather forget.

Avoid stress and exertion by increasing your experience gradually and under proper supervision. One reason your stress level — and thus your breathing rate — might increase is because you're attempting something that's beyond your capability. By staying within your limits you'll be less prone to stress, maintain a comfortable and controlled breathing rate and experience fewer buoyancy problems. When you do decide to extend your capabilities, find a buddy who's experienced at the type of diving you want to pursue. Then, gain experience a little at a time. Don't expect to become an expert in only one dive. Better yet, enroll in a continuing education course and learn under professional supervision. New experiences are a lot less intimidating when there's a seasoned pro at your side.

Develop good breathing patterns that aid buoyancy control. With a little practice, developing good buoyancy control isn't difficult. One excellent way to improve and maintain your skill level is by learning to "hover." This involves maintaining a position in midwater while remaining absolutely motionless — moving neither your hands nor fins. The trick to hovering is complete familiarity with your equipment *and understanding the effect of breathing*. Once you can hover effortlessly you have truly mastered the art of buoyancy control. An added benefit of hovering is that it can be extremely useful in performing safety stops before surfacing.

Consider the Environment

As with all diving skills, mastering buoyancy control is essential to safe diving. But buoyancy control has another equally important aspect that has nothing to do with safety. At least not with human safety. Good buoyancy control protects not only you but also the environment in which you dive. For most, the main reason for diving is to experience the beauty of ecosystems we could never explore on land. But many of these special underwater places, especially coral reefs, are home to fragile inhabitants that are easily broken, squashed or mutilated by even a slight careless or unintended touch. Responsible diving behavior, therefore, requires an awareness of, and ability to perform, what many now call "low-impact diving." The analogy that I like to use is this: When you dive on a coral reef, do you act like a bull or a butterfly? If the answer is bull, it's time you became a butterfly, and here's how.

The first step to reef-friendly diving is maintaining your skills level and underwater awareness. Don't let your knowledge and skill get rusty. If you've been away from diving for a while, take a continuing-education or refresher course. But even more importantly, understand that a truly responsible diver begins preparation in his head long before he enters the water. For example, take the time to learn about where you're going to dive. Between field guides and online resources there are literally thousands of sources of information about any region or ecosystem visited by divers today. So, take some time to gain some insight into where you're diving. Increasing your knowledge helps you become familiar with the organisms you'll see. Keep in mind that the continued health of the environment will largely depend on how you treat it. And how you treat it will depend largely on how much you know about it.

Now let's go diving. Once off the boat, think about your descent not just from the perspective of your own safety, but its effect on the environment. When possible, descend over sand patches rather than directly over the reef. If you're still a bit rusty with buoyancy control, a sandy bottom is a lot more forgiving than a reef. Crashing into the bottom is the worst way to introduce yourself to the reef, so pay attention to your descent rate.

Once on the bottom, you enter the phase of a dive that I term the "terrible 10 minutes." This is, logically, the time when most scientific studies show the greatest amount of diver damage. So, take some time to ac-

climate, and to make your equipment or buoyancy adjustment somewhere away from live coral. Next, before swimming off haphazardly, take a moment to notice what's going on around you. How are the creatures interacting with each other? What's their reaction to you? Are you about to blunder through a cleaning station or destroy an algal patch that's been meticulously farmed by an industrious damselfish? Also make sure that you consider the effect of currents or surge so you're not carried into the reef.

As you swim, try to remain a few feet — what I call the "magic meter" — away from the bottom. In fact, if you try to remain in sand channels, rather than swimming over the reef, all the better. However, be careful around sand, too. Your fins can kick up lots of sand in the water column, creating significant underwater "dust clouds" that can be as harmful as a poison gas attack to many stationary reef residents. Coral, especially, can be highly stressed and use considerable energy reserves in trying to clear itself of sediment.

Be mindful to maintain proper dive posture, with your fins slightly elevated above the level of your head. This means mastery of buoyancy control, and — as emphasized previously— the key to proper buoyancy is using no more weight than is necessary. Wear only enough weight to attain neutral buoyancy with an empty tank; no more and no less. An overweighted diver will swim in a fins-down, diagonal position, unavoidably causing damage to the reef from fin kicks.

If you have difficulty maintaining good body position, consider redistributing your weights by placing small amounts on your BC or tank. Again, avoid using ankle weights, as they tend to make your legs very negative, and make fin impacts much more likely. (Although, a good use of an ankle weight is to secure it around your tank valve to achieve a better "heads-down" swimming position.) Today many BCs are designed with weight pockets especially for this purpose. If you are weighted properly you'll swim in a horizontal, or slightly legs-up position, with your fins well off the bottom. Also, make sure that all of your equipment is secure and nothing — not your SPG (submersible pressure gauge), not your octopus regulator, not even your dive light — is dangling. Secure all equipment close to your body.

Underwater photographers should be particularly careful in avoiding reef contact. No matter how expensive the camera system, it never gives one license to destroy the reef or disrupt its inhabitants just to get the perfect photograph. Good diving etiquette applies to everyone, not just those who don't take pictures. In fact, it's a good idea to first master your diving skills — especially buoyancy control — before tackling the added challenge of photography.

Yet another issue is what to do with your hands. Basically, use them for maneuvering only; don't touch anything. This is for your protection as well as the reef's. Merely touching a coral polyp can kill it. The best way to sensitize yourself to hands-off behavior is by not wearing gloves, except perhaps in circumstances such as wreck diving. (A number of dive destinations no longer allow divers to wear gloves.) You'll learn quickly that, like fish, a good diver doesn't have to touch anything. Only the unskilled grapple with things underwater. Personally, I think the value of gloves has been grossly overblown. I stopped wearing them when diving coral reefs decades ago, and never once regretted it.

Also nix the swordlike dive knives, and opt for something small and sharp. (A pair of shears works better than a knife, anyway.) Most people use large knives more as crowbars or probes than cutting tools; and if just touching something with your hands can cause harm, imagine what a metal instrument can do.

Finally, never forget about your fins, or more accurately what they can do. Studies have proven time and again that most diver damage is a result of unintentional fin contact. Consider that when you are wearing fins, you are more than a foot taller than normal, so make room when you swim over or near the reef. Learn to use a technique called the "stop and tuck." If you ever feel your fins touch something — even slightly — immediately stop kicking and tuck your knees toward your chest. This will pull your feet away from whatever you've contacted, be it a coral reef or another diver. Never continue kicking once you feel you've hit something with your fins. If you must maneuver, use your hands to swim away.

Buoyancy control is such an integral part of the diving experience that I use it as a quick and accurate tool for assessing diver competence. More than the ability to clear a mask, share air or swim a half-mile towing a buddy, a diver's mastery of buoyancy control, or lack thereof, tells me in an instant all I need to know about competence. Without it you aren't really a diver, and until you master it you will never become one.

CHAPTER 37

I Can See for Inches and Inches:
A Guide to Diving In Limited Visibility

Most folks become divers because they're intrigued with what's underwater.

After all, diving is the only way they can see the world beneath the waves firsthand. But this seemingly obvious statement says something important about humans: To us, experience is synonymous with seeing. Indeed, humans are among the most visually oriented creatures on Earth. So, if you tell most divers that they'll encounter conditions so poor that they can barely see anything, their response is likely to be a resounding, "Why bother?"

Still, while every diver dreams of diving in crystal-clear water, this rarely happens. In fact, some spend their entire careers in places where seeing their fins is considered a good day. My own experience is a good example. I learned to dive in the Chesapeake Bay, a body of water known for its blue crabs and oysters, but not for its spectacular clarity. To me, visibility beyond an arm's reach was magical. More typically, in my early days of diving I was happy when I could see beyond the lens of my mask.

Why Dive If You Can't See?

Probably in most cases, divers find themselves in limited visibility not because it's something they planned. Instead, it's because conditions deteriorate, or an error was made in planning. Conditions can change for any number of reasons. For example, a changing tide — especially an outgoing tide — can bring with it dirty water that can quickly turn a great dive into a disappointing experience. On the other hand, a group of inexperienced divers kicking up the bottom can render 30 feet (9 m) of visibility into 30 inches (76 cm) in a matter of seconds.

So, whether we like it or not, sometime or another we all experience limited visibility.

It's certainly understandable that conditions can change, and we have to know how to deal with the cards we're dealt. But what surprises many is that armies of divers actually choose to dive when the water is more like Guinness than gin. In my opinion, one of the advantages to learning to dive in less-than-ideal conditions (yes, there are benefits to poor visibility and cold water) is that visibility isn't everything, nor necessarily the most important factor in a dive. Furthermore, depending on the dive objective, good visibility may not even be necessary. Two examples come to mind immediately: artifact diving and macro (close-up) photography.

Artifact collection is often referred to as "braille diving." It requires sifting through what's most often a muddy bottom, so what little visibility may be present initially is soon gone. Unfortunately, muddy bottoms are ideal environments for finding artifacts, as the low-oxygen environment it creates helps preserve artifacts. So, zero visibility is the norm in some of the best artifact diving locales, like the rivers of coastal South Carolina,

Georgia and North Florida. Here, divers soon become highly adept at diving blind, and don't feel their experience is diminished in the least.

In addition, some of the most outstanding macro photography that I've ever seen was taken in two very different and distant locations — the Lembeh Straits off north Sulawesi, Indonesia, and northern British Columbia. Lembeh is known as the world's best "muck dive" because of the incredible diversity of bizarre and rarely seen invertebrates that thrive in its muddy, trash-strewn bottom. Spectacular visibility isn't necessary. In fact, many of the creatures prefer or require the soft bottom. Off British Columbia the issue isn't necessarily the soft bottom, but here the breathtaking beauty seen in the photos of tiny organisms is belied by the often murky green water resulting from plankton.

What Limits the Visibility?

Common sense tells us that underwater visibility is determined primarily by the concentration of suspended particles in the water. We term this measure of clarity turbidity. Highly turbid water has a higher sediment load than less turbid water. Therefore, areas where low visibility is the norm usually have some continuing input or production of fine particles. Furthermore, the finer the particles the more likely they are to become and remain suspended. Good examples are bodies of water into which silt-laden rivers drain. This explains my early experience in the Chesapeake Bay. As the largest estuary in the United States, this highly productive ecosystem is driven largely by the decay of marsh grass. The decaying organic matter, which scientists call detritus, serves as the base for the estuarine food chain. In addition, sites that are the terminus for rivers receive enormous amounts of sediment carried by these rivers. This soft sediment creates the fine, silty bottom that is easily disturbed, and once suspended in the water tends not to settle quickly.

Interestingly, one way of cleaning highly turbid waters is with seagrass beds. In a way, seagrasses serve as "speed bumps." They create resistance to water flow, allowing the sediments to settle out. This effect is one reason visibility is often better on vegetated bottom as opposed to a barren, soft-sediment bottom. Generally, the courser the bottom type the more it can resist disturbance, and if disturbed, the quicker it will settle. This

is why sandy bottoms typically offer better visibility than mud, and bottoms composed of pebbles or cobble offer better clarity than sand.

While limited visibility is a perpetual condition in some areas, it can occur intermittently even in waters that are normally very clear. The reason for this is usually localized weather phenomena. Runoff caused by heavy rains can devastate visibility, especially if the land proximate to the sea has been cleared for development. This is why, in tropical regions, the sediment load caused by clearing land for agriculture can devastate coral reefs. High winds can also cause heavy seas and make the situation worse or keep it from improving. This is a common occurrence in Florida during the winter months, as strong weather fronts pour down from the north. Furthermore, extremely heavy rainfall can create large amounts of highly turbid freshwater runoff.

At times, however, poor visibility has little or nothing to do with bottom type. Causes of limited visibility not related to bottom type include thermoclines, water staining and plankton blooms. A water mass of one temperature (density) can behave remarkably different from a water mass of another. The result is a stratification or layering effect — caused by the differing densities — that we call thermoclines. (In some situations stratification can be caused by salinity differences in what's termed a halocline.) This occasionally results in layers of clearer water becoming sandwiched between more turbid layers. In my earlier days as a diver, I often encountered this when diving off the coasts of New Jersey and Delaware. We would arrive to find disappointingly low visibility at the surface only to encounter far better conditions once we descended below the thermocline.

Another phenomenon familiar to visitors of coastal rivers in the Deep South is where freshwater bodies are often stained with tannin (tannic acid). Unlike conditions where limited visibility is caused by large suspended particles, tannin is leached from the roots of trees. It actually dissolves in the water, giving many southern rivers their classic reddish-brown coloration. Like diving in a river of fresh-brewed tea, the darkened water may actually provide clear close-up visibility, only to fade quickly into blackness a few feet away. However, as tannin-stained water is often low in suspended particulate matter (the river bottoms are often large-grain sand), this is one limited-visibility situation for which using a dive light can help.

Most often, though, using a dive light in limited visibility is worthless. As many divers have been sad to discover, particulate reflects, scatters and absorbs the light rays. However, if you still insist on using a light in these conditions, try to aim it to the side and above the object you're illuminating. This will minimize backscatter caused by the suspended particulate.

In marine waters, plankton can be a major factor leading to limited visibility. For example, the pea-soup conditions often encountered in northern waters during spring and summer are caused by a high plankton concentration. But this is not limited to colder waters. Generally, the quantity of plankton depends on factors such as the season (which determines both temperature and amount of sunlight), nutrient supply and water movement. During spring and summer, warming temperatures and abundant sunlight can cause plankton to grow so prolifically that "blooms" often occur. In some areas, this may turn the water green or even a reddish-brown. Depending on the species of plankton involved, it can also result in an increasingly common phenomenon called Harmful Algal Blooms or "red tide." (Actually, these have nothing to do with tides, and they're not always red.) Because of possible human health concerns, it's advisable not to dive in areas affected by an active red tide event.

How to Deal With Low Visibility

When diving in limited visibility your diving behavior can make a bad thing even worse. If possible, stay well off the bottom. If you must stay near the bottom, follow the "anti-silting" techniques used by cave divers. This involves swimming in a head-down/fins-up position, which prevents fin movement from disturbing the bottom. Also, keep your knees bent slightly as you kick, and avoid any other unnecessary movement, particularly contact with the bottom. To further reduce the effect from fin turbulence, many cave divers adopt a modified frog kick rather than the standard scissors kick.

Once you've done all you can to maintain what visibility exists, the next consideration is that of your buddy. Some see the primary risk of limited-visibility diving as a case in which buddies can become separated. So, the first and most obvious technique to avoid this is for the buddy team to remain within arm's reach at all times. For divers used to good-visibility conditions — which often allows buddies to separate considerable distances

and still remain within sight — abiding by the practice of "not more than an arm's reach away" may be difficult. Nonetheless, it's an unequivocal rule in limited visibility, and requires diligence from both buddies. Frequent checks to confirm your buddy's presence and position are a necessity as well.

Equipment for Limited Visibility

If you're new to limited-visibility diving, or if the visibility is extremely limited (less than a foot or so), it's probably time to consider using a buddy line. Although popular among European divers, buddy lines are rarely used by the recreational diving community in North America. But the advantage a buddy line can provide in these specialized conditions warrants serious consideration of its use.

A buddy line is a short tether (6-10 feet [1.8-3 m) that allows the buddy team to maintain continuous contact. Usually, ¼-inch to ⅜-inch (0.6 to 1 cm) synthetic braided or three-strand twisted line works best. Polypropylene is especially good as a buddy line because it floats — which keeps the line off the bottom — and its bright yellow color is easily seen. Each end of the line should have some way to allow divers to stay connected. Some prefer simple loops for handholds, or surgical tubing to loop over the wrist. Others prefer to attach the line by snapping it to their buoyancy compensator (BC) — never a weight belt — leaving both hands unencumbered. If this method is used, however, the line should be equipped with quick-release "snap links," which are used by sailors and available in any marine supply store. This allows the line to be immediately detached if necessary.

Using a buddy line has the additional advantage of enabling continuous buddy communication, even in zero visibility. Signals are easily communicated by pulling the line. A commonly used code for simple directions: one pull for "stop," two pulls for "OK" or "proceed," three pulls for "come here," four pulls for "surface" and five pulls for "emergency."

Buddy lines are not without problems, though, as they can create an entanglement risk. This is why you should never use one of excessive length. In addition, swimming with a buddy line requires a level of coordination that you may not be used to from normal diving conditions. Therefore, divers who lack experience using buddy lines should first practice in good-visibility conditions.

Another consideration is exposure protection. Even if the water temperature doesn't require it, some form of exposure suit should always be worn in limited visibility. You won't always be able to see sharp or jagged objects, and it's best to let a suit rather than your body take the wear, tear, scrapes and pokes that can result. And while on the subject of exposure protection, a word about gloves is in order. Although I always advise against wearing them when diving on coral reefs, gloves are a vital piece of gear when diving in murky conditions. You won't always be able to see where you're putting your hands, so these should be more than a pair of cheap cotton gardening gloves.

A good sharp knife is yet another necessity. Personally, I stopped wearing the mini-sword-type dive knife decades ago. Aside from their bulk and tendency to get entangled, big knives rarely keep a sharp edge because of the high-grade stainless steel required to prevent them from rusting. When diving in limited visibility your knife should also be placed somewhere on your upper body, not your leg, to ensure easy accessibility even if you're entangled. Instead, I keep a very sharp Teflon-blade folding knife in my BC pocket along with a shroud-cutter (a plastic-encased razor used by sky divers). The latter makes quick work of fishing line. For heavier entanglements like nets or lines, the knife is a better option.

Finally, in extreme cases, limited-visibility divers sometimes take another lead from cave divers and wear helmets, particularly if they won't be wearing hoods. These, of course, absorb unexpected impacts on the old noggin.

The Mind Game of Limited Visibility

Humans weren't designed to survive underwater, so all dives create some degree of stress. But few things make the stress meter register higher than limited vis-

Navigation and orientation in limited visibility needn't be a guessing game.

Here are a few ways to make sure you know where you are and where you're going when the visibility is bad.

1. **Keep close track of time while you're swimming on the bottom,** and use these mental notes on time in conjunction with your compass heading. By timing the outgoing leg of your trip, a similarly timed reciprocal course should put you back near where you started (assuming there's no current, of course).

2. **Make a mental note of objects, the bottom slope and the angle of the sun.** Remember that if you return on the same course, these objects and features should be on the opposite side.

3. **Sand ripples make excellent orientation devices.** Remember that they generally run parallel to the shoreline.

4. **Changes in depth are often a good indication of direction.** Also, observe the particulate in the water for signs that the current may be changing direction or speed.

5. **If orientation is critical, consider using a reel and line.** But before using it in limited visibility, practice first in good conditions. It's not a good time to start learning a new skill if you can't clearly see what you're doing.

ibility. The reason is simple: Not being able to see envokes the greatest fear of all: the unknown. This added stress can lead to distraction, causing you to make mistakes that would be unlikely under better conditions. Make sure that you factor this additional stress into your dive plan. For example, plan fewer complicated tasks, shorter distances to cover, shallower depths and more frequent checks on both each other and your instruments (air, depth, decompression status). Once in the water, take your time and avoid circumstances in which you might become fatigued or use excessive air. To accomplish this, swim at a slower pace than normal. If you do encounter a problem like exhaustion or entanglement, remember your training — stop, rest, then act in a slow, methodical way.

If you're not using a buddy line, take special care in planning for buddy separation. Other than the standard practice of searching for one minute and surfacing if you don't find him, there are a few other tips for limited-visibility conditions. Before you search, stop all activity and quietly listen for exhaust bubbles. Your buddy may be closer than you realize. In addition, ascend a few feet before you start your search. Visibility is often better a short distance off the bottom. Sometimes you may even be able to follow a silt trail to your buddy.

Getting Where You're Going

Few things in life are as stressful as not knowing where you are. Yet, the lack of either direction or orientation is the essence of limited-visibility diving. And the less experience you have, the greater the stress. Even in clear water, the near-weightless conditions of diving can cause a minor loss of orientation, but the problem is magnified tenfold when visibility is poor. For this reason, it's a good idea to begin a limited-visibility dive while remaining in contact with a stationary object. A vertical descent line is ideal, but using the boat's anchor line will do. In rough seas or if a current is present, consider using a guideline and reel. You can attach the line to the descent/anchor line and easily find your way home no matter how the current alters your navigation. (Never attach a guideline to the anchor itself, as you can easily pull it out of the bottom.) In some popular low-visibility dive sites where open-water training dives are common, permanent lines are set, providing "underwater trails," which even new divers can use to find their way.

In some cases, divers can be struck by vertigo due to the extreme lack of orientation. If this should occur, don't panic. Simply grasp a stationary object, or even your buddy, and wait for the sensation to pass. If this happens in midwater with no reference or object to hold, keep an eye on your bubbles; they always lead upward. If dizziness is anything but minor, ascend to the surface — with your buddy, of course — and think about doing something else that day. Maintaining orientation is another important reason to stay close to your buddy at all times.

Another way to minimize the likelihood of becoming disoriented is to make your first limited-visibility dive at a location where you have lots of experience. That way you'll already have a mental image of the underwater terrain and what you're likely to encounter.

Diving in limited visibility drives home the real value of your underwater navigation and compass skills. In fact, your compass is the only reliable way of maintaining directional control. The trick, however, is learning to trust your compass rather than your intuition. Although you probably learned some very basic compass navigation in your open-water course, you should consider taking a full underwater navigation specialty course if you plan to do a lot of diving in limited visibility.

Most recently, technology has brought the ultimate peace of mind to limited-visibility conditions. Several companies now provide underwater homing devices. Most work by placing a signal station in the water below the boat or at the entry point. The diver then carries a homing device that points the way (and normally indicates the distance) back to where you started. Of course, these are useful even when the visibility is good because you rarely stay within sight of your boat or entry point.

Planning a dive when the water looks like pea soup rather than Perrier® means more than jumping in and hoping for the best. But less-than-ideal visibility shouldn't stop you from enjoying what there is to be experienced. The purpose of diving is to encounter the environment on its own terms — up close and personal — so the ability to see a great distance underwater is rarely a necessity. Don't miss out on a wonderful experience just because you can't see the ripples on the sand a hundred feet below the boat.

CHAPTER 38

Deep Diving Re-examined:
The Forgotten 50 Feet

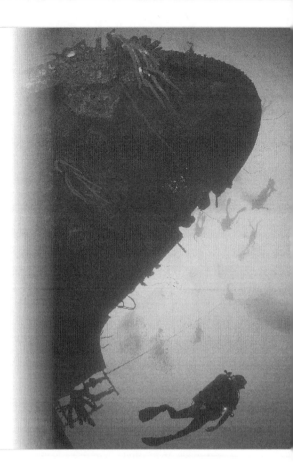

An interesting phenomenon has occurred within the recreational diving community in recent years. In the past, divers were more or less a homogenous crowd; we all had far more in common than not. But that's no longer the case. We've become an extremely diverse group of folks with a wide variety of interests and motivations. On one end of the continuum are those whom I call the "occasional divers" — people who enjoy diving on a limited basis and are happy to confine their underwater forays to shallow tropical water conditions. Rarely will you find this bunch below 60 feet (18 m). The other end of the continuum is reserved for that new breed we now call technical divers. These are the folks who invest as much or more in scuba equipment as they do in their car, and don't feel like they've been diving unless they've had at least 200 feet (61 m) of water over their head.

Of late, much of the diving industry's attention has been focused on these two important and growing segments. Such attention, I believe, is a good thing because each group has much to teach us. The occasional divers, for instance, have shown us that if diving is to grow and prosper, we must provide a higher level of service and supervision than in the past. Conversely, technical divers have helped push the envelope and bring new innovations into the recreational community.

There is one downside to this attention, however. What about those of us in the middle? I, for example, consider myself neither an occasional diver nor a techie; and I sometimes wonder if we haven't forgotten this silent segment of diving. A case in point is deep diving. What exactly should a diver — who is far more than a novice but with no desire to become a techie — know to dive safely in the deeper recreational diving range?

What Is Deep Diving?

The first step in answering the previous question is defining the term "deep." Almost every discussion of deep diving that I've ever read includes an admonition that deep is a relative term. So, to some divers 50 feet (15 m) may be deep, while to others it may be 150 (45 m). Indeed, environmental conditions and personal experience make a huge difference in assigning a meaning, but the quick-and-dirty definition — according to most diver training organizations, at least — is that a deep dive is any excursion below 60 feet (18 m). The rationale for 60 feet is that it's the point where no-decompression limits drop off dramatically, where due to the distance from the surface out-of-air emergencies become much more problematic and the point where, albeit few, some divers begin to experience mild signs of narcosis. Frankly, I've never bought the 60-foot argument and I don't believe most other experienced divers have either. I've opted instead for a somewhat deeper definition of 80 feet (24 m). And my rationale isn't theoretical nor arbitrary, but statistical. In reviewing the diving accident data published by the Divers Alert Network (DAN) over the years, 80 feet seems to jump out as the point which — as the old map makers use to ascribe to unexplored areas — "beyond this, thar be dragons." For whatever reason — and I make no claim to understand why — the risk of accidents seems to increase substantially once divers exceed this depth. (In the "for what it's worth" category, this is also the rationale for why I rarely choose to exceed 80 feet when making a repetitive dive.) So, for the purpose of this chapter, I'll define deep diving as any excursion between the depths of 80 and 130 feet (24 and 39 m) — the forgotten 50 feet (15 m) where occasional divers have no business (unless supervised) and no techie worth the price of his oxygen analyzer cares to stop.

The Mind Game

I'll start with an assumption that you first of all have a good reason to visit the forgotten 50 region, such as a worthwhile dive site. Deep diving simply to satisfy some macho urge or earn testosterone-induced bragging rights is nothing short of stupid; and if that's your motivation might I suggest that you find some other way of injuring or killing yourself that won't reflect on the safety record of scuba diving. The next issue after having a legitimate reason is, should you? A big part of diving is psychological, and deep diving is where head games really come into play. Any candidate for deep diving must have the requisite confidence, experience, self-reliance and common sense. It's not an environment where you can afford to make mistakes or defer to others in case there's a problem. Remember, compliments of our old nemesis nitrogen, psychological factors can be magnified — or suppressed — by the physiology of deep diving.

While a sound mind is the first prerequisite, it's equally important to have a sound body. Certainly you don't have to be a conditioned athlete to be a deep diver. (If that were the case, there'd be very few deep divers.) But if you consider a walk around the block a challenging physical task, it's probably best that your depth gauge never break the 80-foot (24 m) mark. The time-tested measure of fitness that I have given on numerous occasions is the ability to swim 800 yards (727 m) with mask, fins and snorkel in 20 minutes or less. It's not a killer requirement, but I've found it to be an outstanding indicator of aquatic physical fitness. And if you can't do it, it doesn't mean that you can't be a deep diver. It just means that you have some conditioning ahead of you before you try.

Training vs. Trial and Error

Clearly, the best way to be oriented to deep diving is through a formal course of instruction. Every advanced diver course that I'm aware of includes at least some exposure to deep diving, and entire specialty courses exist that provide a much more in-depth (no pun intended) education. The advantage of formal training is that you'll not only gain experience under professional supervision, but you'll also explore the theoretical background necessary to truly understand the full nuance of diving in the forgotten 50 feet (15 m). There's also much to be said for having the safety net of a certified instructor if you make a mistake.

While formal training is the ideal, the reality is that most deep divers do not take a formal course. Most, I hope, are oriented to this unforgiving environment by more experienced friends. But the fact remains that a large portion of divers still use the "this looks easy, so I'll give it a try" method. And while I hope everyone who reads this will take away something of value, it's to this last category of the would-be self-taught that I focus this discussion.

Who and When

I believe that no one has any business even considering deep diving until they're completely at ease diving above 60 feet (18 m). For some, this could mean only a few dozen dives. Others, no doubt, need two or three times this amount of experience. It's a question that only you can answer, and it's not one to which you want to be less than truthful with yourself. It's also a good idea to build up to deeper depths progressively. One important lesson we've learned from the technical diving community is that progressively deeper rehearsal dives are a great way to acclimate to this more challenging environment.

Another vital aspect of character for deep divers is self-discipline. The simple fact is that lazy divers probably won't exercise the judgment and discipline needed to mentally rehearse the dive (another contribution from the technical community, which I'll address later), check and recheck equipment, monitor their buddy, and diligently keep track of decompression, depth and air status. Deep diving is one arena where being considered anal retentive is a compliment.

Yet another important consideration is the person who'll be accompanying you. In deep diving, the wrong buddy isn't just a nuisance; he can be downright dangerous. Competence as a diver, good judgment and self-reliance go without saying, but there's a bit more to choosing a buddy for deep diving. The forgotten 50 is the last place you want to be with someone you don't know well. Therefore, you should always select a buddy with whom you've dived extensively. This prior experience is important in establishing what could be termed a "behavioral baseline." Having this baseline — knowing what's normal behavior for that individual — is really the only way you can detect subtle but significant changes in his behavior at depth, which could indicate the onset of narcosis or other problems.

The Toys

As we're still within standard recreational diving depths, there's no special equipment required for diving in the forgotten 50. But there are some special considerations for that equipment. The first involves exposure protection. If you're diving in an environment where exposure protection is necessary, remember that because of the increased pressure at depth, suit compression becomes a factor. In other words, that 6-millimeter suit, which was toasty-warm at 50 feet (15 m), may not do the job at 120 feet (36 m) simply because the neoprene rubber — which is full of gas bubbles — is a lot thinner. A serious deep diver may well consider the advantage of a dry suit. Tropical divers, as well, should take note that increased depth often means decreased temperature. So, while a T-shirt might be the uniform of the day near the surface, something more substantial is often necessary at depth.

A few words are also in order regarding regulators. Frankly, virtually any regulator on the market will do the job adequately in shallow water. Not so when deep diving, however. The increased pressure at depth causes a concomitant increase in the density of the air you breathe. Therefore, like a racecar, a regulator for deep diving should be of the highest quality and maintained in a flawless condition. If you're not sure about the adequacy of your own system, a long talk with a knowledgeable person at your local dive center is probably a good idea.

Special attention is also warranted with your gas supply. (I use the term "gas" rather than air because of the popularity of enriched-air nitrox.) The key to gas management begins with tank capacity. The general

rule regarding gas supply is that you can never have too much. For example, at 100 feet (30 m) you'll be using air at least four times faster than at the surface, and twice as fast as at 30 feet (9 m). If deep diving is likely to become one of your common menu items, consider a larger-capacity tank. Like the fuel supply of an aircraft, you want to maintain a substantial portion of your air supply — 15-30 percent — in reserve for unexpected circumstances. Although they're a bit heavier and bulkier, high-volume tanks are available.

The most serious and significant emergency consideration in deep diving is running out of air; and this requires some thought beyond use of the standard alternate air source or octopus. Indeed, as in all diving, these devices are considered essential, but the question arises in deep diving: Are they adequate? Standard alternate air sources — spare second stages — do work but with one serious caveat — the diver providing the emergency air must himself have enough air left in the tank for both divers to reach the surface. As this may not always be the case, the answer for many deep divers is a redundant air supply. This may include a pony bottle — a small-capacity tank secured to the side of the main tank — with an independent regulator or a self-contained system like the Spare Air® (a small integrated tank/regulator device).

The Plan

As in any dive plan, the first consideration is that of the environment. Deep diving is not an activity you want to engage in when weather and water conditions are anything but good to ideal, particularly while you're still in the learning curve. Additionally, deeper dive sites are often situated in the most exposed locations, making them especially vulnerable to fast-changing or less-than-ideal weather conditions.

Because most deeper sites are well offshore, you'll probably be diving from a boat. In the less common circumstances in which you may be shore diving, take care to factor into your plan the distance you'll have to swim. This could be an important issue in reducing the risk of decompression illness — due to post-dive exertion — and delay in the event of an emergency. It's also best to have a qualified individual remain at the surface at all times in case assistance is required. (This is a good idea anytime you're diving from a boat.)

Because your bottom time will be significantly less than for a shallow dive, it's important to review your planned dive profile. Most experienced deep divers today use dive computers to assist in managing their profile, but you should never depend entirely on technology to keep you safe. Spend a few minutes familiarizing yourself with your intended profile in conjunction with a dive. This could be vital information in the event your computer malfunctions. Likewise, take the time to familiarize yourself with your buddy's computer and agree that the dive will be dictated by the most conservative device. (Because of the inevitable difference in dive profiles between divers, buddy teams should never share a single computer.) Finally, always bear in mind that the controlling factor in a deep dive may be either your decompression status or your air supply. This requires diligent monitoring of both factors.

To assist with the descent/ascent and to help maintain orientation, you should use some form of "down line" when deep diving. Often, the vessel's anchor line is used for this, but that may not be advised if a lot of line has been let out, especially if current is present. In fact, if the current is anything but mild, a separate descent line and surface float should be used. (Descending along a vertical line can be a lot less fatiguing than along the incline of a lengthy anchor rode.)

Ready, Set, Go

Because of the extra demands of deep diving, it's important that you and your buddy conduct a very thorough final check before entering the water. This predive check is generally no different from what you would do for any dive, but you should pay special attention to factors that might affect your air supply. First, verify that your valve is turned on completely. A partially opened valve will function properly at the surface, and possibly in shallow water, but will not deliver sufficient air at depth. (The telltale sign for this is to watch your SPG [submersible pressure gauge]; if the needle drastically fluctuates between near full to near empty with each breath, your valve is only partially open.) Next, confirm one more time that you have a full tank. When scuba units are assembled, tanks are often left on and unattended for long periods. Therefore, if a minor, unnoticed leak occurs, a

substantial amount of air may escape. Your final predive check is also a good time to confirm that your computer has been turned on and is working properly.

You may want to spend the last few minutes before entry mentally preparing for the dive. Start by closing your eyes and breathing deeply and slowly. Next, visualize the dive (this can be especially effective if you've dived the site before). As vividly as possible, imagine what you expect the dive to be like. Include every phase of the dive from the descent to the ascent. Imagine yourself and your buddy doing everything that you planned without error or omission. This may sound a bit too Zen-like to be worthwhile, but scientific investigation has confirmed the benefit of visual imagery in improving skill performance. The technique is used today by virtually all Olympic athletes.

Finally, don't fall into the trap of entering the water before you're ready. It's your safety and well-being, after all. Don't allow anyone — not your buddy, the divemaster nor even the captain — to rush you into the water unprepared. You, and only you, must decide when and if you'll choose to dive.

Down, Down We Go

Especially for those new to deep diving, a descent line is an important aid. It provides both orientation and control to your descent, which is often into a blue void where you can't initially see the bottom. This can be disconcerting, but there's no need to worry or hurry. The line allows you to easily halt your descent to readjust equipment, clear your ears or simply rest for a moment; and it greatly reduces the risk of being separated from your buddy. A "free descent" — in which you literally fly through the water column with no reference — requires the competence and buddy coordination that comes only with experience. In poor visibility, or when the seafloor is silty, slow your ascent as you near the bottom. A crash landing will do nothing but destroy what little visibility might be present.

On the Bottom

Unless visibility is outstanding, you'll probably need to spend a few seconds getting and setting your bearings (a compass is an invaluable aid anytime you're diving a site where you can't easily ascend back to the surface for orientation). Because of limited bottom time, it isn't likely that you'll cover a large area during a deep dive, so navigation based on physical features is probably even more important than compass use. In very low visibility, when it's important that you ascend back up the line, consider using a line reel. Attaching a "travel line" to the downline will make returning home a simple matter of rewinding the reel.

Between the excitement of a new environment and the effect of nitrogen, it's easy to get distracted and forget to monitor your air and decompression status. Furthermore, you'll also be consuming air at a rate far greater than you're used to on a shallow dive. This means that extra diligence is absolutely essential. So, get in the habit of checking your instruments a lot more frequently than normal. Remind your buddy to do so as well.

Deep diving is also not the time to try and set any speed records. Because of the increased density of the air you're breathing, you can become overexerted much more quickly than at shallower depths. The solution is simple: Slow down and, if you feel your breathing rate increasing, stop and rest. (Studies have shown that excess carbon dioxide can also contribute to the onset of nitrogen narcosis.)

A special warning is also in order if you're using a computer rather than tables to plan your dive. No-decompression time will be eaten up quickly at depth, and you should avoid the practice of remaining at any depth until you reach the no-decompression limit. The practice of not ascending to a shallower depth until your computer display shows no time remaining is sometimes called "riding the zero," and is a foolhardy practice in decompression safety. (Always allow a safety margin of at least five minutes no-decompression time remaining when ascending to a shallower level.)

In many situations when diving the forgotten 50, your dive isn't controlled by decompression status, but rather your air supply. This makes gas management as important as decompression planning. Perhaps the most important factor in gas management is deciding on a "turnaround" point — the amount of gas that will dictate when you begin heading home. Remember, because you'll have some distance to travel to get to your safety stop, having reserve air is important. In some cases, divers use the "half-plus-two" rule; you start heading home when your pressure reaches the halfway point plus 200 psi. In some cases this may be needlessly conservative, but in others it may not be enough air. Regardless, under no circumstance should you delay your turnaround beyond 1,000 psi or one-third of your air supply. And this means when the first buddy reaches that point, no matter how much air the other buddy has left. (If you anticipate a great disparity between you and your buddy's air consumption rates, consider using different-capacity tanks to compensate.) Equally important is that the decision to head home must be clear and unequivocal; the "just one more minute" attitude might work on a shallow dive, but it's asking for trouble in the forgotten 50.

Up, Up and Away

Your ascent is a piece of cake if you've followed your dive plan because it will put you back at the descent line with an ample air supply. My preference has always been to pull myself up the line rather than kick. This allows for a much slower and more precise ascent, plus I don't have to worry about kicking someone's mask who may be ascending behind me. (Descent lines are often crowded at the end of a dive.) Try not to exceed the rate of about one-half foot per second. In other words, it should take you 20 seconds to ascend only 10 feet. I'm not sure how to translate that into anything meaningful for you metric folks, except to say, go slow. Very slow. In my opinion anyone who is diving to the forgotten 50 should have a dive computer anyway, so pay close attention to its ascent rate monitor.

As you approach the depth range of your safety stop, make sure all the air is out of your buoyancy compensator (BC). This is particularly essential when using an aluminum tank because it will be 3 or 4 pounds (1.4 or 1.8 kg) positively buoyant when empty. A buoyant diver is much more likely to be carried past the safety-stop depth.

As it has become such a common practice, it probably goes without saying that you should always make a safety stop before ascending to the surface after a deep dive. (Many advise it after *any* dive.) Plan to stop at a depth range of 15-20 feet (4.5 to 6 m) for three to five minutes. If you have the air and you want to stay longer, fine. It can only help.

In cases in which you think you might reach the minimum limit of your air supply — usually, 500 psi —

by the time you reach the safety stop, you might consider setting up what are termed "hang tanks" at the stop. These are just spare scuba units that act as a reserve air supply. Especially in open-ocean conditions, it's a good idea to attach a weight to the tanks to keep them stable. Some dive operations that do a lot of deep diving use a long length of pipe tether called a "trapeze." The advantage is that a trapeze precludes the need for divers to hover in midwater; and they provide a continual reference point so you needn't worry about depth variations.

Back Home

Most divers assume that their dive is over once they reach the surface. It's not. The surface is really your last decompression stop. In reality, your dive isn't over until your residual nitrogen level has returned to near normal, which requires at least six hours. It's important, therefore, to avoid any excessive exercise during this final period of "off-gassing," and remain alert for any signs of decompression illness. Furthermore, avoid flying for at least 12-18 hours (24 hours is even better).

To the uninformed, deep diving looks deceptively easy. The truth is, it often isn't much more physically difficult than a shallow excursion. But in planning, self-discipline and dealing with psychological challenges, there's a lot more to diving the forgotten 50 — 80 to 130 feet (24 to 39 m) — than meets the eye. 🐟

CHAPTER 39

Lessons From the Whales:
Diving On One Breath

In Europe, freediving has long been more than a sport and more like an obsession, with its champions holding the status of rock stars. In the United States, however, that's not the case. While on this side of the Atlantic competitive freediving enjoys more recognition today than ever, in the 1960s it was far less popular than tiddlywinks. The 1988 film, *The Big Blue*, depicts the pitched battle that took place during the 1960s and '70s between icons Jacques Mayol and Enzo Maiorca for the world freediving record. What the film neglected to include was that an upstart U.S. Navy diver named Bob Croft had challenged, and for a while, beaten this dynamic duo.

As a young diver growing up in the 1960s, I had the good fortune to be taken under the wing of a group of old salts who had spent much of their lives on and under the sea. Through those connections, I met Bob Croft. It was 1969 and Croft was a Navy petty officer serving aboard the famous U.S. Navy midget submarine *X-1*, then stationed in Annapolis, Maryland. To a 17-year-old kid in love with diving, it was like meeting an American version of Jacques Cousteau.

Croft developed an interest in freediving during an earlier billet at the U.S. Naval Submarine Base New London. Termed the "Submarine Capital of the World," this is where Navy submariners are trained, and is the site of an 118-foot-deep (36 m) submarine escape training tank where prospective personnel learn how to escape from a disabled submarine. As a Navy diver, Croft was assigned to train submariners, and soon developed a curiosity about breath-hold diving. Gradually he improved his own breath-hold capability from less than two minutes to more than six. And having mastered the 118-foot limit of the training tank, he was inspired to see exactly how deep he could go.

Over the course of 18 months Croft set the "no-limits" freediving record not once but twice, first in 1967 at 220 feet (67 m) — becoming the first human to ever dive beyond 200 feet while breath-holding — and again in 1968 at 240 feet (73 m). In the process Croft shattered the conventional idea diving physiologists had held for decades that 200 feet was the human physiological limit for a breath-hold dive. An American has never since been a serious challenger for the record. After setting the record Croft retired from freediving, but this bigger-than-life character, and the afternoon that I spent with him, made me a great fan of those who brave the depths without the benefit of compressed air.

Croft's accomplishment meant more than a mere listing in a record book; his feat provided a major insight to our understanding of diving physiology. From 1962 to 1968 he also served as a research subject for Navy scientists. And based on Croft's performance, physiologists discovered something that revolutionized our understanding about the diving ability of humans. The conventional view before Croft was that once a human breath-holder reached a depth at which his lungs

Never, ever, ever even consider freediving alone; and always use the "one up, one down" rule (one buddy diving while the other attentively observes from the surface). As shallow-water blackout is a primary safety concern, you must never create a situation in which both buddies are susceptible at the same time.

Wear a low-volume mask and, if you have the leg strength, relatively long, stiff fins. Weight yourself to be slightly positive at the surface so that wet suit and body compression will not make you too negative at depth. Be sure that all your equipment is as streamlined as possible.

Do not use hyperventilation to extend your breath-hold time. Instead, learn the proper breathing methods, especially the three-step procedure described in the main article.

Once you begin your descent, remove your snorkel mouthpiece. Retaining the mouthpiece, according to many experienced freedivers, increases the urge to breathe.

Be aware that while shallow-water blackout will take place during ascent, deep-water blackout (often caused by insufficient recovery between dives) will generally occur during descent or on the bottom.

During ascent, get in the habit of holding your arms up in front of you. This is not only a more streamlined position, but failure to keep your arms in position is a good sign for your buddy to watch for as an indicator of shallow-water blackout.

While ascending, look straight ahead. Tilting your head down, or looking toward the surface, increases drag.

While ascending, begin a continuous exhale at about 10 feet (3 m) from the surface. This way you'll be able to immediately inhale upon surfacing.

As your buddy reaches the surface, make sure that the two of you are within arm's reach. Remember, your buddy is depending on you if there's a problem from hypoxia. Keep an especially close eye on your buddy during ascent, and know the signs of shallow-water blackout.

Upon surfacing, before doing anything else, take three full recovery breaths. Then, signal your buddy that you're OK. If you're the surface buddy, closely observe the diver for what freedivers sometimes call "the samba" or, more accurately, loss of motor control. Signs and symptoms include a "woozy" feeling, dizziness, euphoria, blue lips and shaking. If a diver experiences any of these symptoms, call it a day; no more diving.

Take several minutes to recover before making another dive. Your body needs this time to blow off excess carbon dioxide, and avoid deep-water blackout on your next dive.

Between dives, relax and "practice" the next dive through mental visualization.

While it's safe to freedive prior to scuba diving, never engage in rigorous freediving after scuba diving, as the practice could increase your susceptibility to decompression sickness.

reached their residual volume (the volume at which one can no longer exhale any more gas), further compression would cause damage from what was termed "thoracic squeeze." However, it was recognized that marine mammals could descend far below the residual volume depth of their lungs because of shifting of blood from peripheral to thoracic circulation, thus preventing lung damage. The discovery of the "blood shift" phenomenon opened a host of theories regarding freediving humans; and it is Croft who served as the research subject in confirming a similar though less pronounced phenomenon in humans. This led to a landmark paper that was published in the prestigious journal *Science* in 1968. The rest, as they say, is history.

Snorkeling vs. Freediving

Because of its lack of popularity here in America, there are lots of misconceptions about freediving. First, to the uninitiated, it may seem like just another word for snorkeling. And everyone knows snorkeling is about as easy as falling out of bed, right? So what's the big deal?

Well, first, comparing snorkeling to freediving is like assuming that your morning jog is kinda like running a marathon. About the only characteristic that snorkeling and freediving have in common is that a mask and fins are involved.

A second misconception among scuba divers is that, because it doesn't involve the use of compressed air systems, freediving is easy. In fact, it's so easy, that unlike scuba diving, it doesn't even require training. After all, how complicated can it be? Place mask on face, insert snorkel, take breath, dive. Here, again, the reality is very different. For many enthusiasts, baseball and basketball look pretty simple. But try playing them on anything but a pick-up game level, and the need for training — as well as a high degree of innate talent — soon becomes embarrassingly obvious.

Third, perhaps the most serious misconception held by scuba divers about freediving is that we have nothing to learn from it. After all, what benefit could we possibly take away from any activity in which your air supply is limited merely to your lung capacity?

Strike three.

The reality is that there are countless lessons and innumerable benefits for bubble blowers in mastering freediving. Several years ago, I took an advanced

freediving course, and it's no exaggeration to say that I learned more in the class to improve my scuba skills than any other course I've ever taken beyond my open-water training.

As a result of my freediving training I developed better breathing techniques, and I gained valuable insight into how to improve my air consumption. I also found the course an excellent refresher on advanced diving physics and physiology because, ironically, the level of theory taught in a freediving class far exceeds that taught to scuba divers. (You'll see why a bit later.) But most importantly I was reintroduced to something that many divers forget or never learn: how to truly relax in the water. So, if freediving is such a great thing, what does it involve?

Lessons With No Bubbles

Although most scuba divers are unaware of it, there are freediving training programs every bit as rigorous — and some more so — than any scuba course. In North America, formal certification is offered through the International Association of Nitrox and Technical Divers (IANTD) and Performance Freediving. They offer a range of freediving courses, from introductory programs to qualification in advanced freediving and even instructor certification.

For those with more than a passing interest, I'd suggest skipping the introductory programs, and jumping right into an advanced course. Unlike in scuba training, freediving allows this option. Typically the course takes two days. Day 1 normally begins in the classroom with a thorough course orientation, brief history of freediving and a review of basic equipment. Freedivers are very proud to point out that their sport, which dates back more than 4,500 years, has the rightful title of the world's "first extreme sport."

Probably the most important safety issue addressed in every freediving course is that the sport isn't about "how deep you can go." In fact, that's the attitude that gets many who are new to freediving — or those who never take formal training — into trouble. How deep you go is merely an outcome of improved performance, concentration and practice. Prudent freedivers should view depth records as the exclusive realm of the competitive elite; and although you may one day get there, it's not a goal you should start with. However, almost everyone who takes an advanced freediving course can expect to be making dives to at least 50 feet (15 m) by the end of their training.

If you're a scuba diver who's taking a freediving course, expect both some similarities and differences from your previous training. For example, what you'll learn about the basic equipment of freediving could come right out of any scuba course. However, there are some special considerations for freediving equipment such as mask volume (the less air inside, the less frequently you need to equalize) and the benefit of specialized fins (the ones you may have seen some scuba divers wear with the extremely long blades).

On the other hand, freediving courses place much more emphasis on physics and physiology than most entry-level scuba courses. For example, anyone who has taken a scuba course over the past decade or so understands that the only thing a student diver is likely to learn about physics is how our bodies' air spaces — mainly our sinuses, ears and lungs — are compressed and expand during the descent and ascent. And the only discussion of physiology is a cursory review of sinus squeeze, lung expansion injuries, narcosis and decompression sickness. The term "partial pressure" hasn't been uttered in most beginning, or even advanced scuba courses since disco was the rage.

Not so with freediving. Comprehending the indomitable Dr. Dalton's law of partial pressures is fundamental to understanding our body's response to freediving. It is, in fact, the basis of the most serious concern that faces freedivers — shallow-water blackout, or what freedivers refer to simply as SWB. Although the mechanisms have nothing in common, it's the freediver's equivalent of air embolism. Just as we scuba divers must understand what causes an air embolism (Boyle's law), freedivers must understand the mechanism responsible for SWB (Dalton's law).

If you haven't read about Dalton's law in Chapter 6, here's the abridged version. For simplicity, let's assume that the air that we breathe at the surface contains 20 percent oxygen. (It's really a bit over 21 percent.) Another way of expressing this is that at the surface — 1 atmosphere — 0.20 of that atmosphere is accounted for by oxygen. Assume now that I immediately descend to 2 atmospheres (33 feet [10 m]) without using any oxygen. (OK, that's another stretch, but bear with me.) While the percentage of oxygen would remain the same (no more could get into my lungs), the portion of the total air pressure in my lungs — the partial pressure — accounted for by oxygen would rise to 0.40 (0.20 X 2 = 0.40). I then remain at depth and use half of my available oxygen. This would reduce the partial pressure from 0.40 back to 0.20.

Finally — and here's where would-be freedivers can't afford to nod off — I begin my ascent. By the time I reach the surface, the partial pressure would reduce by half — down to 0.1 — due to the decreasing ambient pressure. However, a quirky little fact of human physiology comes into play: I cannot sustain consciousness with an oxygen partial pressure of 0.10. In fact, I'll begin experiencing symptoms of hypoxia (low oxygen) once the oxygen partial pressure drops below 1.6. The bottom line to all of this seemingly convoluted physics is quite simple: Long before I reach the surface, I'd fall unconscious from a form of anoxia called shallow-water blackout (SWB). But an SWB itself isn't a problem; on land people faint all of the time and recover with no effect. The nasty little rub is that when one loses consciousness underwater, unless some action is taken in a matter of seconds, drowning is a virtual certainty. Of course, in addition to understanding the cause of SWB, freedivers must be able to recognize its symptoms and, most importantly, know what to do when it occurs.

As a scuba diver, without a doubt the most helpful thing that I took away from my freediving course was how to breathe. Some may find this statement odd, given that breathing is something that we do all our lives without ever getting a single lesson. But that's exactly my point: We never really learn how to breathe in a way that maximizes our breath-holding ability. At least, not until you take a freediving course. Clearly the most practical insight that I gained as a sans-scuba student is what freedivers call "three-step breathing," which is the only way that one can really take a "full" breath. Here's how it's done: The first step involves diaphragmatic breathing. It's also called "belly breathing" because distention of your belly as you inhale is a way to confirm that you're using your diaphragm to draw air deep into your lungs. This is the key to maximizing a full breath of air. Next is chest or thoracic breathing; it's what most of us do all the time. Lastly, there's a technique that I'd never heard or thought of before taking a freediving course. It's called shoulder or subclavian breathing. This uses the muscles of the neck and upper throat to further increase air volume. It's used by highly experienced freedivers in a technique known as "packing" to top off their final breath before descent. This highly efficient and purposeful breathing enables freedivers to get maximum ventilation and use the full lower, middle and upper portions of their lungs.

Interestingly, the person credited with inventing air or lung "packing" (more formally known as *glossopharyngeal inhalation*) is none other than Bob Croft. He actually invented the technique, long before his naval career, as a method to dive deeper and longer than any of his friends.

Freedivers use this three-phased technique in a pre-dive ritual called the "breathe-up." This is a progression from normal breathing, to ventilation, to superventilation, to peak inhalation. The breath-up continues until symptoms are experienced such as slight dizziness, numbness, tingling in the extremities and perhaps even a metallic taste in the mouth. These are all signs of excellent oxygenation, and a clear signal that it's time to take a final breath and start the dive.

One of the biggest surprises that I got from my training was how freedivers view hyperventilation. As every scuba diver learns, hyperventilation (a series of excessive inhalations and exhalations) is a way of extending one's breath-hold time. Scuba instructors often mention the technique only to warn divers against it. (Understanding the mechanism behind why this is so dangerous is another rationale for the in-depth discussion of partial pressures.) What I was astounded to learn is that freedivers do not use hyperventilation, and the rationale is quite convincing. By lowering carbon dioxide levels significantly prior to a dive, which is exactly why hyperventilation works, a freediver becomes susceptible to something else that I'd never heard of before taking a freediving course. It's a condition termed deep-water blackout (DWB). Here the diver falls unconscious at depth because of hypoxia, yet is never warned by any excessive urge to breath. In freediving, the idea is not using tricks to fool our bodies — like hyperventilation — but to instead maximize the efficiency of breathing and of movement. In other words, it's not a matter of tricking your body into not wanting to breathe, but instead taking the maximum amount of oxygen with you, and using it most effectively.

Another subject unique to freediving is a physiology adaptation that we share with our marine mammal brethren known as the mammalian diving reflex. Although our human version is far less intense than that seen in marine mammals, we do demonstrate this adaptation; and in some folks it seems to be more pronounced than others. This fascinating evolutionary holdover is characterized by a slowing of the heart rate and shunting of blood (and, thus, oxygen) from less vital to more vital regions of the body. Water temperature seems to control both the degree and time required for the onset of the response.

Yet another big difference between learning to scuba dive versus freedive is the emphasis placed on what happens in the mind as well as the body. The psychology of freediving is a major topic of discussion in every course. Freedivers rely heavily on mental imagery techniques pioneered and mastered in other athletic fields such as competitive skiing. Research has proven this a successful method for not only practicing the physical movements of an activity, but preparing the mind and reducing anxiety. As most freediving instructors will tell you, while it may seem physically rigorous, freediving is primarily a mental activity. Proof once again that, in the end, the mind does control the body. Clearly, one of the most important lessons you can take away from learning to freedive is how to make your body do things your mind initially said weren't possible.

Theory to Practice

Another distinct difference and benefit of freediving over scuba training is that the former requires no pool training; you may be in open water from the get-go. Beginning in "shallow water" — normally 50 feet (15 m) or so — students first learn ascent and descent procedures, emphasizing the need for streamlining and efficient movement. There's also time spent adapting to unscubalike equipment, like very low-volume masks and exceedingly long fins. Several novel skills found nowhere in any modern scuba course are also included, such as breath-hold mask removal and replacement and swimming with only one fin. The course may also include a skill that's a real throwback to the ancient days of scuba training — what we called back then a "skin bail-out." This involves swimming to depth, removing the mask and fins, returning to the surface; then after taking no more than a few breaths, returning to don the equipment and clear the mask before leaving the bottom.

Given its severe and insidious risk, part of open-water training in freediving also covers how to avoid and deal with SWB. This involves learning how to identify signs of hypoxia in another diver, and should they occur, how to respond and assist the diver until they recover. Of course, should an SWB victim not recover spontaneously, the proper response is standard in-water resuscitation techniques learned in every rescue diver course. So these skills are also part of freediver training.

One interesting approach used to teach descent skills is an introductory warm-up exercise that freediving instructors call "pull downs." As the name implies, this involves pulling yourself to depth using the descent line rather than kicking. The idea is to conserve oxygen by not using the large muscles of the legs. This is normally done in stages, first descending halfway to the bottom, then three-quarters, and finally on the third or fourth attempt, all the way. This is normally done in water about 40-50 feet (12-15 m) deep. With all the rudiments mastered, the rest of open-water training involves applying what you've learned under the watchful eye of an experienced professional.

In the final analysis, I believe learning how to relax and become part of the environment is the single most important lesson any scuba diver can take away from a freediving course. It's also a great way to brush up on some of the theory you may have forgotten, or never learned, in your open-water course. Along the way you'll be treated to a whole new kind of underwater experience — one in which the reef inhabitants don't flee from you as some bubble-blowing freak but welcome you as just an odd and clumsy neighbor. ◯

CHAPTER 40

Lessons From the Edge:
What Rec Divers Can Learn From Tech Divers

A defining theme of the human spirit is exploration. And to explore, we must overcome obstacles, solve problems and extend limits. This spirit is alive and well in those who explore space as well as those who pioneer the depths of the ocean. While we may perceive the undersea explorer as one who pilots futuristic vehicles to unimaginable and crushing depths, there is a segment of this group who brave the depths directly with no more external protection than a few millimeters of rubber or nylon. These intrepid trailblazers are called technical divers. Not so long ago they were viewed as daredevil cowboys, disdained by most of the diving community. Today, while still outside the mainstream of recreational diving, techies, as they're now affectionately known, are considered by many to be the "test pilots" of diving.

Just as spin-off technology from space exploration has brought improvements to everyday life, technical diving has made its contributions to recreational diving. And while the intent of this article is not meant to encourage (nor discourage) you from technical diving, it is intended to demonstrate what we can learn from those who "push the envelope." But before examining what we can learn from the technical community, let's first establish what it is.

Tech Versus Rec

Recreational diving has been defined for decades quite simply as diving on air to depths no greater than 130 feet (39 m), and within no-decompression limits. The ubiquitous use of nitrox has required some minor adjustments to that age-old definition, but it's still pretty easy to tell when someone is outside the bounds of recreational diving. Not so with tech diving.

Technical diving is a bit harder to define. One could view it simply as any form of diving beyond the range and parameters of recreational diving. In fact, some even use the term "extended range diving" rather than the more familiar term technical diving. But you're sorely mistaken — and maybe an accident waiting to happen — if you think that technical diving means nothing more than going a little deeper or staying a little longer. As many techies will tell you, the essence of what they do can't be summed up as succinctly as rec diving because, by its very nature, technical diving has no arbitrary limitations. At its core, tech diving is defined more by attitude than any technique, equipment configuration or environment. And it is understanding the nature and implications of this attitude that's the greatest lesson tech divers have for us in the recreational community.

Karl Shreeves, technical development executive for PADI (Professional Association of Diving Instructors) and primary developer of the PADI TecRec program, says that the essential difference between tech divers and their rec diving cousins is approach. "It doesn't matter if it's a dive to 20 feet or 200 feet [6 or 61 m], tech divers are far less casual than rec divers when it comes to dive planning," Shreeves says. "Whether it's a prediving equipment check, or planning for reserve air and other contingencies, what characterizes a technical dive is the thoroughness of preparation, and that's something that every rec diver can learn from." Indeed, planning a tech dive isn't, like rec diving, something you normally do on the boat as you ride to the dive site. A general rule in the tech community is that for every one hour spent underwater, you will spend 30 minutes to an hour planning a dive, though it may take more than that if you have a complex objective.

In the realm of planning, perhaps the greatest lesson to be learned from tech diving is the almost fanatical use of something we discussed in previous chapters on narcosis and freediving — visualization or mental rehearsal. While to some this may sound like a journey into some New Age, pop psychology fad, the truth is that mental imagery is anything but hocus-pocus. Its effectiveness has been documented in several studies on skill acquisition and performance enhancement. Like yoga or biofeedback therapy, it takes time and discipline to develop the skill to its fullest, but the basic concept is pretty simple. The diver begins long before entering the water by concentrating on breath control and relaxation. Then, in as vivid detail as possible, he or she imagines making the dive. Through this imaginary voyage, the diver anticipates what could go wrong and, most importantly, mentally rehearses the proper response to any problems.

Shreeves actually recommends doing the procedure in reverse as well as forward because, he says, chaining events together backward makes problems and omissions all the more obvious. "Thinking through the dive backwards enables you to more easily determine what's necessary for a certain outcome," he says.

The Redundant Mentality

Another aspect of tech diving that rec divers can learn from is the importance of redundancy. To understand why there's such attention paid to having numerous backups and contingencies, let's look at another problem unique to tech diving. My own quick definition of technical diving is any underwater excursion that places the diver under a "ceiling." This may be a literal ceiling, such as the confines of a cave or bowels of a shipwreck, or a physiologic ceiling as when making a multistaged decompression dive. In both instances, the diver doesn't have the luxury afforded a recreational diver of immediately ascending to the surface if he encounters a problem. Instead, a technical diver must not only bring with

him everything he'll need — or thinks he'll need, but safety dictates he also must bring a spare. In tech diving, redundancy isn't just a matter of convenience, it's a matter of life or death. This idea is so important that many tech divers even use buoyancy compensators (BCs) that have redundant air bladders. While that may be overkill for recreational divers, tech divers using open-circuit scuba depend on a BC because, if properly weighted, the diver may be 20-plus pounds (9 kg) negative at the start of the dive. This is because the diver must be weighted to decompress with nearly empty cylinders (worst-case scenario). The negative buoyancy is the weight of all the gas. This makes the very profound point that in technical diving, there's no room for failure.

Perhaps the most important redundancy involves gas supply. While spare second stages are the norm for rec diving, the standard octopus is all but useless for most tech applications. When true redundancy is needed, the answer is a completely independent tank and regulator system. The sizes of the reserve tanks vary according to circumstance. While small, compact, integrated systems such as the Spare Air™ are adequate for most recreational diving applications, they don't provide enough air for technical diving. A popular option in the tech world for open-circuit diving is a double-tank configuration (side or back-mounted) with dual, independent valves. With this system, separate regulators are attached to each valve, and the manifold is designed to allow access to the entire gas supply by either regulator. In many situations, tech divers use both tanks — as well as what are termed "travel bottles" — depending on the nature, depth and duration of the dive.

While double tanks may be inconvenient, or unnecessary, for the average recreational diver, a smaller independent tank and regulator — called a pony bottle — can be a wise choice. Although it does add bulk, and they can be a real pain to travel with, its advantage over a standard alternate air source is that a pony bottle provides a true air reserve. It's a lot like the reserve parachute carried by a skydiver. Another reason for a totally redundant air supply is because most out-of-air situations occur near the end of a dive when even the diver sharing his air supply is probably low. In this case, a spare regulator alone will be of little value if there's not enough air left for the buddy team to reach the surface. Furthermore, a pony bottle also gives an out-of-air diver an independent means of solving his own problem, something that a traditional octopus regulator cannot.

Redundancy is also important in monitoring decompression status. Just as in recreational diving, dive computers have revolutionized tech diving. And, as you might suspect, tech divers routinely wear two or more computers. Admittedly, multiple computers probably aren't necessary when rec diving, but a single backup device can be of great benefit if the primary goes south. Although dive computer technology is very reliable, and malfunctions are rare, even once is too much when it's your safety at stake. In reality, a computer malfunction is always an uncertain situation because rarely do you realize immediately that your device has quit. So, when it stopped tracking your decompression status is anyone's guess. (This is why manufacturers' guidelines normally specify that you make a prolonged safety stop before surfacing whenever your computer quits at depth.) Using dual computers also gives you the option of adding a measure of safety to your dive by following the more conservative device.

With the availability of small, inexpensive models now on the market, a backup computer is a wise and realistic alternative for serious rec divers. And in addition to increasing safety, they prevent the needless inconvenience of switching over to a dive table if your computer quits. Frankly, switching from your computer back to a dive table is never the best option because, as most tables can't calculate multilevel profiles or don't do it very well, tables actually penalize you for time you didn't actually spend underwater. This could be a very serious consideration given the amount of time, effort and money you invest for each minute spent underwater.

Another item for which redundancy's a good idea is your dive knife. Especially in environments where entanglement is common, losing your knife — or being unable to reach it — could have serious consequences. To avoid this, tech divers often attach a small, sharp backup knife to the upper portion of the body, such as the upper arm or BC. Another approach is to carry a shroud cutter — a hook-shaped device containing a razorblade — like that used by skydivers. They make short work of all but the thickest lines, and cut through monofilament like butter. Many techies prefer carrying shears, such as those used by paramedics, instead of a knife of any kind. Maybe I'm paranoid, but my preference is to carry all three. And make sure that you position your cutting instruments so that you can reach at least one device with either hand in case your movement is restricted when you need it.

Equipment Modifications

Aside from redundancy, there are other helpful — and potentially life-saving — equipment modifications developed by tech divers. One that seems to be catching on in the rec community is the extra-long (often up to five feet [1.5 m]) alternate air source hose. The extra maneuvering room afforded the out-of-air diver can mean the difference between a calm, controlled situation and a disaster.

Tech divers, particularly cave divers, have also learned a lot about using weights more effectively. Most importantly, they've shown the benefit of not necessarily wearing them all around our waist, but redistributing them. For example, placing weight somewhere above your waistline affords a more comfortable — and environmentally responsible — head-down posture. Modern BC design is recognizing this by adding features such as weight pockets on the backs of units, and numerous rings where clip weights can be easily attached. Systems are also available enabling weight to be attached to the tank rather than the BC or weight belt.

Another innovation tech divers have brought us is the use of a delayed surface marker buoy (DSMB). These devices can be inflated and deployed near the surface as a float to maintain a more comfortable and stable position while making a safety stop. In addition, the DSMB allows you to make a safety stop even if you're blown off the dive site, and away from the descent line, by current. Still another advantage is that the lift bag serves as a marking buoy, so the dive boat can continually observe your position as you drift, and facilitate your recovery after you surface.

Tech divers are also teaching us a lot about reducing drag, and the risk of entanglement, by streamlining equipment. To a tech diver, this is almost a religious ritual. One concern is avoiding clips or hooks that might catch on submerged objects. Or, if you insist on using clips, use "dog" clips, which require thumb activation to open, rather than passive snap clips. Some unwary divers have accidentally fastened themselves to objects on the bottom because of unsecured or improperly located snap clips. The same caution goes for all of your hoses. (Although a properly stowed alternate air source is important, it shouldn't be so well secured that access to it becomes difficult.) Improved streamlining also explains why today you see fewer tech divers using gauge consoles, opting instead for wrist-mounted gauges.

Managing Your Gas

Aside from redundancy issues and equipment modification we can learn a great deal from the techniques and guidelines of tech divers. One of the most important is gas management. The key to proper gas management is simple: Always have more than you think you'll need and even then, plan to have a bit more. But accurate gas management is impossible unless you know how much air you consume. As a result, most technical diving courses spend considerable time determining precise air consumption rates. With this information you can then estimate the amount of air you're likely to use at a particular depth. This attention to detail is the antithesis of the typical recreational diver, who normally allows his decompression status to control his bottom time, and merely "keeps an eye" on his air pressure.

Another important air usage guideline used by the tech community is determining when it's time to go home. Often, recreational divers give little consideration to this, and you've probably seen or experienced the result: A diver well downstream of the boat who has to swim back on the surface because he exhausted his air supply. In tech diving the famous "rule of thirds" is often used. It specifies that you use only one-third of your air for the excursion out. The next third is for your return, and the final third is kept in reserve as a contingency. While this may be a bit more conservative than necessary for most recreational applications, it can be a good idea in circumstances in which you're dealing with extreme currents (assuming you're not drift diving), or in cases in which you know you'll encounter an overhead environment, such as a wreck.

A final tenet of tech diving that should become standard operating procedure for all diving operations is the ability and willingness to abort a dive. In the tech community, they live by the adage, "Any diver can abort any dive at any time for any reason." In tech diving, the community peer pressure is to be disciplined, detail-oriented and completely transparent when it comes to safety issues. You speak up if you have concerns and no one tells you you're overreacting. You don't second-guess an aborted dive during the dive, and you don't chastise your teammate if it turned out to be a false alarm. Instead, you say, "Good call — if it had been what you thought and we hadn't aborted, we'd have been in big trouble." Tech divers also recognize that "not feeling right" is itself a step toward a problem, and therefore a reason to turn the dive. This attitude is at the heart of how being a tech diver improves someone's diving at all levels.

Unfortunately, in the recreational community, many divers are reluctant to make such a call due to peer pressure and feelings of embarrassment. Techies have long ago realized that death is far too high a price to pay to preserve face.

Taking the Next Step

Technical diving clearly isn't an activity for everyone. And it's not intended to be. Yet, that doesn't mean that every diver can't benefit from a little technical training. Much of what you'll learn in a tech course concerning dive planning, discipline, equipment modification and general diving theory is entirely applicable to the no-decompression world above 130 feet (39 m). Be forewarned that, compared with most recreational courses, the training tends to be longer, more demanding and, with the additional required equipment, a lot more expensive. But the result could be you becoming a better diver than you ever imagined. ❧

NITROX   AIR   TRIMIX

CHAPTER 41

Mixing It Up:
A Primer On Mixed-Gas Diving

As every diver knows, when it comes to scuba, myths and misconceptions abound.

Who among us hasn't fielded questions from friends and relatives about the danger of being eaten by sharks or explained that, no, we can't yet "breathe water" like that guy in the movie, *Abyss*. Yet, the winner and still champion in the misconception race has got to be the old stand-by regarding our "oxygen" tanks.

Frankly, the oxygen misconception is so common that I'm sure more than a few of you reading this entered your own Open Water training with this assumption, only to learn that, in most cases, our tanks contain nothing more than good-old regular air. But there are some compelling reasons for divers to sometimes alter the gas we breathe.

Nitrox: From Villain to Vogue

Not long ago the idea of recreational divers putting anything other than air into their tanks was considered a cross between suicide and heresy. In fact, the debate between the early nitrox pioneers and the mainstream diving community was quite rancorous. Nitrox diving was branded as too far outside the mainstream to be considered recreational; and there were even attempts to ban it from popular diving destinations due to assumed safety concerns. Of course, it's a different world today; it's common to see a dive boat leaving the dock with more green-and-yellow-labeled nitrox tanks on board than those without. Using nitrox, also known as enriched air, is now standard operating procedure even among divers right out of Open Water courses.

The truth is that, while technical diving inspired the use of nitrox in recreational diving, its widespread acceptance is simply because nitrox does what it's supposed to do.

How so?

Theoretically, the answer is simple. For land-based animals that breathe at normal atmospheric pressure, regular old air does the job of sustaining life quite well. But, when we venture either to altitude or into the depths, there are certain disadvantages to regular or what's formally called normoxic air. At altitude we're all aware that the reduced atmospheric pressure robs us of precious oxygen. That's why pilots must breathe pure oxygen when flying at high altitude, and why the cabins of jet aircraft are pressurized.

Problems arise from breathing air, too, when we venture underwater. In recreational diving, however, these problems have less to do with oxygen than the other component of air, nitrogen. The problem created by nitrogen is, of course, decompression sickness. As you probably know, how long a diver can remain at depth, or how long he must decompress before surfacing, depends upon the amount of nitrogen absorbed during the dive. When using air, you breathe a gas mixture containing about 79 percent nitrogen. In a nitrox mixture, though, additional oxygen is used to replace some of the nitrogen. So, instead of a breathing mixture containing 79 percent, an enriched-air mixture contains less. Usually it's either 68 percent or 64 percent nitrogen, but the mixture could be blended to contain whatever nitrogen "fraction" is desired. What's important is that when breathing nitrox, the diver absorbs less nitrogen, resulting in both an extension of the decompression limits and, if required, reduced decompression time.

Nitrox: Our Friend

The advantages of nitrox are often stated as providing increased safety and extending bottom time. But, like the old saying goes, you can't have your cake and eat it, too. More accurately, the claim should be that nitrox provides *either* increased safety or more bottom time, not both.

Let's look first at extending no-decompression limits. Clearly, nitrox can extend bottom times, and at some depth ranges, more than double the no-decompression limit of air tables. In addition, using nitrox can shorten the required surface interval between repetitive dives. Or, the diver can make a longer repetitive dive with the same surface interval as a comparable air dive. Either option is possible, again, because the diver absorbs less nitrogen than on an air dive of the same bottom time. It's important to recognize, however, that when using any nitrox tables, the risk of decompression sickness (DCS) is probably similar to breathing regular air and using air tables. Indeed, you will absorb less nitrogen breathing nitrox, but if you also extend your bottom time, the risk of decompression sickness is likely commensurate with diving on air.

Many divers say that the real benefit of nitrox is not in extending one's bottom time, but in decreasing the risk of decompression sickness. This is accomplished by breathing nitrox while using standard air dive tables or computers to determine your decompression status. Air tables and computers assume you're breathing air containing 79 percent nitrogen. But, as the nitrox mixture has less nitrogen, the diver doesn't absorb as much as the air tables or computers assume.

While no dive is absolutely risk-free in terms of decompression sickness, many believe that using nitrox in this manner does provide a reduced risk as compared with diving the same profile on air. Hence, nitrox could be a good way to factor into your dive profile the conservatism that so many authorities advise without sacrificing bottom time. It's also been suggested as a way of reducing risks from factors such as age, obesity, cold, fatigue and dehydration. However, others maintain that, as the risk of getting the bends breathing regular air is already very low, the added advantage of nitrox is negligible. The truth is, we currently have no empirical evidence for whether using nitrox in this way might make a dive safer or not, but the theory behind the practice is solid.

Another benefit experienced nitrox divers often report is what some call its "post-dive effect." Many say strongly that the fatigue they experience after a dive on air does not happen when they use nitrox. Some explain this lack of fatigue by the higher percentage of oxygen reducing or eliminating silent bubbles. Some also say that it results from better tissue oxygenation. The problem is, experience shows that post-dive fatigue — or lack of it — when using nitrox is a highly individual matter; and the phenomenon has not been scientifically documented nor refuted. Others believe it's more of a "placebo effect" than reality.

A final benefit of nitrox, oddly enough, occurs when a diver is stricken with DCS. Because the breathing gas contains a higher-than-normal level of oxygen, it's theorized that tissues affected by decompression sickness will survive longer than if the diver was breathing air. Again, this hasn't been established through a controlled study, but makes sense given our assumptions about the mechanism of the bends.

Nitrox: Our Enemy

Like most good things in life, nitrox comes with a downside, and this is due to that Dr. Jekyll/Mr. Hyde gas, oxygen. The main issue, as explained in Chapter 22, is the risk of acute or central nervous system (CNS) oxygen toxicity or "oxtox."

The current recommended oxygen tolerance limit for recreational diving is a maximum partial pressure of 1.4 ATA (atmospheres absolute) for no longer than 45 minutes. Dives longer than 45 minutes require further reduction. Under normal circumstances, this limit has no effect on recreational divers who restrict their diving to 130 feet (39 m) or less. The concern over breathing nitrox is that, because of its higher oxygen content, it reaches the oxygen tolerance limit at much shallower depths than does air. This makes the risk of CNS oxygen toxicity a very real concern even at recreational diving depths. This is why every nitrox mixture has a specific maximum operating depth or MOD. For example, using the recommended maximum oxygen partial pressure of 1.4 ATA, for the two most commonly used mixes, NOAA Nitrox I (68 percent nitrogen) and NOAA Nitrox II (64 percent nitrogen), the MODs are 111 feet (34 m) and 95 feet (29 m), respectively. Exceeding these depths exposes divers to the same risk of oxygen poisoning as breathing air at 187 feet (57 m)!

Oxygen tolerance is the reason for probably the nitrox diver's most critical rule: You must closely adhere to the maximum operating depth of the nitrox mixture used. We're all aware that recreational diving is limited to a maximum depth of 130 feet. The primary rationale for this limit is to avoid the risk from severe symptoms of nitrogen narcosis below that depth, and reduce the risk of decompression sickness. Yet, most divers know that dives beyond 130 feet are often possible without significant effect from narcosis; and when using a computer to control the profile, diving below 130 feet can be done with a reasonable degree of safety. As a result, knowing they can sometimes get away with exceeding it, some divers come to view 130 feet as a relatively "soft" or forgiving limit.

With nitrox, however, it's the onset of CNS oxygen toxicity that determines the depth limit, not the effect of nitrogen. And unlike nitrogen narcosis, CNS oxygen poisoning does not always come about gradually (a diver who lacks nitrox training probably won't recognize the subtle symptoms, anyway). Still, while the diver might experience minor symptoms before convulsions occur — the result of oxygen toxicity — convulsions often begin with virtually no warning. So, when diving nitrox, the MOD isn't as "forgiving" as the 130-foot limit for recreational air diving.

The irony of nitrox is that the very thing that makes it so useful in avoiding DCS — breathing a higher percentage of oxygen — is also what limits the depth at which it can be used. So, to proceed any deeper we need to reduce the amount of oxygen in the gas mixture. Another irony is that in this depth range beyond where nitrox is safe, it seems that air once again becomes the gas of choice because the ppO_2 in a 21 percent oxygen mixture (air) doesn't reach 1.4 ATA — a commonly agreed-upon maximum limit — until 198 feet (60 m).

Unfortunately, the problem isn't resolved by reverting to air. Or rather, in solving one problem, yet another arises. While the concern of oxygen toxicity may be put to rest in what's sometimes called the "deep air" range, the gas we have to worry about is, once again, nitrogen. But now it's a double whammy because, in addition to concerns over decompression sickness, we now have to take into account nitrogen's sedating effect, nitrogen narcosis. Here we reach the limit of what we can do with our two actors, nitrogen and oxygen, and to continue still deeper a new character must come on stage.

The plot thickens.

The Munchkin Gas

It should be clear now that, while it has its advantages, nitrox is not a gas for deep diving. Of course, when we dive deeper, we absorb both more oxygen and nitrogen; and as we saw, this leads to an increased risk of both oxygen toxicity and decompression sickness. Therefore, one way to solve these problems is to reduce the amount of both gases in the mixture. The problem is, what gas to replace them with? The answer is a gas that's actually quite rare on Earth, and is famous for the party trick that enables someone to talk like the munchkins out of *The Wizard of Oz* — helium.

Helium has two fundamental advantages as a deep-diving breathing gas. First, it does not cause narcosis, even at very high partial pressures. (If you want to know why it's non-narcotic, read Chapter 16.) Actually, there is a theoretical depth at which helium could become narcotic, but it's so deep as to be irrelevant to any human diver. The second advantage, which isn't immediately obvious, is that it's a much smaller molecule, and therefore much less dense than nitrogen. Neon is another inert gas that's sometimes used in deep commercial diving, but is very expensive. Like helium, it is less narcotic than nitrogen, but unlike helium, it does not create the "munchkin voice" problem.

The density of a gas — how closely packed the molecules are — is important because it determines how much breathing resistance a diver will experience while at depth. Although the average recreational diver may not consider this significant, under the high pressures of very deep dives, the density of a gas is what determines the amount of work required for breathing. In the case of helium, it's less dense at 300 feet (91 m) than nitrogen is at sea level.

While the narcosis problem is solved by substituting helium for nitrogen, that alone isn't enough as we go still deeper. As stated earlier, air with its 21 percent oxygen content reaches its safe maximum limit at around 200 feet (61 m). So even replacing all the nitrogen with helium does nothing to reduce the risk of oxygen toxicity. Now, we must reduce the toxicity risk in a similar way that we reduced the DCS risk — by cutting the amount of oxygen in the mixture. For example, if you reduce the oxygen in a breathing mixture to just 10 percent, rather than 21, you don't reach the ppO_2 limit of 1.4 ATA until over 400 feet (121 m) of depth. A breathing mixture containing only helium and oxygen is called "heliox."

The problem with such a low-oxygen mixture is, of course, that it's hypoxic — it won't sustain life if breathed at the surface or even in shallow depths. So how can such a gas mixture be useful? The answer is to use two different mixtures for our dive. One source, called the "travel mix," has an ample oxygen content and is used to descend to a prescribed depth where we then switch over to a lower-oxygen content "bottom mix." At that depth, the bottom mix has a high enough ppO_2 for the diver to breathe safely — enough to sustain life but not so much as to risk oxygen toxicity. (By the way, the need for various gas mixtures, each contained in a different tank or tanks, explains the photos you see of technical divers carrying multiple tanks strapped under their arms.) The downside of the need to switch gases, both on the bottom and during decompression, explains why one of the most common accidents in mixed-gas diving is making a switch to the wrong gas, or making a switch at the wrong depth.

By convention, a trimix is named by its oxygen and helium percentage (it's understood that the balance is nitrogen). For example, "trimix 10/70" consists of 10 percent oxygen, 70 percent helium (the remaining 20 percent is nitrogen), and is suitable for a 330-foot (100 m) dive. Furthermore, trimix can be classified as either "normoxic" or "hypoxic." A normoxic mix has a minimum of 18 percent oxygen (ppO_2 0.18 ATA); thus it can sustain life even at the surface and can be used without a travel mix to a depth of around 200 feet (61 m). On the other hand, a "hypoxic" mix is a mixture containing less than 18 percent, and thus is not breathable at the surface. Dives deeper than 200 feet require a hypoxic mix like 10/50 and can be used only as a bottom gas.

Mixing or, more accurately "blending," trimix can be done in two ways. The partial pressure method involves putting oxygen and helium into a cylinder, then topping up the mix with compressed air. An accurate mix requires that the cylinder be allowed to cool after each gas transfer until the correct pressure is achieved. This process is a very labor-intensive process, often taking hours or days and usually requires a gas booster.

The second technique is termed "continuous blending" and is the preferred method. Here, oxygen, helium and air are blended on the intake side of a compressor. The oxygen and helium are fed into the air stream using flow meters to achieve the rough mix. The low-pressure air is analyzed for oxygen content and the oxygen (and helium) flows adjusted accordingly. On the high-pressure side of the compressor a regulator is used to reduce pressure and the trimix is metered through an analyzer (preferably helium and oxygen) so that the fine adjustment to the intake gas flows can be made. The benefit of continuous blending is that the tank delivering the gas need not be as high a pressure as that used in the partial pressure method. In addition, a partially used tank can be refilled to a desired mix after the dive. Additional educational resources on mixed-gas diving can be found at www.fillexpress.com.

Mixed-Up Gases

So our problem of diving deeper seems to be solved. Replace some of the nitrogen with helium and vary the percentage of oxygen according to the depth you plan to operate. Well, not so fast. As it turns out, even helium has it problems. The first is that it's expensive and, as Earth's natural reserves are quickly depleting, getting more so. Currently, helium costs between 75 cents and a dollar per cubic foot. That means the gas alone for a typical technical dive can cost well over $100. So, as many diving instructors caution those considering technical diving, "deep diving requires deep pockets." Of course, if you're in the military or a commercial diving company — and cost is a secondary consideration — then no problem. You can make whatever heliox mixture you desire, and off you go. End of story.

Unlike either military or commercial operations, though, no one subsidizes the cost for technical divers; and fortunately, to gain the advantage of helium you don't have to replace all the nitrogen in a mixture. An alternative is to use only the amount needed by concocting a gas mixture with just the right amount of oxygen required for the desired depth, and dilute that oxygen-nitrogen mixture with enough helium to reduce the narcotic effects of the nitrogen. In fact, by altering the amount of helium in a mix, you can actually decide how "narked" you want to be by setting what's termed the "equivalent narcotic depth." For example, you could dive to 200 feet (61 m), but have a gas mix that's the equivalent of diving to only 100 feet (30 m) on air. This new triple blend is termed "trimix," and it's typically the gas of choice for technical diving operations.

Another problem with helium is that it conducts heat five times faster than air. The concern here is that technical diving, due to extended time spent at depth, almost always means wearing a dry suit; and dry suits must be inflated with gas. But the low thermal capacity of any gas mixture containing helium makes it a poor choice for staying warm in a dry suit. To solve this problem, many technical divers inflate their dry suit using a small, dedicated cylinder of yet another gas with excellent thermal insulation properties — argon.

There are also a few other problems with helium, but fortunately they don't appear to be a concern until our dive exceeds 400 feet (121 m). The first is a condition called high-pressure neurological syndrome (HPNS) that manifests itself as tremors, muscle twitching and coordination difficulties. This is the condition that James Cameron tried to depict — though more than a bit unrealistically — in the segment involving the "diver gone mad" in the aforementioned film, *Abyss*. As it turns out, adding a small amount of nitrogen to the mix can alleviate these symptoms, and it's another reason why some see trimix as a superior choice to straight heliox. The second problem with helium is less common than HPNS and is called hyperbaric arthralgia (pain in the joints). Both conditions can occur on descent and while at depth. Unfortunately, in a real "damned if you do and damned if you don't" scenario, a rapid descent rate seems to be helpful in avoiding HPNS, while a slow descent rate appears to mitigate hyperbaric arthralgia.

Going Up: Decompression Issues

Aside from the extreme depths encountered in technical diving, another characteristic that sets it apart from recreational diving is that you dive under a "ceiling." Sometimes that ceiling is a physical barrier to the surface, like a cave ceiling or deck of a ship. But even when there's a clear path to the surface, technical divers almost always encounter the "physiologic ceiling" imposed by the need for lengthy decompression stops. Both types of ceilings preclude what is perhaps the greatest safety factor in recreational diving: the ability to, in an emergency, ascend immediately to the surface.

A common myth about heliox and trimix is that by breathing helium you can reduce decompression time. Being a smaller molecule, it does enter and leave the tissues faster than nitrogen, and it does not enter slow tissues as readily as nitrogen. Paradoxically, though, compared with decompression on air, helium requires a little more decompression on short dives, but less decompression on long dives. So, from the perspective of decompression, helium is not an ideal gas for dives of less than one or two hours of bottom time. In fact, if heliox or trimix were used for the entire duration of a dive, including decompression, the total time in the water would be extremely long compared with air. However, decompression time on either heliox or trimix can be dramatically decreased if, during ascent, the breathing mixture is changed once again to something that doesn't contain any helium.

Although air contains virtually no helium it's not an ideal choice for decompression from a mixed-gas dive. Breathing air would make the helium outgas more quickly, but the nitrogen component of air would ingas, hindering the decompression process. The better option is, rather than air, using a mixture with less nitrogen — nitrox or trimix. Unlike recreational diving, for which nitrox is used to extend bottom time, in mixed-gas deep diving nitrox is used to accelerate decompression. Moreover, for decompression stops in 20 feet (6 m) or less, you can breathe pure oxygen to further accelerate decompression by eliminating any inert gas component from the mixture.

It's clear that the term mixed-gas diving is quite apt. Not only do technical divers breathe mixtures of various gases, but these mixtures are also switched back and forth at appropriate points during descent and ascent to maximize their advantage and eliminate potential dangers. Clearly, this illustrates the need for the extremely high level of planning and training required by anyone considering taking on such an advanced form of diving. As many technical diving instructors will tell you, learning to dive beyond the recreational range isn't as much a progression as it is starting all over again. It requires learning a whole new set of skills and attitudes as well as an entire new way of managing risk. As some have noted, recreational diving is like walking in the park, but technical diving is like walking on the moon.

CHAPTER 42

Look, Ma, No Bubbles:
A Look at Rebreathers

To divers, bubbles are a fact of life.

But when we think of them, it's normally in the context of the bubbles we hope to avoid — ones that cause decompression sickness. Ironically, these tiniest of bubbles cause the greatest problems. The big bubbles — the ones we exhale — are so common to our experience that we rarely even think about them. It's just part of diving. Fish have scales, sharks have teeth and divers have bubbles. Bubbles are the "white noise" of diving that goes virtually unnoticed. Like the constant drone of traffic to a city dweller, we can hardly imagine a life underwater without this ever-present cacophony whizzing past our ears. That is, at least, until you make your first bubbleless dive.

Diving sans bubbles sounds like something out of a dream. But to more and more recreational divers, it has become an exciting reality that's opening up a whole new world that most divers could never imagine. The technology that makes bubble-free diving possible is called a rebreather; and over the past few years they've come a long way.

Sixty years of experience has proven that open-circuit systems — our beloved bubble machines — are simple, safe, reliable and relatively inexpensive. They certainly get the job done of extending time underwater. But had history taken a slightly different path, what we now call scuba might have been a bubbleless breathing bag rather than the familiar device we all know today.

Why No Bubbles?

Although simple, safe and cheap, open-circuit scuba poses one disadvantage. Like the behemoth cars of decades past, they waste lots of gas. Humans consume only a small portion of the oxygen we inhale with each breath. In fact, at most, only a few percent at the surface; and at depth, even less. If that's hard to believe, then consider mouth-to-mouth resuscitation. The technique works precisely because the high level of oxygen in every exhalation is more than enough to sustain someone who can't breathe on their own.

Most of the oxygen in a diver's scuba cylinder goes unused in the exhaled air released as bubbles. Just how much oxygen is lost? A fit person working hard may breathe at a rate of 100 liters per minute but will only metabolize a maximum of six liters per minute of oxygen. And with increased depth, the proportion of oxygen used is even less due to the increase in partial pressure.

Rebreathers are a way to reduce — literally, reuse — the wasted oxygen. They recapture the exhaled air and scrub out the carbon dioxide, recycling the air time and time again in a closed loop. Hence they're termed "closed-circuit" systems. But of course, some oxygen has to be consumed, so over time this closed circuit would become dangerously hypoxic (low in oxygen). To prevent this, small amounts — and only small amounts — of oxygen are added to replenish the circuit, or what's also called the "breathing loop." With a need to carry

How a Rebreather Works

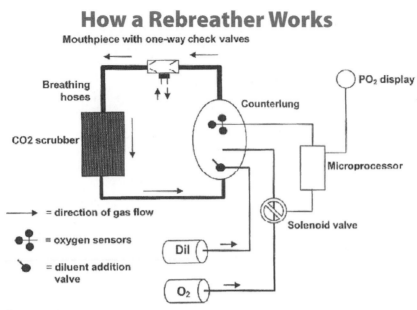

Mouthpiece with one-way check valves

Breathing hoses

CO2 scrubber

Counterlung

PO₂ display

Microprocessor

Solenoid valve

Dil

O₂

→ = direction of gas flow

= oxygen sensors

= diluent addition valve

Figure 1: In a CCR the breathing loop is maintained by adding gas from both an oxygen source and diluent. The diver can use this diluent gas supply as an open-circuit emergency bailout system in the event of a system failure, which is why diluent is never a pure gas, but always has some oxygen. The proportion of oxygen depends upon the planned dive depth. The diluent gas supply can also be used to inflate the integrated buoyancy compensator. Check valves in the mouthpiece ensure that air flows only in one direction. Multiple (usually three) electronic oxygen sensors monitor the oxygen partial pressure (PO₂). The setpoint is the PO₂ that the rebreather maintains. Most eCCRs and eSCRs vary the setpoint, which is called a floating setpoint or a dynamic setpoint. Most systems give an alarm or an alert if you're more than 0.1 from setpoint, though this will vary with sophistication. If you exceed 1.4 or drop below 0.7 (underwater), they all give top-level alarms. The oxygen sensor readings are displayed on two separate and redundant readouts. When needed, oxygen is added to the breathing loop by a solenoid. The volume of gas is maintained in the breathing loop by two counter lungs, one for inhalation and one for exhalation. As gas circulates, the breathing loop is scrubbed of carbon dioxide through a chemical reaction with a substance called soda lime. This is a granulated compound consisting primarily of hydrated lime (Ca[OH]₂) blended with small amounts of sodium hydroxide (NaOH). While the unit can carry enough gas for perhaps 10 or more hours of diving, the absorbent material must be changed more frequently, normally after around three hours.

only a small oxygen supply to refresh the loop, the system can carry far less gas than an open-circuit unit. (See Figure 1, "How a Rebreather Works.")

New Technology?

As rebreathers are relative newcomers to the recreational diving scene, most assume that this is brand-new technology. In fact, a diver recently told me, with complete conviction, that had it not been for the space program, we wouldn't have rebreathers. I suppose that's a logical assumption, given all the technological benefits we've gleaned from space exploration, but it's simply not true. The reality is — something you already know if you read Chapter 2 — that rebreathers existed long before the eminent Jacques Cousteau was even a twinkle in his daddy's eye. The first successful scuba of any kind was built in 1878 — that's 1878, not 1978 — by an Englishman, Henry Fleuss. His apparatus consisted of a rubberized fabric hood, a breathing bag, a back-mounted copper cylinder containing oxygen and a carbon dioxide scrubber. As the diver rebreathed his expired gas and consumed the oxygen, more was added manually from the oxygen supply tank. Although crude, it worked quite well.

Another historical tidbit is that rebreathers weren't initially developed for diving; they were designed for mining operations. So, early diving rebreathers had a serious limitation in that they were severely depth-limited because they used pure oxygen in them. Humans can breathe pure oxygen safely to a depth of only about 20 feet (6 m). As addressed extensively in Chapter 22, under higher pressure (deeper depth), life-giving oxygen becomes poisonous, resulting in a condition known as acute oxygen toxicity. It's most problematic symptom is seizure which, when it happens underwater, means drowning. So what good is a diving system that will kill you with little or no warning if you dive deeper than 20 feet?

Not surprisingly, in the early days of diving, rebreathers took a backseat to more familiar systems — helmets, hoses and compressors. But what breathed the life back into rebreathers was World War II, and the need for clandestine (no bubble) underwater operations. The Fleuss system was refined by British Royal Navy researchers Kenneth Donald and J.B.S. Haldane, son of diving's most famous decompression researcher. Spurred on by the heroic exploits of Italian and British frogmen, rebreather technology was well-refined by the time Cousteau and Gagnan perfected their aqualung. Now, here's one of history's little ironies. As it turns out, had Cousteau himself not nearly drowned while testing a rebreather of his own design — causing him to abandon closed-circuit systems as too dangerous — the face of modern scuba might be vastly different today. We might all be diving bubble-free.

Would You Like It Open or Closed?

The most basic systems, like the ones used by the frogmen of the Second World War and Special Operations troops today, are termed oxygen rebreathers. Using oxygen as the only gas in the breathing loop, the diver's breath is chemically scrubbed of carbon dioxide each time it's cycled. Additional oxygen is added when necessary to replace that consumed by the diver. But, like the earliest rebreathers, even modern systems aren't designed for use below 20 feet (6 m). Well, actually, that's not quite true. Operationally, military systems are used regularly to depths of around 60 feet (18 m), but taking calculated risks is what warfare is all about. Still, any dive deeper than 20 feet is playing Russian Roulette, so mechanical oxygen rebreathers have no place in recreational diving. Case closed.

The first rebreathers to appear widely in the recreational diving community were the mechanical "semi-closed" systems. A semi-closed system uses a single gas source, but not pure oxygen. Instead, a nitrox mixture is used with a predetermined oxygen percentage. This is why these units are also referred to as "nitrox rebreathers." However, about 20 percent of the exhalation isn't recirculated, but expelled as bubbles; hence the term "semi-closed."

In semi-closed systems the on-board gas is fed into the breathing loop in one of two ways, and thus there are two different designs. One controls the input of oxygen by flow, normally passing the gas through a calibrated orifice. The second is somewhat more elaborate and uses a bellows system to control gas inflow. Their advantage is that, by recovering most of the exhalation, a relatively small tank can last a very long time. In addition, they're relatively inexpensive compared with the more sophisticated fully closed systems. The downside, however, is that their operational depth is predetermined by the oxygen content of the on-board gas. (Remember all that stuff about maximum operating depths in your nitrox class?)

Mechanical nitrox rebreathers never gained a foothold, mainly because they provided little advantage over open-circuit diving. They also suffered from bad press due to a number of well-publicized accidents. Currently, however, manufacturers are taking a fresh look at semi-closed systems by overcoming the shortcomings of the mechanical design with electronic control. Several electronically controlled semi-closed rebreathers (eSCRs) may be on the market by the time you read this. They cover most of what a recreational diver may want from a rebreather, with more mechanical and operational simplicity.

The most sophisticated rebreather technology, and the one that offers the most benefits, is the electronic computer-controlled, fully closed system or eCCR. Exactly how the oxygen is handled is what makes them different from the shallow-water systems used by the military. In these units, the oxygen content of the breathing loop isn't controlled by mechanics but by an array of primary, back-up and even tertiary electronic oxygen sensors. Information from the sensor is monitored by an on-board computer (also with a backup), which controls when and how much oxygen is added to the breathing loop. This precise computer control takes human guesswork and mechanical limitations out of the equation by adding only the exact amount of oxygen needed to maintain a constant and predetermined oxygen partial pressure or PO_2.

PO_2 is the percentage of oxygen in the breathing loop times the ambient pressure in atmospheres absolute (ATA). For example, at the surface — 1 ATA — the oxygen component of air is 21 percent, making the PO_2 0.21 ATA (0.21 ATA x 1). At 33 feet (10 m), or 2 ATA, it becomes 0.42 ATA (2 x 0.21). Because there must be at least one other gas in the breathing loop to dilute the oxygen, CCRs also carry a second gas supply termed a *diluent*. Depending on the depth of the dive, this may be air, nitrox or even a mixed gas such as trimix for deep tech diving. The diver can use this diluent gas supply as an open-circuit emergency bailout system in the event of a system failure, which is why diluent is never a pure gas, but always has some oxygen. The proportion of oxygen depends upon the planned dive depth.

As the PO_2 is computer-controlled, and only a very small amount of gas is required to maintain the breathing loop, these systems are usable to extreme depths, while still carrying tanks no larger than pony bottles (about 20 cubic feet). Currently, technical divers commonly use closed-circuit systems to depth ranges of 200-300 feet (61-91 m), and in some cases as deep as 500-700 feet (151-212 m).

Below is a list of features required for a Type R rebreather as suited to PADI-sanctioned Recreational Rebreather courses.

The unit should be of robust design and engineered to prevent incorrect assembly by the user.

The unit will not operate without a scrubber canister present, or it will warn the diver.

The unit can be used with prepacked scrubber cartridges.

The diver is warned* if the diluent or oxygen supply becomes too low.

The unit switches set points automatically.

The unit will function to a depth of 130 feet (39 m).

The diver is prompted to check the mouthpiece mushroom valve function and to perform a loop positive/negative pressure check during predive checks.

The unit should automatically attempt to sustain life or prevent the user from diving if predive procedures are not performed correctly.

The unit self-calibrates its O_2 cells.

The unit will self-initiate or warn the diver if the electronics are not turned on, or when the diver starts to use it.

The diver should have a simple status indicator in his line of sight indicating that all is well or if a bailout is required (e.g., heads-up display).

The diver should be able to switch to open-circuit bailout using single-hand action and without removing his mouthpiece.

The unit automatically adds diluent to the loop as required if the bag volume is reduced.

The diver is warned if he starts to use the unit with the diluent or oxygen supply not properly turned on, or it will turn the relevant gas on automatically.

The diver is provided with an indicator of remaining battery life and is warned if it becomes critically low.

The diver is warned if the diluent or oxygen supply becomes too low.

The unit switches setpoints automatically.

The unit will function to a depth of 130 feet (39 m).

The unit will maintain a pO_2 close to the target level in normal use.

The diver is warned if pO_2 is too high.

The diver is warned if pO_2 is too low.

The unit has a system to warn the diver if pCO_2 is too high or it has a system for estimating remaining scrubber duration.

The loop includes an automatic overpressurization relief valve.

The unit should have a provision to fit a mouthpiece that can be used by a second diver.

The unit has a "black box" data recorder function.

The rebreather has undergone nationally or internationally recognized third-party testing against an appropriate standard. Examples would Include EN14143 (and having attained CE marking) or meeting the NOAA Minimum Manufacturing & Performance Requirements for Closed Circuit Mixed Gas rebreathers.

*Note: Warnings must be very apparent and not likely to be missed by the diver. A vibrating mouthpiece alarm is ideal, coupled with a visual alarm in the diver's line of sight and/or an audible alarm. A secondary warning discernible to other divers on the back is highly desirable.

Type R Rebreather Features

A Rec Revolution?

While the technology and theory of rebreathers may sound interesting, one might ask, "Of what possible significance is this for recreational diving?" Well, how would you like to dive all weekend — perhaps all week — and never have to refill your tank? And what if that tank was no bigger than a large pony bottle? What if marine life showed almost no fear, allowing you to approach without them running for the hills? What if you could spend three hours on a multilevel dive from 60 to 100 feet (18 to 30 m)? Or spend an hour at 100 feet with minimal decompression? With a rebreather all of these advantages are possible, even for recreational divers.

One way to view a CCR is as a computerized gas-mixing machine. In this way, aside from giving you a virtually unlimited air supply, it minimizes your decompression. This is done by maximizing the pO_2 in the breathing loop, thereby minimizing inert gas update, as your depth changes. (By the way, for you nitrox divers, the maximum oxygen partial pressure — "set point" in rebreather parlance — is 1.2 to 1.3 ATA versus the open-circuit standard of 1.4 to 1.6 ATA.)

Until recently, their cost, complexity, maintenance requirements and poor safety record have limited CCRs to tech divers who needed their exceptional capabilities. Learning to use a CCR also demanded many hours of training and in-water experience. Furthermore, because each system is materially different, each model required its own specialized training. This meant repeating training again if you decided to opt for a different model. However, this all changed with the recent introduction of what are now termed "Type R" (recreational) CCRs intended for recreational, mainstream no-stop dives to 130 feet (39 m).

Some now see these next-generation, more user-friendly systems as not only a viable alternative to open-circuit scuba, but as the ultimate future of diving. The reason for such enthusiasm is twofold. First, the technology has progressed significantly in recent years to where some of the most common concerns over CCRs can be virtually eliminated, especially through redundancy (much like with aircraft design). Second, the CCR training and support infrastructure within the diving industry has matured tremendously in the past decade or so. Perhaps most significantly, CCR use by recreational divers has now been endorsed and formally supported with the introduction of PADI's (Professional Association of Diving Instructors) Rebreather Diver and Advanced Rebreather Diver courses. These courses specially train recreational divers in the use of Type R rebreathers (there are also the PADI Tec CCR Diver courses for using Type T CCRs for technical diving).

"There's no question that rebreathers are a growing part of mainstream diving," says Karl Shreeves, PADI technical development executive. "They're here to stay and you'll see them more and more as the support they need — oxygen fills and absorbent — become more widely available in the dive community. Open-circuit scuba will be with us for years to come — it still has its place and advantages — but don't be surprised if you find yourself sitting next to a diver in a rebreather the next time you head out on a charter boat."

The real beauty in this new approach to Type R rebreathers is that much of the complexity that was thought to be inherent in the technology can be largely eliminated through better engineering. A good analogy is computing. What made computers easy to use were Windows/Mac OS. DOS is a simpler program, but burdened the user. The more complex programs burden the device and free the user. Additionally, better engineering can reduce or prevent many of the common mistakes and omissions made by divers, thus reducing operator error. To help manufacturers achieve this, in 2009 PADI put forth a list of features that it saw as important for rebreathers to transition from tech diving to recreational diving. Several manufacturers saw the opportunity, and the Type R rebreather emerged.

Yet, aside from efficiency, extensive bottom time and minimum decompression, there are some less obvious benefits to CCRs. One that is of no small consequence addresses the bane of all divers — staying warm. It turns out that the chemical reaction in the carbon dioxide scrubber gives off heat (what chemists call an *exothermic* reaction), keeping the air in the breathing loop much warmer than in an open-circuit system. And warm air equals a warm diver. In my own admittedly limited experience with CCRs, I've spent as long as three hours on a dive and never got cold. On one occasion I even had to push back my hood because I was getting overheated.

Speaking of long dives, most open-circuit divers probably can't imagine spending three hours even in warm water because by the end their airway would be as dry as a piece of beef jerky. However, like your own lungs, the closed-circuit loop is kept moist naturally from the moisture in your airway, so the "dry mouth" experienced when breathing air from a standard scuba system simply doesn't happen. It's hard to explain how pleasant this feels until you experience it.

"A three-hour dive on a rebreather is 'shorter' than the same-length dive in open-circuit. It's not really, of course, but it feels that way — you have to experience it to understand what I mean," Shreeves says. His comments are not unusual among rebreather divers.

Safety Issues

Although CCRs provide enormous benefits, the advantages also come at a cost. Although the data are weak and the actual number of rebreather divers is still speculative, accident analysis shows that CCR divers could be at about a fivefold increased fatality risk compared with those using the more familiar bubble machine. That translates into about 20 deaths per year in a population of well under 30,000 (compared with open-circuit diving with fewer than 100 fatalities in a population of hundreds of thousands). Yet, in digging deeper into the root cause of CCR accidents it becomes clear that equipment failure is almost never the reason a CCR diver doesn't come home from a dive. As in open-circuit scuba diving and in aviation alike, the primary "triggering event" in the vast majority of CCR fatalities is not equipment failure but operator error. In one analysis researchers found that in two-thirds of fatalities divers engaged in "high-risk behaviors" such as ignoring checklists, or pushing limits.

To me, putting aside the issue of the price tag, at issue in the cost-benefit analysis comparing open-circuit systems with CCRs is weighing benefit versus complexity. Our trusty old bubble machine is highly reliable, simple and forgiving. If something does go wrong with it — a free-flowing regulator, burst O-ring, or forgetting to open a tank valve all the way — you'll know it almost immediately and most often in a pretty obvious way. A CCR is much more subtle and therefore the nature of the problems it may pose are far more insidious. An inattentive CCR diver can lapse into unconsciousness quickly and with no warning from too little oxygen or too much carbon dioxide, or succumb to convulsions due too much oxygen. If CCRs were people, they'd be the most unforgiving SOBs on earth.

As I've said about technical diving in general, this article is not intended to either encourage nor discourage the use of CCRs by recreational divers. Its intent is merely to examine the option. Perhaps aviation provides the most useful analogy for comparison. Diving open circuit is like flying a plane visually, whereas CCR diving is like flying on instruments. As one CCR manufacturer said, "Just because you can afford one doesn't mean that you possess the background or experience and skills to use a rebreather. The overwhelming majority of sport divers are better off on open circuit, which is far more forgiving."

I agree wholeheartedly and, for one, have no plans to give up my beloved bubble machine. ♺

Index

Bahamas, 113
bailout, 318-320
Balestra, C., 184, 214
ballast, 8, 12
Banyash, LW, 132
barbiturates, 101
baroreceptors, 185-186
barotrauma, 58, 63, 130, 157
Barron, RJ, 132
basal metabolism, 101, 108
Bassett, Bruce, 32
BC, 72, 214-215, 236-237, 250-251, 253, 272-275, 281-282, 291, 304-305
behaviors, 47, 237, 322
Behnke, Albert, 32, 122
Benadryl, 149
Bennett, Dr. Peter, 213-214
Bernoulli, Daniel, 47
Bert, Paul, 22-23, 25, 94, 171
beverages, 95, 108, 146, 197
bicarbonate, 70
bilipid layer, 199
billet, 295
billfish, 106
biochemical, 168, 173, 200-201, 206
blackout, 59, 96, 124, 296, 298-299
bladders, 63, 186, 274, 304
Blatteau, J.M., 184
blended, 310, 312, 318
blindness, 138, 228
blockage, 57, 77, 86, 88, 102, 147, 193, 198
bloodstream, 51, 70, 76, 79, 101, 167, 199, 202
blurred, 77, 79, 96, 113, 115, 138, 149
BMi, 60
bodies, 5, 41, 55, 86, 94-95, 99, 105, 107, 109, 117, 137, 167-168, 174, 183-185, 197-199, 205, 280, 298-299
Bonine, 151
Bonuccelli, C., 214
Bookspan, Dr. Jolie, 192
boomers, 85, 165, 265
Borelli, Giovanni, 11
Bouton, Louis, 13
Bove, A.A., 58, 89
bowels, 150, 304
Boyle, Sir Robert, 6, 21, 42-43, 45, 47-49, 51, 63, 298

braille, 279
brain, 37, 40, 69, 76-77, 81, 95-96, 100-101, 110, 113-117, 122, 146-151, 161, 171, 173-174, 185, 193, 220, 228, 236, 265, 267
Braithwaite, John and William, 5
breastbone, 78
breath, 4, 47-48, 50, 63, 69, 71, 75-76, 78-79, 86-87, 90, 94, 96, 115, 129, 131, 172, 177-180, 193, 236-238, 250, 257, 290, 295-299, 304, 312, 317, 319
Bridges, Lloyd, 11, 75
British Columbia, 280
Brock, Ken, 17
bronchitis, 59, 79, 180
bronchoconstriction, 130
Brooklyn Bridge, 22, 26
BSAC, 139
bubbles, 22-23, 31-34, 50-51, 76-77, 79, 81, 87, 89, 95-96, 100-101, 113, 156-157, 167-168, 184, 192, 194, 197-199, 201-202, 205-207, 212-214, 227, 231, 271, 283, 289, 310, 317, 319
bubbling, 32, 199, 201, 207, 211-212, 214-215
buddy, 8, 31, 60, 65, 72, 78, 90, 123, 125-126, 140, 142, 146, 155, 158-159, 161, 214-215, 236, 238, 241, 245, 250-253, 257-260, 263-267, 271, 274, 276, 281-283, 288-291, 296, 304
Buhlmann, Dr. Albert, 33
buoyancy, 6-7, 12, 17-18, 37, 40-41, 63, 71-72, 140, 214-215, 236, 243-244, 250-251, 259, 271-276, 281, 291, 304, 318
Bussoz, Rene, 16
Butler, Steve, 14

C

Cadaques bell, 5
cadavers, 157
caffeine, 101, 146-147, 149, 186
CAGE, 77
caissons, 22, 26
calcium, 146

calculation, 33, 40-41, 43, 48-49, 207
Cali-Corleo, P., 214
calories, 101, 171
Cambridge University, 37
camera, 38, 273, 276
Cameron, James, 313
Campbell, Dr. Ernest, xiii, 201
cancer, 99, 101-102, 116, 166
capillaries, 8, 64, 70, 76-77, 178, 198, 201
Capp of Maintenance, 6
carbohydrates, 137, 184
carbon, 101
carbon dioxide, 5, 50-51, 69-72, 76, 93, 95-96, 115, 122-123, 167, 174, 184, 197, 291, 296, 299, 317-319, 321-322
carbon monoxide, 50, 102, 193
Carcharodon carcharias, 37
cardio-respiratory decompression sickness, 178
cardiovascular disease, 58, 138
cardiovascular endurance, 165
cardiovascular system, 86
career, 3, 16, 22, 86, 137, 142, 279, 299, 326
Caribbean, 15, 58, 265, 273
Carlston, C.B., 58
carotid, 69, 90, 185
catheter, 223
cave, 16, 34, 75, 140, 207, 252, 281-282, 304-305, 313
cavern, 113-114, 244
cavity, 64, 78, 199
CCRs, 318-319, 321-322
cells, 24, 70, 76, 95, 101-102, 115-117, 122, 137-139, 147, 149, 151, 165, 167, 173, 184, 194, 199-202, 207, 320
cerebral arterial gas embolism, 77
certification, 16, 57, 121, 155-156, 159, 171, 219, 245, 251, 266, 297
certified, 27, 59, 129, 139, 158, 197, 288, 326
cesarean, 194
cetirizine, 150
Challenger Deep, 44
Chalons, France, 22
Charles, Jacques, 47, 49-51

checklists, 322
checkout, 18
checkups, 59, 166
chemistry, 94, 146, 201
chemists, 321
chemoreceptors, 70
Chesapeake Bay, 279-280
chest, 13, 59, 71, 77-79, 86, 107, 115,130-131, 157, 178, 228, 250, 253, 272, 274, 276, 298
childbirth, 193
children, 8, 55, 129, 155-159, 161, 191
chills, 138
choking, 115
cholesterol, 59-60, 88, 102, 145
Churchill, Owen, 14
cigarettes, 191
circulation, 76, 78-79, 87-88, 100, 107, 168, 193-194, 198-199, 202, 297
Claritin, 150
Clark, Bob, 16
Clark, Dr. Eugenie, 191
climate, 141, 275
closed-circuit rebreathers, 174
clot, 89, 201
clotting, 199
Club des Scaphandres et de la Vie Sous L'Eau, 14
CNS, 94, 146, 149, 157, 171-172, 310-311
central nervous system, 94, 146, 171, 184, 310
CO_2, 72
coastal, 4, 15, 242, 279-280
cocaine, 101
cochlea, 65
cognitive exercises, 123
cognitive development,159, 161
Cohen, Dr. Sheldon, 117
colds, 57, 59, 66, 79
Columbus, 4
coma, 138, 141, 156
Commeinhes, George, 14
communication, 281
compensator, 12, 17, 63, 71-72, 214, 243, 250-251, 273, 281, 291, 318
competence, 264-265, 276, 290
compression, 23, 27, 71, 125, 141, 157, 179, 205, 207, 212, 224, 227, 289-290, 296, 310, 321

compressors, 25, 312, 318
computer, xv, 18, 21, 25, 27, 31-34, 75, 95, 100, 187, 207, 211-212, 214-215, 227-228, 257, 290-291, 305, 319
computers, 21, 27, 31, 33-34, 43, 81, 197, 207, 213-215, 290, 305, 310, 321
Condert, Charles, 12
confidence, 228, 237, 259, 264-265, 267, 288
confusion, 44, 81, 107, 123-124, 133, 150-151, 167, 178, 228
congenital, 64
consciousness, 58-59, 72, 77, 96, 107, 138-139, 148, 167, 173, 178, 298
convulsions, 13, 15, 23, 59, 77, 80, 93, 96, 173-174, 311, 322
Cooper, Dr. Kenneth, 90
coral, 113, 243-245, 251, 272-273, 275-276, 280, 282
Corlieu, 14
coronary disease, 85-86, 166, 202
Corporal Jones, 8
Council for National Cooperation in Aquatics, 16
countercurrents, 243
Cousteau, Jacques, 3, 11, 14-16, 121, 155, 295, 318
CPR, 80-81, 221
crepitus, 78
Crilley, Frank, 26
Crimean War, 7
Croft, Bob, 295, 297, 299
cromoglycate, 130
cromolyn sodium, 150
Cronin, John, 16
Cronje, Frans, 213-214
Curaçao, 15
currents, 242-243, 265, 275, 306
CVD, 85-86, 88, 90
Cyana, 4
cylinder, 6, 13, 304, 312-313, 317-318

D

Da Vinci, Leonardo, 5, 11
Dalmatian coast, 15
Dalton, John, 45, 47, 49-51, 94, 172, 298

Printed in Great Britain
by Amazon.co.uk, Ltd.,
Marston Gate.